KT-436-219

MEI STRUCTURED MATHEMATICS

THIRD EDITION

A2 Further Pure Mathematics

Terry Heard
David Martin
Bernard Murphy

FOR
REFERENCE ONLY

Series Editor: Roger Porkess

NORWICH CITY COLLEGE			
Stock No.	238 301		
Class	510 HEA		
Cat	SSA	Proc	NAFL

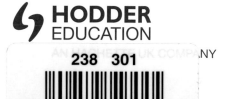

HODDER
EDUCATION
AN HACHETTE UK COMPANY

238 301

The Publishers would like to thank the following for permission to reproduce copyright material:

Photographs: page 1, TEK IMAGE/Science Photo Library; page 20, Claude Nuridsany and Marie Perennou/Science Photo Library; page 32, Astrid and Hanns-Frieder Michler/Science Photo Library; page 123, H. Steinhaus 'Mathematical Snapshots', OUP New York, new edition 1960; page 138, Dewitt Jones/CORBIS

Every effort has been made to trace all copyright holders, but if any have been inadvertently overlooked the Publishers will be pleased to make the necessary arrangements at the first opportunity.

OCR accept no responsibility whatsoever for the accuracy or method of working in the answers given.

Hachette UK's policy is to use papers that are natural, renewable and recyclable products and made from wood grown in sustainable forests. The logging and manufacturing processes are expected to conform to the environmental regulations of the country of origin.

Orders: please contact Bookpoint Ltd, 130 Milton Park, Abingdon, Oxon OX14 4SB. Telephone: (44) 01235 827720. Fax: (44) 01235 400454. Lines are open 9 am to 5 pm, Monday to Saturday, with a 24-hour message-answering service. Visit our website at www.hoddereducation.co.uk.

© Terry Heard, David Martin, Bernard Murphy 1996, 2003, 2005

First Edition published in 1996
Second Edition published in 2003
Third Edition published in 2005 by
Hodder Education, an Hachette UK Company
338 Euston Road
London NW1 3BH

Impression number   10 9 8 7
Year   2010 2009

All rights reserved. Apart from any use permitted under UK copyright law, no part of this publication may be reproduced or transmitted in any form or by any means, electronic or mechanical, including photocopying and recording, or held within any information storage and retrieval system, without permission in writing from the publisher or under licence from the Copyright Licensing Agency Limited. Further details of such licences (for reprographic reproduction) may be obtained from the Copyright Licensing Agency Limited, Saffron House, 6-10 Kirby Street, London EC1N 8TS.

Typeset in 10.4pt Minion by Tech-Set, Gateshead, Tyne & Wear.
Printed and bound in Great Britain by Martins The Printers, Berwick-upon-Tweed.

A catalogue record for this title is available from the British Library

ISBN-13: 978 0 340 88995 4

MEI Structured Mathematics

Mathematics is not only a beautiful and exciting subject in its own right but also one that underpins many other branches of learning. It is consequently fundamental to the success of a modern economy.

MEI Structured Mathematics is designed to increase substantially the number of people taking the subject post-GCSE, by making it accessible, interesting and relevant to a wide range of students.

It is a credit accumulation scheme based on 45 hour units which may be taken individually or aggregated to give Advanced Subsidiary (AS) and Advanced GCE (A Level) qualifications in Mathematics and Further Mathematics. The units may also be used to obtain credit towards other types of qualification.

The course is examined by OCR (previously the Oxford and Cambridge Schools Examination Board) with examinations held in January and June each year.

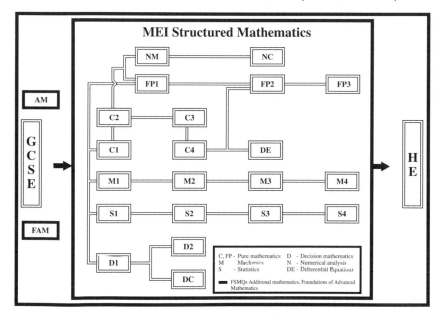

This is one of the series of books written to support the course. Its position within the whole scheme can be seen in the diagram above.

Mathematics in Education and Industry (MEI) is an independent curriculum development body which aims to promote links between education and industry in mathematics. MEI produce relevant examination specifications at GCSE, AS and A Level (including Further Mathematics) and for Free Standing Mathematics Qualifications (FSMQs); these are examined by OCR.

In partnership with Hodder Murray, MEI are responsible for three major series of textbooks: Formula One Maths for Key Stage 3, Hodder Mathematics for GCSE and the MEI Structured Mathematics series, including this book, for AS and A Level.

As well as textbooks, MEI take a leading role in the development of on-line resources to support mathematics. The books in this series are complemented by a major MEI website providing full solutions to the exercises, extra questions including on-line multiple choice tests, interactive demonstrations of the mathematics, schemes of work, and much more.

In recent years MEI have worked hard to promote Further Mathematics and, in conjunction with the DfES, they are now establishing the national network of Further Mathematics Centres.

MEI are committed to supporting the professional development of teachers. In addition to a programme of Continual Professional Development, MEI, in partnership with several universities, co-ordinate the Teaching Advanced Mathematics programme, a course designed to give teachers the skills and confidence to teach A Level mathematics successfully.

Much of the work of MEI is supported by the Gatsby Charitable Foundation.

MEI is a registered charity and a charitable company.

MEI's website and email addresses are www.mei.org.uk *and* office@mei.org.uk.

Introduction

This book covers the MEI Structured Mathematics A2 unit (or module) FP2, *Further Methods for Advanced Mathematics*. This unit is a requirement for an A level in Further Mathematics in this specification. The material in this book is also relevant to other Further Mathematics specifications and so it will be found useful by all students at this level.

Throughout the series the emphasis is on understanding rather than mere routine calculations, but the various exercises do nonetheless provide plenty of scope for practising basic techniques. Extensive on-line support is available via the MEI website, *www.mei.org.uk*.

This is the third edition of this series. Much of the content of this book was previously covered in *Pure Mathematics 5* but it has now been reorganised to meet the requirements of the new specification being first examined in January 2006.

The final chapter, *Investigation of curves*, is, however, completely new. This exciting topic replaces the previous syllabus item of conics; it is based on the assumption that the reader has a graphic calculator, and looks at the properties of curves in a much more general way. Because of the many diagrams this chapter looks rather long, but the actual work involved is comparable with that in the other chapters.

I would like to thank all those who have worked on this book, particularly David Martin for preparing this new edition and Bernard Murphy for his creativity in writing the final chapter.

Readers who are interested in a possible career in mathematics may wish to visit the website *www.mathscareers.org.uk* for more information.

Roger Porkess
Series Editor

Key to symbols in this book

? This symbol means that you may want to discuss a point with your teacher. If you are working on your own there are answers in the back of the book. It is important, however, that you have a go at answering the questions before looking up the answers if you are to understand the mathematics fully.

⚠ This is a warning sign. It is used where a common mistake, misunderstanding or tricky point is being described.

 This is the ICT icon. It indicates where you should use a graphic calculator or a computer.

e This symbol and a dotted line down the right-hand side of the page indicates material which is beyond the criteria for the unit but which is included for completeness.

☆
☆ Harder questions are indicated with stars. Many of these go beyond the usual examination standard.

Contents

Calculus

The moving power of mathematical invention is not reasoning but imagination.

Augustus De Morgan, 1806–1871

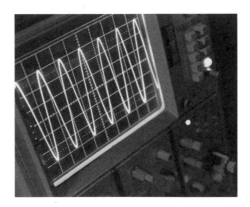

What is the mean voltage?

In this chapter you will build on the following techniques that you learnt previously.

Differentiation

- The product rule: $\dfrac{d}{dx}(uv) = v\dfrac{du}{dx} + u\dfrac{dv}{dx}$

- The quotient rule: $\dfrac{d}{dx}\left(\dfrac{u}{v}\right) = \dfrac{v\dfrac{du}{dx} - u\dfrac{dv}{dx}}{v^2}$

- The chain rule: $\dfrac{dy}{dx} = \dfrac{dy}{du} \times \dfrac{du}{dx}$

Integration

- By substitution, as in

$$\int (3x - 2)^5 \, dx = \int \tfrac{1}{3} u^5 \, du$$
$$= \tfrac{1}{3} \times \tfrac{1}{6} u^6 + c$$
$$= \tfrac{1}{18}(3x - 2)^6 + c.$$

$u = 3x - 2$
$\Rightarrow \dfrac{du}{dx} = 3$
$\Rightarrow \tfrac{1}{3} du = dx$

In a simple example like this you may well be able to go straight to the result, mentally checking that differentiating $\tfrac{1}{18}(3x - 2)^6 + c$ gives $(3x - 2)^5$, without having to make a substitution. This is described as 'by inspection'. One important example of this is when integrating a fraction in which the numerator is the derivative of the denominator: $\displaystyle\int \dfrac{f'(x)}{f(x)} \, dx = \ln|f(x)| + c.$

- By parts, using the formula $\displaystyle\int u \dfrac{dv}{dx} \, dx = uv - \int \dfrac{du}{dx} v \, dx.$

Differentiation and integration of trigonometric functions

- $\dfrac{d}{dx}(\sin x) = \cos x \qquad \dfrac{d}{dx}(\cos x) = -\sin x \qquad \dfrac{d}{dx}(\tan x) = \sec^2 x.$

- $\displaystyle\int \sin x \, dx = -\cos x + c \qquad \int \cos x \, dx = \sin x + c.$

For example

$$\int \sin 5x \, dx = \int \tfrac{1}{5}\sin u \, du$$
$$= -\tfrac{1}{5}\cos u + c$$
$$= -\tfrac{1}{5}\cos 5x + c.$$

$u = 5x$
$\Rightarrow \dfrac{du}{dx} = 5$
$\Rightarrow dx = \tfrac{1}{5} du$

Again you may well be able to do this integration by inspection, or by quoting the general result,

$$\int \sin kx \, dx = -\frac{1}{k}\cos kx + c.$$

Similarly, $\displaystyle\int \cos kx \, dx = \frac{1}{k}\sin kx + c.$

EXAMPLE 1.1

Find $\displaystyle\int 2x \cos(x^2 + 1) \, dx$.

SOLUTION

$$\int 2x \cos(x^2 + 1) \, dx = \int \cos u \, du$$
$$= \sin u + c$$
$$= \sin(x^2 + 1) + c$$

$u = x^2 + 1$
$\Rightarrow \dfrac{du}{dx} = 2x$
$\Rightarrow 2x \, dx = du$

Notice that Example 1.1 involved integrating the product of the function, $2x$, and the 'function of a function', $\cos(x^2 + 1)$. It is because $2x$ is the derivative of $(x^2 + 1)$ that the substitution $u = x^2 + 1$ is useful. Example 1.2 is of a similar type.

EXAMPLE 1.2

Find $\displaystyle\int \cos x \sin^2 x \, dx$.

SOLUTION

This integral is the product of the function, $\cos x$, and the 'function of a function', $\sin^2 x = (\sin x)^2$. Here $\cos x$ is the derivative of $\sin x$, so the substitution $u = \sin x$ should be helpful.

Differentiating, $\dfrac{du}{dx} = \cos x \Rightarrow du = \cos x \, dx.$

Therefore

$$\int \cos x \sin^2 x \, dx = \int u^2 \, du$$
$$= \tfrac{1}{3}u^3 + c$$
$$= \tfrac{1}{3}\sin^3 x + c.$$

With practice you will learn how to work out this kind of integral by inspection. But if in doubt it is best to write down the whole substitution process.

Using trigonometric identities in integration

Sometimes trigonometric identities can help when you are integrating a trigonometric function. The next example uses the identity $\sin^2 x + \cos^2 x \equiv 1$. The method is typical when you have an odd power of $\sin x$ or $\cos x$.

EXAMPLE 1.3

Find $\int \cos^3 x \, dx$.

SOLUTION

Notice that

$$\cos^3 x = \cos x \cos^2 x$$
$$= \cos x(1 - \sin^2 x)$$
$$= \cos x - \cos x \sin^2 x.$$

Integrating $\cos x$ is easy.

You integrated $\cos x \sin^2 x$ in Example 1.2. Use either substitution or inspection.

Therefore

$$\int \cos^3 x \, dx = \int (\cos x - \cos x \sin^2 x) \, dx$$
$$= \sin x - \tfrac{1}{3} \sin^3 x + c.$$

When you have an even power of $\sin x$ or $\cos x$, use one of the identities associated with $\cos 2x$, as in the next example.

EXAMPLE 1.4

Find $\int \sin^2 x \, dx$.

SOLUTION

The identity $\cos 2x \equiv 1 - 2\sin^2 x \Rightarrow 2\sin^2 x \equiv 1 - \cos 2x$.
Then

$$\int \sin^2 x \, dx = \tfrac{1}{2} \int (1 - \cos 2x) \, dx$$
$$= \tfrac{1}{2}\left(x - \tfrac{1}{2}\sin 2x\right) + c$$
$$= \tfrac{1}{2}x - \tfrac{1}{4}\sin 2x + c.$$

The same method can be used to integrate $\cos^2 x$, using $\cos^2 x \equiv \tfrac{1}{2}(\cos 2x + 1)$. Higher even powers of $\sin x$ and $\cos x$ can be integrated in a similar way, but you have to use the identity more than once.

ACTIVITY 1.1

By expressing $\cos^4 x$ as $(\cos^2 x)^2$ and $\cos^2 x$ as $\tfrac{1}{2}(\cos 2x + 1)$ show that

$$\cos^4 x = \tfrac{1}{8}\cos 4x + \tfrac{1}{2}\cos 2x + \tfrac{3}{8}$$

and hence find $\int \cos^4 x \, dx$.

The *mean* value of the function $f(x)$ over the interval $a \leqslant x \leqslant b$ is defined as

$$\frac{1}{b-a} \int_a^b f(x)\, dx.$$

Over the same interval the *root mean square* value of $f(x)$ is defined as

$$\sqrt{\frac{1}{b-a} \int_a^b (f(x))^2 dx}.$$ When the function is periodic, the interval chosen is usually a whole number of periods. These processes are useful in both physics and statistics.

ACTIVITY 1.2
(i) Find the root mean square value of $a \sin t$ over a single period.

(ii) In the UK, mains electricity is usually supplied as alternating current at a nominal 240 volts. This is the root mean square of the supply voltage, $a \sin t$. Show that the supply peaks at about 339 V.

Starting from the compound angle formulae $\sin(\theta \pm \phi) = \sin\theta\cos\phi \pm \cos\theta\sin\phi$ you can readily show that $\sin\theta\cos\phi = \frac{1}{2}(\sin(\theta+\phi) + \sin(\theta-\phi))$. This enables you to express the integral of the product of a sine and a cosine as the integral of the sum of two sines. For example

$$\int \sin 3x \cos 2x\, dx = \tfrac{1}{2}\int (\sin 5x + \sin x)\, dx$$

$$= -\tfrac{1}{10}\cos 5x - \tfrac{1}{2}\cos x + c.$$

ACTIVITY 1.3
(i) Starting from $\cos(\theta \pm \phi) = \cos\theta\cos\phi \mp \sin\theta\sin\phi$ show that

$$\cos\theta\cos\phi = \tfrac{1}{2}(\cos(\theta+\phi) + \cos(\theta-\phi))$$

and state and prove a similar result for $\sin\theta\sin\phi$.

(ii) Hence find
(a) $\int \cos 3x \cos x\, dx$
(b) $\int \sin 5x \sin 2x\, dx$.

Another trigonometric identity is $\tan x = \dfrac{\sin x}{\cos x}$. This allows you to find the integral of $\tan x$. Since $\dfrac{d}{dx}(\cos x) = -\sin x$, $\displaystyle\int \frac{-\sin x}{\cos x}\, dx = \ln(\cos x) + c$.

So
$$\int \frac{\sin x}{\cos x}\, dx = \int \tan x\, dx = -\ln|\cos x| + c.$$

$$= \ln\left|\frac{1}{\cos x}\right| + c$$

$$= \ln|\sec x| + c.$$

EXAMPLE 1.5

Find $\int \tan kx \, dx$.

SOLUTION

Notice that $\tan kx = \dfrac{\sin kx}{\cos kx}$ and $\dfrac{d}{dx}(\cos kx) = -k \sin kx$.

So
$$\int \tan kx \, dx = -\frac{1}{k} \int -\frac{k \sin kx}{\cos kx} \, dx$$

$$= -\frac{1}{k} \ln |\cos kx| + c$$

$$= \frac{1}{k} \ln |\sec x| + c.$$

EXERCISE 1A

1 Integrate these functions with respect to x.

(i) $\cos^2 x$ **(ii)** $\sin^2 3x$ **(iii)** $\sec^2 x$

(iv) $\sin^3 x$ **(v)** $\sin^4 x$ **(vi)** $\cos^5 x$

(vii) $\tan 2x$ **(viii)** $\cot x$ **(ix)** $\cot x + \tan x$

2 Find the following indefinite integrals.

(i) $\int \sin x \cos^2 x \, dx$ **(ii)** $\int \cos^2 3x \, dx$ **(iii)** $\int \sin 5x \cos 2x \, dx$

(iv) $\int (1 + \sin x)^2 \, dx$ **(v)** $\int (\sin x + \cos x)^2 \, dx$ **(vi)** $\int \sec^2 x \tan x \, dx$

3 Evaluate these definite integrals, using substitution where necessary.

(i) $\displaystyle\int_0^{\frac{\pi}{4}} \cos x \sin^3 x \, dx$ **(ii)** $\displaystyle\int_0^{\frac{\pi}{4}} \frac{\sec^2 x}{1 + \tan x} \, dx$ **(iii)** $\displaystyle\int_0^{\sqrt{\pi}} x \sin (x^2) \, dx$

(iv) $\displaystyle\int_0^{\frac{\pi}{4}} \tan^2 x \, dx$ **(v)** $\displaystyle\int_0^{\frac{\pi}{2}} \sin 6x \cos 4x \, dx$ **(vi)** $\displaystyle\int_0^{\frac{\pi}{4}} \sin 3x \sin 4x \, dx$

4 (i) Use a graphic calculator or a computer to sketch the graph of

$$y = \sin x (\cos x - 1)^2 \text{ for } 0 \leqslant x \leqslant 4\pi.$$

(ii) Find the area enclosed between the x axis and the positive part of one cycle of the curve.

5 By expressing $\cos x$ in terms of $\cos \dfrac{x}{2}$ find $\displaystyle\int \frac{1}{1 + \cos x} \, dx$.

6 (i) Find $\dfrac{d}{dx}(\cos 2x)$ and hence show that $\int \sin 2x \, dx = -\frac{1}{2} \cos 2x + A$.

(ii) Use the identity $\sin 2x \equiv 2 \sin x \cos x$ and the fact that

$\dfrac{d}{dx}(\sin x) = \cos x$ to show that $\int \sin 2x \, dx = \sin^2 x + B$.

(iii) Use the identity $\sin 2x \equiv 2 \sin x \cos x$ and the fact that

$\dfrac{d}{dx}(\cos x) = -\sin x$ to show that $\int \sin 2x \, dx = -\cos^2 x + C$.

(iv) Explain how these three different looking answers can all be correct!

7 Find the mistake in the following argument.

$$I = \int \tan x \, dx = \int \sin x \sec x \, dx$$
$$= -\cos x \sec x + \int \cos x \sec x \tan x \, dx$$
$$= -1 + \int \tan x \, dx$$
$$= -1 + I$$

Therefore $0 = -1$.

The inverse trigonometric functions

The arcsine function

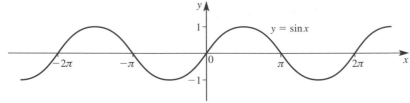

Figure 1.1

Figure 1.1 shows the graph of $y = \sin x$. The sine function is a many-to-one function: many values of x (for example: -2π, $-\pi$, 0, π, 2π, etc.) give the same value of y.

You can find the inverse of any function by interchanging x and y in the defining equation; this is equivalent to reflecting the graph in the line $y = x$.
In the case of $y = \sin x$ you obtain the graph shown in figure 1.2; its equation is $x = \sin y$. For any value of x (between -1 and 1) there are infinitely many values of y, so figure 1.2 is not the graph of a function. However, by restricting the range of y you can define a function, so that each value of x (between -1 and 1) is associated with a unique value of y. There are infinitely many ways of doing this, but it is conventional (and sensible) to include $0 \leqslant y \leqslant \dfrac{\pi}{2}$ (i.e. angles in the first quadrant) as part of the required range, corresponding to $0 \leqslant x \leqslant 1$.

To keep the function continuous (and to have as large a domain as possible) you include $-\dfrac{\pi}{2} \leqslant y < 0$, fourth quadrant angles, corresponding to $-1 \leqslant x < 0$. Figure 1.3 shows the complete graph of this function. Its equation is $y = \arcsin x$. (Older textbooks and many modern calculators use the notation $\sin^{-1} x$.) You will notice that the gradient of $y = \arcsin x$ is always positive, and that the gradient tends to infinity as $|x|$ tends to 1.

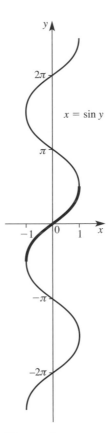

Figure 1.2

Now
$$y = \arcsin x$$

$\Rightarrow \quad \sin y = x$

$\Rightarrow \quad \dfrac{dy}{dx} \cos y = 1$

$\Rightarrow \quad \dfrac{dy}{dx} = \dfrac{1}{\cos y}$

$$= \dfrac{1}{\pm\sqrt{1 - \sin^2 y}}$$

$$= \dfrac{1}{\pm\sqrt{1 - x^2}}.$$

But $y = \arcsin x \Rightarrow -\dfrac{\pi}{2} \leqslant y \leqslant \dfrac{\pi}{2} \Rightarrow \cos y \geqslant 0$,

so that $\cos y = +\sqrt{1 - x^2}$. The conclusion is

that $\dfrac{d}{dx}(\arcsin x) = \dfrac{1}{\sqrt{1 - x^2}}.$

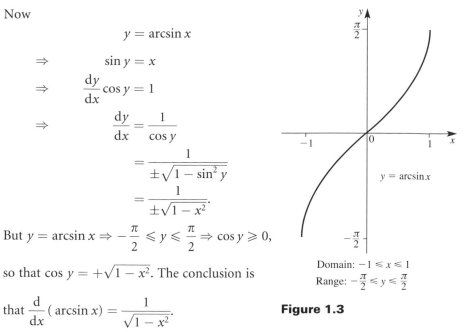

Domain: $-1 \leqslant x \leqslant 1$
Range: $-\dfrac{\pi}{2} \leqslant y \leqslant \dfrac{\pi}{2}$

Figure 1.3

Notice that the expression $\dfrac{1}{\sqrt{1 - x^2}}$

- is positive and only defined for $-1 < x < 1$

- has a minimum at $x = 0$

- tends to ∞ as x tends to ± 1

all of which is consistent with the graph in figure 1.3.

The arccosine function

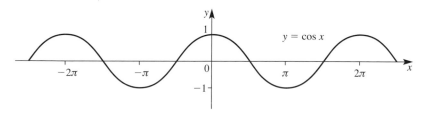

Figure 1.4

The inverse of the cosine function is dealt with in much the same way.
Figure 1.4 shows the graph of $y = \cos x$. Reflecting the graph of figure 1.4 in the
line $y = x$ produces the graph with equation $x = \cos y$, shown in figure 1.5. This
is not the graph of a function. However, a function can be defined by restricting
the range of y so that each value of x (between -1 and 1) is associated with a

unique value of y. Again the values $0 \leqslant y \leqslant \dfrac{\pi}{2}$ are included (first quadrant angles), corresponding to $0 \leqslant x \leqslant 1$. To maximise the domain and preserve continuity, the range includes $\dfrac{\pi}{2} < y \leqslant \pi$, second quadrant angles. Figure 1.6 shows the complete graph of this function. Its equation is $y = \arccos x$.

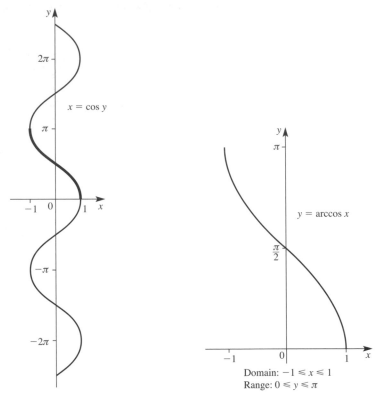

Figure 1.5   Figure 1.6

ACTIVITY 1.4
(i)   From the various graphs (without using calculus) what can you say about the gradient of $y = \arccos x$?

(ii) Use calculus to show that $\dfrac{\mathrm{d}}{\mathrm{d}x}(\arccos x) = -\dfrac{1}{\sqrt{1 - x^2}}$.

The arctangent function

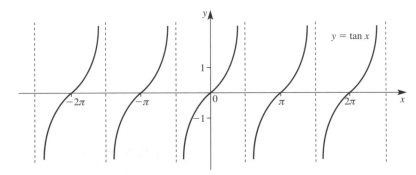

Figure 1.7

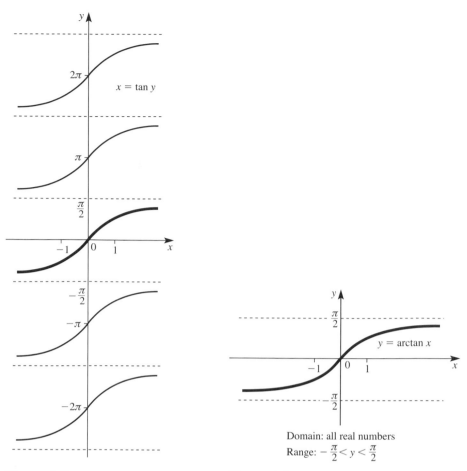

Figure 1.8

Domain: all real numbers
Range: $-\frac{\pi}{2} < y < \frac{\pi}{2}$

Figure 1.9

ACTIVITY 1.5 Describe the relationship of the various graphs shown in figures 1.7, 1.8 and 1.9.

Notice that the graph of $y = \arctan x$ has horizontal asymptotes. Describe qualitatively how its gradient varies and then use calculus methods to show that

$$\frac{\mathrm{d}}{\mathrm{d}x}(\arctan x) = \frac{1}{1 + x^2}.$$

The results $\dfrac{\mathrm{d}}{\mathrm{d}x}(\arcsin x) = \dfrac{1}{\sqrt{1 - x^2}}$ and $\dfrac{\mathrm{d}}{\mathrm{d}x}(\arctan x) = \dfrac{1}{1 + x^2}$ are particularly important, allowing you to integrate additional functions, as is shown in the next section.

ACTIVITY 1.6 Show that
(i) $\operatorname{arcsec} x \equiv \arccos\left(\dfrac{1}{x}\right)$

(ii) $\operatorname{arccosec} x \equiv \arcsin\left(\dfrac{1}{x}\right)$

(iii) $\operatorname{arccot} x \equiv \arctan\left(\dfrac{1}{x}\right)$ with $\operatorname{arccot} 0 = \dfrac{\pi}{2}$.

These formulae are useful as calculators, spreadsheets and other mathematical software frequently include only the three elementary trigonometric functions and their inverses.

General solutions

If you are looking for the *general solution* of an equation, you want a rule or formula which will give you all the solutions, but no other values.

For example: one root of the equation $\sin x = \dfrac{1}{2}$ is $x = \arcsin\dfrac{1}{2} = \dfrac{\pi}{6}$; another root is $x = \pi - \dfrac{\pi}{6} = \dfrac{5\pi}{6}$; all roots are in the first or second quadrants as $\sin x$ is positive. Every solution may be regarded as a number of complete rotations plus $\dfrac{\pi}{6}$ or $\dfrac{5\pi}{6}$.

These two forms may be written as

$$x = 2m\pi + \frac{\pi}{6} \text{ or } (2m+1)\pi - \frac{\pi}{6}, \text{ where } m \text{ is any integer.}$$

Alternatively you may combine these two expressions and write the general solution of $\sin x = \dfrac{1}{2}$ as $x = n\pi + (-1)^n\dfrac{\pi}{6}$, where n is any integer.

The table shows the other important forms.

Equation	Form of the general solution (n is any integer)
$\sin x = y$	$x = n\pi + (-1)^n \arcsin y$
$\cos x = y$	$x = 2n\pi \pm \arccos y$
$\tan x = y$	$x = n\pi + \arctan y$

EXERCISE 1B

1 State the domain and range of the inverse sine, cosine and tangent functions.

2 Show that $\arcsin x + \arccos x \equiv \dfrac{\pi}{2}$.

3 Show that $\arcsin(-x) = -\arcsin x$, and that $\arctan(-x) = -\arctan x$. State and prove a formula connecting $\arccos(-x)$ and $\arccos x$.

4 Show that $\arcsin(\sin \pi) \neq \pi$. Under what circumstances is $\arcsin(\sin x) = x$?

5 Show that $\arccos\sqrt{1-x} \equiv \arcsin\sqrt{x}$.

6 Differentiate the following with respect to x.
   (i) $\arcsin x$ **(ii)** $\arcsin 5x$
   (iii) $\arctan\dfrac{3x}{2}$ **(iv)** $\arctan(2-3x)$

7 Differentiate the following with respect to x.

    (i) $\arcsin 2x$ **(ii)** $\arctan 5x$

    (iii) $\arcsin 3x^2$ **(iv)** $\arccos 2x$

    (v) $\arctan(e^x)$ **(vi)** $\arctan(1 - x^2)$

    (vii) $\arccos(5x^2 - 2)$ **(viii)** $\arcsin \sqrt{x}$

8 If $f(x) \equiv \sin x + \cos x$, $-\dfrac{\pi}{4} < x < \dfrac{\pi}{4}$, find $f^{-1}(x)$.

9 Write down the derivatives of $\arcsin x$ and $\arccos x$. Hence show that

$\displaystyle\int \dfrac{1}{\sqrt{1 - x^2}}\, dx$ may be expressed as $\arcsin x + c_1$ and as $-\arccos x + c_2$, where c_1 and c_2 are arbitrary constants. Explain how the two results are compatible, and express c_2 in terms of c_1.

10 In each of the following, find the general solution of the equation. Where possible give your answer as a rational multiple of π; otherwise leave your answer in a form involving an inverse trigonometric function.

    (i) $\sin 2x = \sin x$ **(ii)** $\cos x - \sin x = \sqrt{2}$

    (iii) $3\cos x + 4\sin x = 2.5$ **(iv)** $\tan 2x = 4\tan x$

    (v) $\cos x = \cos\frac{1}{2}x$ **(vi)** $2\sin x = \cos x + 1$

11 State the domain and range of

    (i) $y = \text{arcsec}\,x$ **(ii)** $y = \text{arccosec}\,x$

    (iii) $y = \text{arccot}\,x$.

12 **(i)** **(a)** By sketching the graph of $y = \text{arcsec}\,x$ show that $\dfrac{d}{dx}(\text{arcsec}\,x) > 0$.

      (b) Show that $\dfrac{d}{dx}(\text{arcsec}\,x) = \dfrac{1}{|x|\sqrt{x^2 - 1}}$.

    (ii) Find

      (a) $\dfrac{d}{dx}(\text{arccosec}\,x)$ **(b)** $\dfrac{d}{dx}(\text{arccot}\,x)$.

13 **(i)** Evaluate $\text{arcsec}\,x + \text{arccosec}\,x$.

    (ii) Evaluate $\arctan x + \text{arccot}\,x$.

Integration using inverse trigonometric functions

The inverse sine and tangent functions are particularly useful in integration.

Integration using the arcsine function

Since $\dfrac{d}{dx}(\arcsin x) = \dfrac{1}{\sqrt{1 - x^2}}$ you know that $\displaystyle\int \dfrac{1}{\sqrt{1 - x^2}}\, dx = \arcsin x + c.$

You will see the similarity between $\displaystyle\int \dfrac{1}{\sqrt{9 - x^2}}\, dx$ and $\displaystyle\int \dfrac{1}{\sqrt{1 - x^2}}\, dx$ and you may well (correctly) guess that $\displaystyle\int \dfrac{1}{\sqrt{9 - x^2}}\, dx$ takes a similar form, but you will perhaps be unsure what effect the number 9 has on the expression. Try treating 9 as a factor:

$$\int \frac{1}{\sqrt{9-x^2}}\,dx = \int \frac{1}{\sqrt{9\left(1-\dfrac{x^2}{9}\right)}}\,dx$$

$$= \int \frac{1}{3\sqrt{1-\left(\dfrac{x}{3}\right)^2}}\,dx$$

Let $3u = x$ so that $3\,du = dx$.

$$= \int \frac{1}{3\sqrt{1-u^2}} \times 3\,du$$

$$= \int \frac{1}{\sqrt{1-u^2}}\,du = \arcsin u + c = \arcsin \frac{x}{3} + c.$$

You can now construct the formula for $\displaystyle\int \frac{1}{\sqrt{a^2-x^2}}\,dx$, where a is a positive constant.

As $x = 3u$ was a useful substitution when the denominator was $\sqrt{9-x^2}$, it makes sense to use the substitution $x = au$ so that $dx = a\,du$:

$$\int \frac{1}{\sqrt{a^2-x^2}}\,dx = \int \frac{1}{\sqrt{a^2-(au)^2}} \times a\,du$$

$$= \int \frac{1}{a\sqrt{1-u^2}} \times a\,du$$

$$= \int \frac{1}{\sqrt{1-u^2}}\,du = \arcsin u + c = \arcsin \frac{x}{a} + c.$$

EXAMPLE 1.6

Find **(i)** $\displaystyle\int \frac{1}{\sqrt{16-x^2}}\,dx$ **(ii)** $\displaystyle\int \frac{1}{\sqrt{16-3x^2}}\,dx.$

SOLUTION

(i) $\displaystyle\int \frac{1}{\sqrt{16-x^2}}\,dx = \arcsin \frac{x}{4} + c.$

This is of the form $\int \frac{1}{\sqrt{a^2-x^2}}\,dx$ with $a = 4$.

(ii) $\displaystyle\int \frac{1}{\sqrt{16-3x^2}}\,dx = \frac{1}{\sqrt{3}}\int \frac{1}{\sqrt{\frac{16}{3}-x^2}}\,dx = \frac{1}{\sqrt{3}}\arcsin \frac{x\sqrt{3}}{4} + c.$

Take out the factor $\sqrt{3}$, then as in **(i)** with $a = \frac{4}{\sqrt{3}}$.

Integration using the arctangent function

In the same way knowing that $\dfrac{d}{dx}(\arctan x) = \dfrac{1}{1 + x^2}$ so that

$\displaystyle\int \dfrac{1}{1 + x^2}\,dx = \arctan x + c$ may well lead you to guess that $\displaystyle\int \dfrac{1}{a^2 + x^2}\,dx$ takes a similar form. But

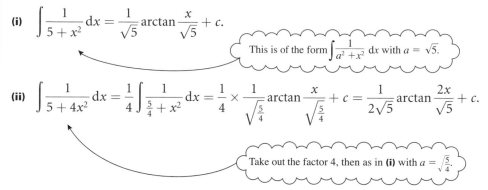

$$\int \dfrac{1}{a^2 + x^2}\,dx = \int \dfrac{1}{a^2 + a^2 u^2} \times a\,du \qquad \text{putting } au = x \text{ so that } a\,du = dx$$

$$= \int \dfrac{1}{a(1 + u^2)}\,du \qquad \text{Notice the factor } \dfrac{1}{a}.$$

$$= \dfrac{1}{a}\arctan u + c = \dfrac{1}{a}\arctan\dfrac{x}{a} + c.$$

EXAMPLE 1.7

Find **(i)** $\displaystyle\int \dfrac{1}{5 + x^2}\,dx$ **(ii)** $\displaystyle\int \dfrac{1}{5 + 4x^2}\,dx.$

SOLUTION

(i) $\displaystyle\int \dfrac{1}{5 + x^2}\,dx = \dfrac{1}{\sqrt{5}}\arctan\dfrac{x}{\sqrt{5}} + c.$

> This is of the form $\displaystyle\int \dfrac{1}{a^2 + x^2}\,dx$ with $a = \sqrt{5}$.

(ii) $\displaystyle\int \dfrac{1}{5 + 4x^2}\,dx = \dfrac{1}{4}\int \dfrac{1}{\frac{5}{4} + x^2}\,dx = \dfrac{1}{4} \times \dfrac{1}{\sqrt{\frac{5}{4}}}\arctan\dfrac{x}{\sqrt{\frac{5}{4}}} + c = \dfrac{1}{2\sqrt{5}}\arctan\dfrac{2x}{\sqrt{5}} + c.$

> Take out the factor 4, then as in **(i)** with $a = \sqrt{\frac{5}{4}}$.

Note

Dimensions will help you understand (and remember) why the factor $\dfrac{1}{a}$ is needed in

$$\int \dfrac{1}{a^2 + x^2}\,dx = \dfrac{1}{a}\arctan\dfrac{x}{a} + c \qquad\qquad\qquad ①$$

but not in

$$\int \dfrac{1}{\sqrt{a^2 - x^2}}\,dx = \arcsin\dfrac{x}{a} + c. \qquad\qquad\qquad ②$$

Integration is a form of summation. In both integrals dx is a length. In ② the expression $\dfrac{1}{\sqrt{a^2 - x^2}}$ is a number divided by the square root of an area; multiplying by dx gives a dimensionless number; the sum of a series of numbers is dimensionless; $\arcsin\dfrac{x}{a}$ is an angle, also dimensionless – $r\theta$ is well known as an expression for the length of an arc of a circle, where r is the radius (a length) and θ the angle of the arc, in radians. So ② is dimensionally correct. In ① the expression $\dfrac{1}{a^2 + x^2}$ is a number divided by an area; multiplying by dx gives the dimension L^{-1} (i.e. the reciprocal of a length); summing these does not change the dimension; $\arctan \dfrac{x}{a}$ is dimensionless and multiplying it by something like $\dfrac{1}{a}$ (with the dimension L^{-1}) makes the two sides of ① agree dimensionally. (In ① the constant c has the dimension L^{-1}; in ② the constant c is dimensionless.)

The next example involves definite integration.

EXAMPLE 1.8

Evaluate $\displaystyle\int_0^2 \dfrac{1}{4 + x^2}\,dx$.

SOLUTION

$$\int_0^2 \dfrac{1}{4 + x^2}\,dx = \left[\dfrac{1}{2}\arctan\dfrac{x}{2}\right]_0^2 = \dfrac{1}{2}(\arctan 1 - \arctan 0) = \dfrac{\pi}{8}.$$

ALTERNATIVE APPROACH

Alternatively you may make the substitution $x = 2\tan u$, remembering to change the limits of integration at the same time. But the equation $x = 2\tan u$ does not define u uniquely: given $x = 0$, for example, u may be 0, or π, or any multiple of π. However, though it looks more cumbersome, the equation $u = \arctan\dfrac{x}{2}$ does define u uniquely, and is the preferred way of stating the substitution. Then

$$\int_0^2 \dfrac{1}{4 + x^2}\,dx = \int_0^{\frac{\pi}{4}} \dfrac{2\sec^2 u}{4\sec^2 u}\,du \quad \text{where } u = \arctan\dfrac{x}{2} \Rightarrow x = 2\tan u$$

$$\Rightarrow dx = 2\sec^2 u\,du;$$

$$= \int_0^{\frac{\pi}{4}} \dfrac{1}{2}\,du \qquad \text{when } x = 2,\ u = \dfrac{\pi}{4}; \text{ when } x = 0,\ u = 0.$$

$$= \dfrac{1}{2}\left[u\right]_0^{\frac{\pi}{4}} = \dfrac{\pi}{8}.$$

EXERCISE 1C

1 Find the following indefinite integrals.

(i) $\displaystyle\int \dfrac{1}{25 + x^2}\,dx$ (ii) $\displaystyle\int \dfrac{1}{\sqrt{36 - x^2}}\,dx$

(iii) $\displaystyle\int \dfrac{5}{x^2 + 36}\,dx$ (iv) $\displaystyle\int \dfrac{4}{25 + 4x^2}\,dx$

(v) $\displaystyle\int \dfrac{1}{\sqrt{9 - 4x^2}}\,dx$ (vi) $\displaystyle\int \dfrac{7}{\sqrt{5 - 3x^2}}\,dx$

2 Evaluate the following definite integrals, leaving your answers in terms of π.

(i) $\displaystyle\int_0^3 \frac{1}{9+x^2}\,\mathrm{d}x$

(ii) $\displaystyle\int_0^{\sqrt{2}} \frac{1}{\sqrt{4-x^2}}\,\mathrm{d}x$

(iii) $\displaystyle\int_{-\frac{1}{\sqrt{3}}}^{\frac{1}{3}} \frac{1}{1+9x^2}\,\mathrm{d}x$

(iv) $\displaystyle\int_0^{\frac{1}{4}} \frac{1}{\sqrt{1-4x^2}}\,\mathrm{d}x$

(v) $\displaystyle\int_{-\frac{1}{2}}^{\frac{1}{2}} \frac{1}{\sqrt{3-6x^2}}\,\mathrm{d}x$

(vi) $\displaystyle\int_{\sqrt{5/6}}^{\sqrt{5/2}} \frac{1}{5+2x^2}\,\mathrm{d}x$

3 (i) Find $\displaystyle\int \frac{1}{9+16x^2}\,\mathrm{d}x$.

(ii) Using the substitution $x = 2\sin\theta$, or otherwise, show that

$$\int_1^2 \sqrt{4-x^2}\,\mathrm{d}x = \frac{2\pi}{3} - \frac{\sqrt{3}}{2}.$$

[MEI, part]

Harder integrations

You have been integrating functions of the form: $\dfrac{1}{a^2+x^2}$ and $\dfrac{1}{\sqrt{a^2-x^2}}$.

The example below shows how the formula $\displaystyle\int \frac{1}{a^2+x^2}\,\mathrm{d}x = \frac{1}{a}\arctan\frac{x}{a}+c$ helps you integrate rational functions with constant numerator, and a denominator which is quadratic with no real roots.

EXAMPLE 1.9

Find $\displaystyle\int \frac{4}{x^2-2x+3}\,\mathrm{d}x$.

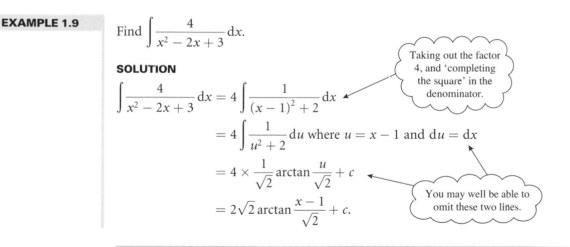

SOLUTION

$$\int \frac{4}{x^2-2x+3}\,\mathrm{d}x = 4\int \frac{1}{(x-1)^2+2}\,\mathrm{d}x$$

Taking out the factor 4, and 'completing the square' in the denominator.

$$= 4\int \frac{1}{u^2+2}\,\mathrm{d}u \text{ where } u = x-1 \text{ and } \mathrm{d}u = \mathrm{d}x$$

$$= 4 \times \frac{1}{\sqrt{2}}\arctan\frac{u}{\sqrt{2}}+c$$

You may well be able to omit these two lines.

$$= 2\sqrt{2}\arctan\frac{x-1}{\sqrt{2}}+c.$$

❓ When trying to integrate $\dfrac{1}{Ax^2+Bx+C}$ how can you tell if Ax^2+Bx+C has no real roots? And what should you do if A is negative?

The next example shows how the formula $\int \dfrac{1}{\sqrt{a^2 - x^2}} dx = \arcsin \dfrac{x}{a} + c$ helps you integrate functions that can be arranged as a fraction, with constant numerator, and a denominator which is the square root of a quadratic; this quadratic must have distinct real roots and the coefficient of x^2 must be negative.

EXAMPLE 1.10

Find $\int \dfrac{5}{\sqrt{2 + 4x - 4x^2}} dx$.

SOLUTION

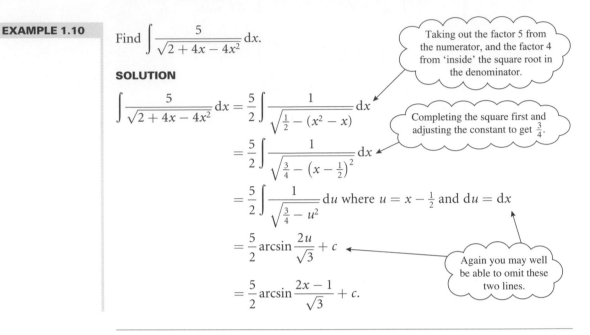

$$\int \frac{5}{\sqrt{2 + 4x - 4x^2}} dx = \frac{5}{2} \int \frac{1}{\sqrt{\frac{1}{2} - (x^2 - x)}} dx$$

Taking out the factor 5 from the numerator, and the factor 4 from 'inside' the square root in the denominator.

$$= \frac{5}{2} \int \frac{1}{\sqrt{\frac{3}{4} - \left(x - \frac{1}{2}\right)^2}} dx$$

Completing the square first and adjusting the constant to get $\frac{3}{4}$.

$$= \frac{5}{2} \int \frac{1}{\sqrt{\frac{3}{4} - u^2}} du \text{ where } u = x - \frac{1}{2} \text{ and } du = dx$$

$$= \frac{5}{2} \arcsin \frac{2u}{\sqrt{3}} + c$$

Again you may well be able to omit these two lines.

$$= \frac{5}{2} \arcsin \frac{2x - 1}{\sqrt{3}} + c.$$

? When using the formula $\int \dfrac{1}{\sqrt{a^2 - x^2}} dx = \arcsin \dfrac{x}{a} + c$ to integrate

$\dfrac{1}{\sqrt{Ax^2 + Bx + C}}$ why is it necessary to have A negative and $B^2 > 4AC$?

The final example illustrates other ways these techniques may be used.

EXAMPLE 1.11

Find **(i)** $\int \dfrac{x + 5}{x^2 + 4} dx$ **(ii)** $\int \dfrac{x}{\sqrt{1 - x^2}} dx$ **(iii)** $\int \dfrac{9x - 8}{(x^2 + 9)(x + 2)} dx$.

SOLUTION

(i) $\int \dfrac{x + 5}{x^2 + 4} dx = \int \left(\dfrac{x}{x^2 + 4} + \dfrac{5}{x^2 + 4} \right) dx$

The fraction being integrated is split into two parts: one numerator = constant × derivative of denominator; the other numerator is constant.

$$= \frac{1}{2} \int \frac{2x}{x^2 + 4} dx + 5 \int \frac{1}{x^2 + 4} dx$$

$$= \frac{1}{2} \ln (x^2 + 4) + 5 \times \frac{1}{2} \arctan \frac{x}{2} + c$$

$$= \frac{1}{2} \ln (x^2 + 4) + \frac{5}{2} \arctan \frac{x}{2} + c.$$

(ii) $\displaystyle\int \frac{x}{\sqrt{1-x^2}}\,dx$ is best found by inspection:

$$\frac{d}{dx}(1-x^2)^{\frac{1}{2}} = \frac{1}{2}(1-x^2)^{-\frac{1}{2}} \times (-2x) = -\frac{x}{\sqrt{1-x^2}}$$

> Alternatively use any of the substitutions $u = \arcsin x$; $u = 1 - x^2,\ u^2 = 1 - x^2.$

so that $\displaystyle\int \frac{x}{\sqrt{1-x^2}}\,dx = -\sqrt{1-x^2} + c.$

(iii) $\displaystyle\int \frac{9x-8}{(x^2+9)(x+2)}\,dx = \int\left(\frac{2x+5}{x^2+9} - \frac{2}{x+2}\right)dx$

> The rational function being integrated is expressed in partial fractions.

$$= \int \frac{2x+5}{x^2+9}\,dx - \int \frac{2}{x+2}\,dx$$

$$= \int \frac{2x}{x^2+9}\,dx + \int \frac{5}{x^2+9}\,dx - \int \frac{2}{x+2}\,dx$$

$$= \ln(x^2+9) + 5 \times \frac{1}{3}\arctan\frac{x}{3} - 2\ln|x+2| + c$$

$$= \ln\frac{x^2+9}{(x+2)^2} + \frac{5}{3}\arctan\frac{x}{3} + c.$$

> As x^2+9 and $(x+2)^2$ are clearly positive you do not need to use modulus signs here.

---

1 Find the following integrals.

(i) $\displaystyle\int \frac{1}{4+(x+2)^2}\,dx$

(ii) $\displaystyle\int \frac{7}{\sqrt{5+4x-x^2}}\,dx$

(iii) $\displaystyle\int \frac{3}{3+2x^2}\,dx$

(iv) $\displaystyle\int \frac{3}{9x^2+6x+5}\,dx$

(v) $\displaystyle\int \frac{1}{\sqrt{3+2x-x^2}}\,dx$

(vi) $\displaystyle\int \frac{7}{\sqrt{3-4x-4x^2}}\,dx$

2 (i) By writing $\arcsin x$ as $1 \times \arcsin x$ use integration by parts to find $\int \arcsin x\,dx$.

(ii) Use a similar method to find the following integrals.

(a) $\int \arccos x\,dx$

(b) $\int \arctan x\,dx$

(c) $\int \text{arccot}\,x\,dx$

3 (i) Use the substitution $x = a \sin u$ to find

$$\int_0^b \sqrt{(a^2 - x^2)}\, dx, \text{ where } a > b > 0.$$

(ii) Draw a sketch to show the significance of the area you calculated in part **(i)**, and explain both terms of your answer to part **(i)** geometrically.

4 Find the following integrals.

(i) $\displaystyle\int \frac{1}{x^2 - 6x + 13}\, dx$

(ii) $\displaystyle\int \frac{1}{\sqrt{7 - 12x - 4x^2}}\, dx$

(iii) $\displaystyle\int \frac{1}{4x^2 + 20x + 29}\, dx$

(iv) $\displaystyle\int \frac{1}{x^2 - 6x + 9}\, dx$

(v) $\displaystyle\int \frac{1}{\sqrt{5 - 12x - 9x^2}}\, dx$

5 Find the following integrals.

(i) $\displaystyle\int \frac{x + 1}{x^2 + 1}\, dx$

(ii) $\displaystyle\int \frac{4}{(x^2 + 1)(1 + x)}\, dx$

(iii) $\displaystyle\int \frac{1 - x}{\sqrt{1 - x^2}}\, dx$

(iv) $\displaystyle\int \frac{x + 3}{(x + 1)(x^2 + 1)}\, dx$

6 Evaluate the following.

(i) $\displaystyle\int_1^3 \frac{1}{\sqrt{4x - x^2}}\, dx$

(ii) $\displaystyle\int_2^5 \frac{2x^2 + 3}{(x - 1)(x^2 + 4)}\, dx$

7 Find $\dfrac{d}{dx}(\operatorname{arcsec} x)$ and $\displaystyle\int \frac{dx}{x\sqrt{x^2 - a^2}}$.

1 When integrating $\sin^2 x$ or $\cos^2 x$ use the identities

$$\sin^2 x \equiv \tfrac{1}{2}(1 - \cos 2x), \qquad \cos^2 x \equiv \tfrac{1}{2}(1 + \cos 2x).$$

2 $\displaystyle\int \tan kx \, dx = \frac{1}{k}\ln|\sec kx| + c$

3 Inverse trigonometric functions

Function	Domain	Range	Derivative
$y = \arcsin x$	$-1 \leqslant x \leqslant 1$	$-\dfrac{\pi}{2} \leqslant y \leqslant \dfrac{\pi}{2}$	$\dfrac{1}{\sqrt{1 - x^2}}$
$y = \arccos x$	$-1 \leqslant x \leqslant 1$	$0 \leqslant y \leqslant \pi$	$-\dfrac{1}{\sqrt{1 - x^2}}$
$y = \arctan x$	all x	$-\dfrac{\pi}{2} < y < \dfrac{\pi}{2}$	$\dfrac{1}{1 + x^2}$

4 $\displaystyle\int \frac{1}{a^2 + x^2}\, dx = \frac{1}{a}\arctan\frac{x}{a} + c$

Use when integrating rational functions with constant numerator, and a quadratic denominator with no real roots.

5 $\displaystyle\int \frac{1}{\sqrt{a^2 - x^2}}\, dx = \arcsin\frac{x}{a} + c$

Use when integrating functions that can be arranged as a fraction, with constant numerator, and a denominator which is the square root of a quadratic; this quadratic must have distinct real roots, and the coefficient of x^2 must be negative.

Polar co-ordinates

$M\eta\delta\epsilon\grave{\iota}\varsigma\ \grave{\alpha}\gamma\epsilon\omega\mu\acute{\epsilon}\tau\rho\eta\tau o\varsigma\ \epsilon\grave{\iota}\sigma\acute{\iota}\tau\omega\ \mu o\upsilon\ \tau\grave{\eta}\nu\ \sigma\tau\acute{\epsilon}\gamma\eta\nu$

[Let no one ignorant of geometry enter my door].

Inscription over the entrance to the Academy of Plato, c.430–349 BC

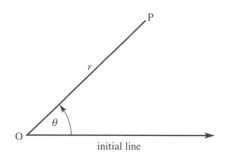

This Nautilus shell forms an equiangular spiral. How could you describe this mathematically?

You will be very familiar with using cartesian co-ordinates (x, y) to specify the position of a point P in a plane. A second system of co-ordinates uses the idea of describing the position of point P by giving its distance r from a fixed point O and the angle θ between OP and a fixed direction. In this system, first used by Newton in 1671, O is called the *pole* and the angle θ is measured from the initial line, which is usually drawn to the right across the page, like the positive x axis; the numbers (r, θ) are called the *polar co-ordinates* of P; see figure 2.1.

Figure 2.1

The angle θ is positive in the anticlockwise sense from the initial line; at the pole itself $r = 0$ and θ is undefined. Each pair of numbers (r, θ) gives a unique point, but the converse is not true, for two reasons. Firstly, a point is not changed if you add any integer multiple of 2π to the angle θ. Secondly, it is sometimes convenient to let r take negative values, with the natural interpretation that the point $(-r, \theta)$ is the same as $(r, \theta + \pi)$.

ACTIVITY 2.1   Check by drawing a diagram that the polar co-ordinates

$$\left(5, \frac{\pi}{3}\right), \left(5, \frac{7\pi}{3}\right), \left(5, -\frac{11\pi}{3}\right) \text{ and } \left(-5, -\frac{2\pi}{3}\right) \text{ all describe the same point.}$$

Give three other pairs of polar co-ordinates for the point $\left(-6, \frac{3\pi}{4}\right)$.

If it is necessary to specify the polar co-ordinates of a point uniquely then you use those for which $r > 0$ and $-\pi < \theta \leqslant \pi$; these are called the *principal polar co-ordinates*.

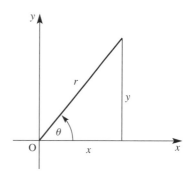

Figure 2.2

It is easy to change between polar co-ordinates (r, θ) and cartesian co-ordinates (x, y) since, from figure 2.2,

$$x = r \cos \theta \qquad y = r \sin \theta \qquad r = \sqrt{x^2 + y^2} \qquad \tan \theta = \frac{y}{x}$$

You need to be careful to choose the right quadrant when finding θ, since the equation $\tan \theta = \frac{y}{x}$ always gives two values of θ, differing by π. Always draw a sketch to check which one of these is correct.

1 Plot the points A, B, C, D with polar co-ordinates $\left(3, \dfrac{\pi}{5}\right)$, $\left(2, \dfrac{7\pi}{10}\right)$, $\left(3, -\dfrac{4\pi}{5}\right)$, $\left(-4, \dfrac{7\pi}{10}\right)$ respectively. What shape is ABCD?

2 One vertex of an equilateral triangle has polar co-ordinates $\left(4, \dfrac{\pi}{4}\right)$. Find the polar co-ordinates of all the possible other vertices

   (i) when the origin O is the centre of the triangle

   (ii) when O is another vertex of the triangle

   (iii) when O is the mid-point of one side of the triangle.

3 The diagram shows a regular pentagon OABCD, in which A has cartesian co-ordinates (5, 2).

   (i) Show that OB = 8.71 (correct to 2 decimal places).

   (ii) Find the polar co-ordinates of A, B, C, D.

   (iii) Hence find the cartesian co-ordinates of B, C, D.

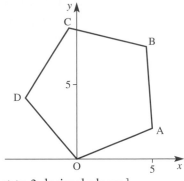

[In parts **(ii)** and **(iii)** give your answers correct to 2 decimal places.]

4 In this question r is in millimetres and θ is in degrees. The scoring region of a dartboard is marked by six concentric circles, called inner bull, outer bull, inner treble, outer treble, inner double, outer double, with radii 6, 16, 99, 107, 162, 170 mm respectively (to the nearest mm, ignoring the thickness of the dividing wire). The part between the outer bull and outer double circles is divided into twenty equal 'sectors', numbered as shown below, and the board is hung with the 20 sector vertically above the centre so that the initial line bisects the 6 sector. A dart scores 50 in the inner bull and 25 in the outer bull, where $6 < r < 16$. A dart in a sector scores the sector number, except that within the doubles ring ($162 < r < 170$) or trebles ring ($99 < r < 107$) it scores double or treble the sector number respectively.

   (i) Find the score in the region for which $16 < r < 99$ and $27 < \theta < 45$.

   (ii) Give conditions on r and θ which define the boundary between sectors 10 and 15.

   (iii) Give conditions on r and θ for the regions in which the score is

   (a) treble 14

   (b) 17

   (c) 18.

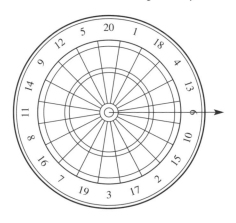

The polar equation of a curve

The points (r, θ) for which the values of r and θ are linked by a function f form a curve whose *polar equation* is $r = f(\theta)$. The polar equation of a curve may be simpler than its cartesian equation, especially if the curve has rotational symmetry. Polar equations have many important applications, for example in the study of orbits.

EXAMPLE 2.1

Investigate the curve with polar equation $r = 10\cos\theta$.

SOLUTION

This can be tackled in three ways.

(i) *By plotting.* Make a table of values. This one has θ increasing by $\dfrac{\pi}{12}$ (i.e. 15°), which gives a convenient number of points.

θ	0	$\dfrac{\pi}{12}$	$\dfrac{\pi}{6}$	$\dfrac{\pi}{4}$	$\dfrac{\pi}{3}$	$\dfrac{5\pi}{12}$	$\dfrac{\pi}{2}$	$\dfrac{7\pi}{12}$	$\dfrac{2\pi}{3}$	$\dfrac{3\pi}{4}$	$\dfrac{5\pi}{6}$	$\dfrac{11\pi}{12}$	π
r	10	9.7	8.7	7.1	5.0	2.6	0	-2.6	-5.0	-7.1	-8.7	-9.7	-10

Values of θ from 0 to $-\pi$ (or from π to 2π) give the same points again: for example, $\theta = -\dfrac{\pi}{12} \Rightarrow r = 9.7$, which is the same point as $(-9.7, \dfrac{11\pi}{12})$.

Plotting these points gives the curve shown in figure 2.3. It looks like a circle – the other methods will prove that it is a circle.

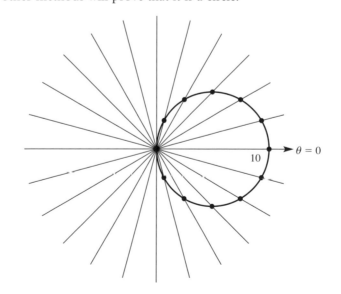

Figure 2.3

(ii) *By converting to cartesian form.*

If $r \neq 0$ then

$$r = 10 \cos \theta$$
$$\Leftrightarrow \qquad r^2 = 10r \cos \theta$$
$$\Leftrightarrow \qquad x^2 + y^2 = 10x.$$

If $r = 0$ then $x = y = 0$, which also satisfies $x^2 + y^2 = 10x$.

Therefore the cartesian equation is

$$x^2 + y^2 = 10x \Leftrightarrow (x - 5)^2 + y^2 = 25,$$

which proves that the curve is the circle with radius 5 and centre $(5, 0)$ (in cartesian co-ordinates).

(iii) *By geometrical reasoning.* Knowing the answer makes it even simpler! Consider the circle with radius 5 and centre $(5, 0)$, shown in figure 2.4. If P is the point on this circle with polar co-ordinates (r, θ) then OPA is a right angle (the angle in a semi-circle) and so $r = 10 \cos \theta$ as required, and the same applies to points on the lower semi-circle since the cosine function is an even function.

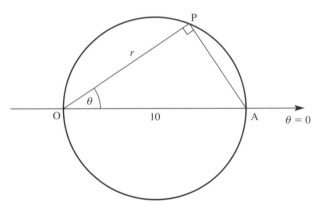

Figure 2.4

Notes

1 Plotting and joining points as in part **(i)** above gives a good idea of the shape of the curve, but the argument in parts **(ii)** or **(iii)** is needed before you can be sure that this is truly a circle.

2 As the value of θ increases from $-\pi$ to π the point moves twice around the circle.

ACTIVITY 2.2   If you have access to a graphic calculator or a computer with suitable software, find out how to draw a curve from its polar equation. Check that you can adjust the scales so that in this case you get a circle, not just an ellipse.

❓   Some graphic calculators will not draw the curve $r = f(\theta)$ directly, but instead you can take θ as a parameter and draw the curve with parametric equations $x = f(\theta)\cos\theta,\; y = f(\theta)\sin\theta$. Explain why this works.

EXAMPLE 2.2   **(i)**   Describe the motion of a point along the curve $r = 1 + 2\cos\theta$ as θ increases from 0 to 2π.

(ii)   Do the same for the curve $r = \dfrac{1}{1 + 2\cos\theta}$.

SOLUTION

(i)   The curve is shown in figure 2.5.

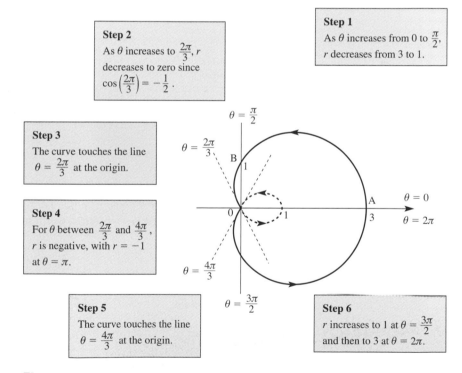

Step 1
As θ increases from 0 to $\frac{\pi}{2}$, r decreases from 3 to 1.

Step 2
As θ increases to $\frac{2\pi}{3}$, r decreases to zero since $\cos\left(\frac{2\pi}{3}\right) = -\frac{1}{2}$.

Step 3
The curve touches the line $\theta = \frac{2\pi}{3}$ at the origin.

Step 4
For θ between $\frac{2\pi}{3}$ and $\frac{4\pi}{3}$, r is negative, with $r = -1$ at $\theta = \pi$.

Step 5
The curve touches the line $\theta = \frac{4\pi}{3}$ at the origin.

Step 6
r increases to 1 at $\theta = \frac{3\pi}{2}$ and then to 3 at $\theta = 2\pi$.

Figure 2.5

This double loop is one of a family of curves called *limaçons* (snail curves).

(ii) The value of r is now the reciprocal of the value found in **(i)**; the curve is shown in figure 2.6.

This curve has two separate branches; it is an example of a *hyperbola*.

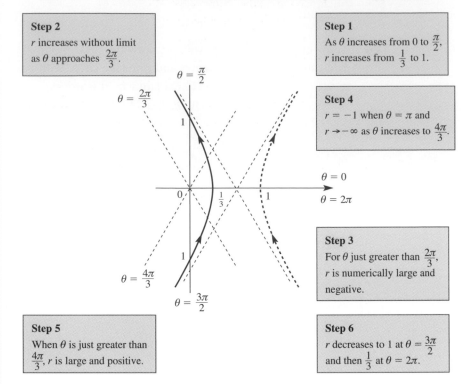

Step 2
r increases without limit as θ approaches $\frac{2\pi}{3}$.

Step 1
As θ increases from 0 to $\frac{\pi}{2}$, r increases from $\frac{1}{3}$ to 1.

Step 4
$r = -1$ when $\theta = \pi$ and $r \to -\infty$ as θ increases to $\frac{4\pi}{3}$.

Step 3
For θ just greater than $\frac{2\pi}{3}$, r is numerically large and negative.

Step 5
When θ is just greater than $\frac{4\pi}{3}$, r is large and positive.

Step 6
r decreases to 1 at $\theta = \frac{3\pi}{2}$ and then $\frac{1}{3}$ at $\theta = 2\pi$.

Figure 2.6

Note

The diagrams in the example above use the convention that the parts of the curve for which $r < 0$ are shown by a broken line. In some applications it is physically impossible for r to be negative, so it is sometimes worth distinguishing such portions in this way.

EXERCISE 2B

In this exercise you should make full but critical use of a graphic calculator or computer if these are available.

1 Make a table of values of $8 \sin \theta$ for θ from 0 to π at intervals of $\frac{\pi}{12} (= 15°)$, and say what happens when $\pi \leqslant \theta \leqslant 2\pi$. By plotting points draw the curve $r = 8 \sin \theta$. Prove that this curve is a circle, and give its cartesian equation.

2 Draw the graph of the *spiral of Archimedes*

$$r = \frac{4\theta}{\pi} \text{ for } -2\pi \leqslant \theta \leqslant 2\pi.$$

3 A curve with polar equation $r = k \sin n\theta$, where k and n are positive and n is an integer, is called a *rhodonea* (rose curve). Throughout this question take $k = 10$.

    (i) What shape is the curve when $n = 1$?

    (ii) Draw the curve when $n = 2$.

    (iii) Draw the curve when $n = 3$.

    (iv) From these examples (and others if you wish) form a conjecture about how the number of 'petals' depends on n.

4 A curve with polar equation $r = a(1 + \cos\theta)$ is called a *cardioid*. Draw the curve when $a = 8$, and account for its name.

5 Prove that $r = a \sec\theta$ and $r = b \operatorname{cosec}\theta$, where a and b are non-zero constants, are the polar equations of two straight lines. Find their cartesian equations.

6 The straight line ℓ passes through the point A with polar co-ordinates (p, α) and is perpendicular to OA. Prove that the polar equation of ℓ is $r \cos(\theta - \alpha) = p$.

    Use the expansion of $\cos(\theta - \alpha)$ to find the cartesian equation of ℓ.

7 Sketch on the same diagram the curves with polar equations $r = 2a \cos\theta$, $2r(1 + \cos\theta) = 3a$ and find the polar co-ordinates of their points of intersection.

    What is the polar equation of the common chord of the two curves?

                                                                               [MEI]

The area of a sector

The region bounded by an arc UV of a curve and the two lines OU and OV is called a *sector*. In order to find the area of the sector for which OU and OV are the lines $\theta = \alpha$ and $\theta = \beta$ and the curve is $r = \mathrm{f}(\theta)$ you first divide it into small sectors such as OPQ, where P and Q have co-ordinates (r, θ) and $(r + \delta r, \theta + \delta\theta)$, as in figure 2.7.

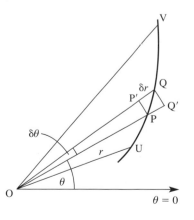

Figure 2.7

Let the areas of sectors OUP and OPQ be A and δA respectively. Then since the area of sector OPQ lies between the area of the circular sectors OPP′ and OQQ′,

$$\tfrac{1}{2}r^2\delta\theta < \delta A < \tfrac{1}{2}(r+\delta r)^2\delta\theta$$

> Remember that θ is in radians.

and so $\quad \tfrac{1}{2}r^2 < \dfrac{\delta A}{\delta\theta} < \tfrac{1}{2}(r+\delta r)^2.$

Now as $\delta\theta \to 0$, $\dfrac{\delta A}{\delta\theta} \to \dfrac{dA}{d\theta}$ the rate of change of A with respect to θ.

But $\dfrac{\delta A}{\delta\theta}$ is trapped between $\tfrac{1}{2}r^2$, which is fixed, and $\tfrac{1}{2}(r+\delta r)^2$, which tends to $\tfrac{1}{2}r^2$, and so $\dfrac{\delta A}{\delta\theta}$ must also tend to $\tfrac{1}{2}r^2$. Therefore

$$\frac{dA}{d\theta} = \tfrac{1}{2}r^2.$$

From this key result the area of the sector can be found by integration:

$$\text{area OUV} = \int_\alpha^\beta \tfrac{1}{2}r^2 d\theta.$$

? The argument given above is based on figure 2.7 in which

(i) $\delta\theta$ is positive $\qquad\qquad$ **(ii)** r increases as θ increases.

Consider how the argument must be adapted if

(a) $\delta\theta$ is negative
(b) r decreases as θ increases
(c) both **(a)** and **(b)**.

Note that the final result remains the same in all cases.

EXAMPLE 2.3

Find the area of the inner loop of the limaçon $r = 1 + 2\cos\theta$ drawn in figure 2.5.

SOLUTION

The inner loop is formed as θ varies from $\dfrac{2\pi}{3}$ to $\dfrac{4\pi}{3}$, so its area is

$$\int_{2\pi/3}^{4\pi/3} \tfrac{1}{2}(1+2\cos\theta)^2\,d\theta = \int_{2\pi/3}^{4\pi/3} \tfrac{1}{2}(1+4\cos\theta+4\cos^2\theta)\,d\theta$$

$$= \int_{2\pi/3}^{4\pi/3} \left(\tfrac{1}{2}+2\cos\theta+(1+\cos 2\theta)\right)d\theta$$

> using $\cos^2\theta = \tfrac{1}{2}(1+\cos 2\theta)$

$$= \left[\frac{3\theta}{2}+2\sin\theta+\tfrac{1}{2}\sin 2\theta\right]_{2\pi/3}^{4\pi/3}$$

$$= \pi - \frac{3\sqrt{3}}{2}.$$

Note

Even though r is negative for $\dfrac{2\pi}{3} < \theta < \dfrac{4\pi}{3}$, the integrand $\frac{1}{2}r^2$ is always positive, so there is no problem of 'negative areas' as there is with curves below the x axis in cartesian co-ordinates.

ACTIVITY 2.3 For the limaçon $r = 1 + 2\cos\theta$ find

(i) the total area contained by the outer loop

(ii) the area between the two loops.

EXERCISE 2C

1 Check that $\int \frac{1}{2}r^2\,\mathrm{d}\theta$ gives the area of the circle $r = 10\cos\theta$ correctly when the integral is evaluated from $-\dfrac{\pi}{2}$ to $\dfrac{\pi}{2}$ or from 0 to π. What happens when the integration is from 0 to 2π?

2 Find the area bounded by the spiral $r = \dfrac{4\theta}{\pi}$ from $\theta = 0$ to $\theta = 2\pi$ and the initial line.

3 Find the areas of the two portions into which the line $\theta = \dfrac{\pi}{2}$ divides the upper half of the cardioid $r = 8(1 + \cos\theta)$.

4 The diagram below shows the *equiangular spiral* $r = ae^{k\theta}$, where a and k are positive constants, and the lines $\theta = 0$ and $\theta = \dfrac{\pi}{4}$. Prove that the areas of the regions $A, B, C, \ldots$ between these lines and successive whorls form a geometric sequence, and find its common ratio.

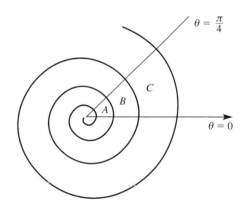

5 Sketch *Bernoulli's lemniscate* (ribbon bow) $r^2 = a^2\cos 2\theta$, and find the area of one of its loops.

6 A curve has polar equation $r = a(1 - \cos\theta)$, for $0 \leqslant \theta \leqslant 2\pi$, where a is a positive constant.

(i) Sketch the curve.

(ii) Find the area of the region enclosed by the curve.

[MEI, part]

7 The interior of the circle $r = 3a \cos \theta$ is divided into two parts by the cardioid $r = a(1 + \cos \theta)$. Find the area of the part whose boundary passes through the origin.

[MEI]

8 A curve is defined by the parametric equations $x = f(t)$, $y = g(t)$. By differentiating the relation $\tan \theta = \dfrac{y}{x}$ with respect to t show that

$$r^2 \frac{d\theta}{dt} = x\frac{dy}{dt} - y\frac{dx}{dt}.$$

As t increases from t_1 to t_2 the point on the curve moves from P_1 to P_2, and θ increases. Prove that the area of the sector OP_1P_2 is

$$\frac{1}{2}\int_{t_1}^{t_2} \left(x\frac{dy}{dt} - y\frac{dx}{dt} \right) dt.$$

9 The arc PQ is defined by $x = t^2$, $y = t^3$, $1 \leqslant t \leqslant 2$. Use Question 8 to find the area of the sector bounded by this arc, OP and OQ.

10 Sketch the *astroid* $x = a\cos^3 t$, $y = a\sin^3 t$, and find the area it encloses.

11 Prove that the area enclosed by the curve

$$x = a\cos t + b\sin t, \quad y = c\cos t + d\sin t$$

is $\pi|ad - bc|$.

12 (i) Sketch the curve with polar equation $r = a\sin 3\theta$ for $0 \leqslant \theta \leqslant \pi$, where a is a positive constant. Use a continuous line for sections where $r > 0$, and a broken line for sections where $r < 0$.

(ii) Find the area enclosed by one loop of this curve.

The point P on the curve corresponds to $\theta = \frac{1}{4}\pi$.

(iii) Mark the point P on your sketch, and give the co-ordinates of P in polar and in cartesian form.

You are given that the cartesian equation of the curve is

$$x^4 + 2x^2y^2 + y^4 = 3ax^2y - ay^3.$$

(iv) Differentiate this cartesian equation to obtain an equation involving x, y and $\dfrac{dy}{dx}$.

(v) Find the gradient of the curve at the point P.

[MEI]

13 A curve has polar equation $r = 2\sqrt{\cos 2\theta}$, for $-\frac{1}{4}\pi \leqslant \theta \leqslant \frac{1}{4}\pi$.

(i) Sketch the curve.

(ii) Find the area of the region enclosed by the curve.

(iii) By first writing the polar equation of the curve as $r^2 = 4(\cos^2\theta - \sin^2\theta)$, show that the cartesian equation of the curve is

$$x^4 + 2x^2y^2 + y^4 - 4x^2 + 4y^2 = 0.$$

(iv) Differentiate this cartesian equation to obtain a relationship between x, y and $\dfrac{dy}{dx}$.

(v) If P is a point on the curve where $\dfrac{dy}{dx} = 0$, show that $OP = \sqrt{2}$, where O is the origin.

(vi) Find the *polar* co-ordinates of the two points on the curve where $\dfrac{dy}{dx} = 0$.

[MEI]

INVESTIGATION

The curve C has equation $r = \dfrac{k}{1 + e\cos t}$. By working through the following investigate the shape of C.

(i) Draw C for $k = 4$ and e taking the values **(a)** 0   **(b)** 0.5   **(c)** 1   **(d)** 2   **(e)** 5.

You may use a graphic calculator or graph-drawing software.

(ii) What happens to C if the value of k is changed?

(iii) Describe C for **(a)** $e = 0$ **(b)** $0 < e < 1$ **(c)** $e = 1$ **(d)** $e > 1$.

KEY POINTS

1 The principal polar co-ordinates (r, θ) are those for which $r > 0$ and $-\pi < \theta \leqslant \pi$.

2 $x = r\cos\theta$, $y = r\sin\theta$, $r = \sqrt{x^2 + y^2}$, $\theta = \arctan\dfrac{y}{x}$ ($\pm\pi$ if necessary).

3 The area of a sector is $\displaystyle\int_\alpha^\beta \frac{1}{2}r^2 d\theta$.

Complex numbers

The shortest path between two truths in the real domain passes through the complex domain.

Jacques Hadamard, 1865–1963

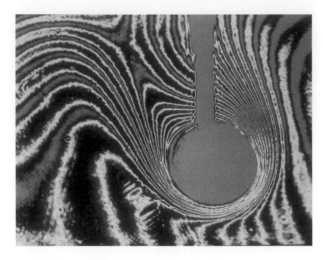

Graphical representation of fluid-flow around a pipe

Complex numbers may appear to be a mere mathematical curiosity but this is far from the truth. They have many applications in the real world. For example, electrical engineers use j to analyse oscillating currents. Physicists have found that imaginary numbers provide the best language for describing some real-world phenomena, such as the flow of fluid around a pipe or solutions to differential equations modelling shock absorbers.

The polar form of complex numbers

The position vector of the point z in an Argand diagram can be described by means of its length r and the angle θ it makes with the positive real axis (figure 3.1).

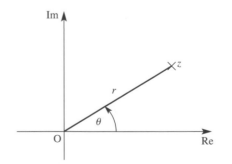

Figure 3.1

The distance r is of course $|z|$, the modulus of z. The angle θ is slightly more complicated: it is measured anticlockwise from the positive real axis, normally in radians, but is not uniquely defined since adding $2k\pi$ (for any integer k) to θ gives the same direction. To avoid confusion, it is usual to choose that value of θ for which $-\pi < \theta \leqslant \pi$; this is called the *principal argument* of z, denoted by arg z. Then every complex number except 0 has a unique principal argument: the argument of 0 is undefined. For example, with reference to figure 3.2,

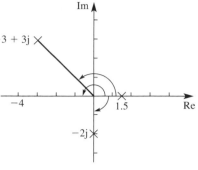

$$\arg(-4) = \pi$$
$$\arg(-2\mathrm{j}) = -\frac{\pi}{2}$$
$$\arg(1.5) = 0$$
$$\arg(-3 + 3\mathrm{j}) = \frac{3\pi}{4}.$$

Figure 3.2

ACTIVITY 3.1   Find   **(i)** arg j   **(ii)** $\arg(\sqrt{3} + \mathrm{j})$ **(iii)** $\arg(-4 - 4\mathrm{j})$ **(iv)** arg $\left(\dfrac{-1 - \sqrt{3}\mathrm{j}}{2} \right)$.

It is clear from figure 3.3 that

$$x = r\cos\theta \qquad y = r\sin\theta$$
$$r = \sqrt{x^2 + y^2} \qquad \tan\theta = \frac{y}{x}$$

and the same relations hold in the other quadrants too.

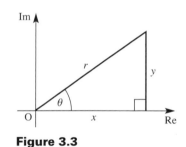

Figure 3.3

These can be used to find the real and imaginary parts from the modulus and argument, and vice versa, but care is needed in finding the argument from the real and imaginary parts. It is tempting to say that $\theta = \arctan\left(\dfrac{y}{x}\right)$, but this gives a value between $-\dfrac{\pi}{2}$ and $\dfrac{\pi}{2}$, which is correct only if z is in the first or fourth quadrants. For example, the point $z_1 = 2 - 3\mathrm{j}$ is in the fourth quadrant, and its argument is correctly given by $\arctan\left(\dfrac{-3}{2}\right) \approx -0.98\,\text{rad}\ (\approx -56°)$.

But $z_2 = -2 + 3\mathrm{j}$ is in the second quadrant, where its argument is $\arctan\left(\dfrac{3}{-2}\right) + \pi \approx 2.16\,\text{rad}\ (\approx 124°)$ as in figure 3.4 overleaf.

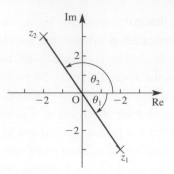

Figure 3.4

The general results for all quadrants are shown in figure 3.5. It is wise to draw a sketch diagram each time.

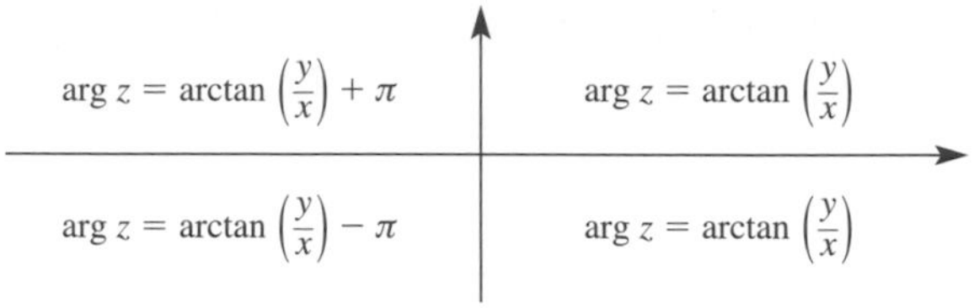

$$\arg z = \arctan\left(\frac{y}{x}\right) + \pi \qquad\qquad \arg z = \arctan\left(\frac{y}{x}\right)$$

$$\arg z = \arctan\left(\frac{y}{x}\right) - \pi \qquad\qquad \arg z = \arctan\left(\frac{y}{x}\right)$$

Figure 3.5

ACTIVITY 3.2 Mark the points $1 + j$, $1 - j$, $-1 + j$, $-1 - j$ on an Argand diagram. Find $\arg z$ for each of these, and check that the statements in figure 3.5 are correct.

ACTIVITY 3.3 Most calculators can convert from (x, y) to (r, θ) (called *rectangular* to *polar*, often shown as $R \rightarrow P$) and from (r, θ) to (x, y) (polar to rectangular, $P \rightarrow R$). Find how to use these facilities on your calculator, and compare with other available types of calculator. Does your calculator always give the correct θ, or do you sometimes have to add or subtract π?

Since $x = r \cos\theta$ and $y = r \sin\theta$ we can write the complex number $z = x + yj$ in the form

$$z = r(\cos\theta + j\sin\theta).$$

This is called the *polar* or *modulus–argument* form. For example

$$-1 + j = \sqrt{2}\left(\frac{3\pi}{4} + j\sin\frac{3\pi}{4}\right)$$

$$7j = 7\left(\cos\frac{\pi}{2} + j\sin\frac{\pi}{2}\right)$$

$$-3 = 3(\cos\pi + j\sin\pi)$$

$$4 + 3j = 5(\cos\alpha + j\sin\alpha) \text{ where } \alpha = \arctan\left(\frac{3}{4}\right) \approx 0.644.$$

In Questions 1–16, *find the modulus and principal argument. Give the argument in radians, either as a simple rational multiple of π or correct to 3 decimal places.*

1 1 **2** -2 **3** $3j$ **4** $-4j$

5 $1 + j$ **6** $-5 - 5j$ **7** $1 - \sqrt{3}j$ **8** $6\sqrt{3} + 6j$

9 $-\sqrt{18} + \sqrt{18}j$

10 $8\left(\cos \dfrac{\pi}{5} + j \sin \dfrac{\pi}{5} \right)$

11 $\dfrac{\cos 2.3 + j \sin 2.3}{4}$

12 $-3(\cos(-3) + j \sin(-3))$

13 $3 - 4j$ **14** $-12 + 5j$ **15** $4 + 7j$ **16** $-58 - 93j$

17 Given that $\arg(5 + 2j) = \alpha$, find the principal argument of each of the following in terms of α.

     (i) $-5 - 2j$ **(ii)** $5 - 2j$ **(ii)** $-5 + 2j$

     (iv) $2 + 5j$ **(v)** $-2 + 5j$

In Questions 18–22, *write the complex numbers in polar form.*

18 $\cos \alpha - j \sin \alpha$

19 $3(\sin \alpha + j \cos \alpha)$

20 $j(\cos \alpha + j \sin \alpha)$

21 $\dfrac{10}{\cos \alpha + j \sin \alpha}$

22 $1 + j \tan \alpha$

23 (i) Given that $z = \cos \theta + j \sin \theta$, plot the points $0, 1, z, 1 + z$ on an Argand diagram. What sort of quadrilateral do these points form? Hence find the modulus and argument of $1 + \cos \theta + j \sin \theta$.

     (ii) Obtain the same result by expressing $1 + \cos \theta + j \sin \theta$ in terms of $\cos \dfrac{\theta}{2}$ and $\sin \dfrac{\theta}{2}$.

     (iii) Find the modulus and argument of $1 - \cos \theta - j \sin \theta$.

24 (i) Given that $\alpha = -1 + 2j$, express α^2 and α^3 in the form $a + bj$. Hence show that α is a root of the cubic equation
$$z^3 + 7z^2 + 15z + 25 = 0.$$

     (ii) Find the other two roots of this cubic equation.

     (iii) Illustrate the three roots of the cubic equation on an Argand diagram, and find the modulus and argument of each root.

     (iv) L is the locus of points in the Argand diagram representing complex numbers z for which $\left| z + \tfrac{5}{2} \right| = \tfrac{5}{2}$. Show that all three roots of the cubic equation lie on L and draw the locus L on your diagram.

[MEI]

Sets of points using the polar form

EXAMPLE 3.1

Draw Argand diagrams showing the sets of points z for which

(i) $\arg z = \dfrac{\pi}{4}$ **(ii)** $\arg(z - j) = \dfrac{\pi}{4}$

(iii) $0 \leqslant \arg(z - j) \leqslant \dfrac{\pi}{4}$ **(iv)** $\arg(z - j) = \arg(z - 2 + j)$

SOLUTION

(i) $\arg z = \dfrac{\pi}{4}$

    $\Leftrightarrow$ the vector z has direction $\dfrac{\pi}{4}$

    $\Leftrightarrow$ z lies on the half-line from the origin

        in the $\dfrac{\pi}{4}$ direction, see figure 3.6.

    (Note that the origin is not included,
    since arg 0 is undefined.)

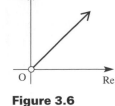

Figure 3.6

(ii) $\arg(z - j) = \dfrac{\pi}{4}$

    $\Leftrightarrow$ the vector $z - j$ from the point j

        to the point z has direction $\dfrac{\pi}{4}$

    $\Leftrightarrow$ z lies on the half-line from the

        point j in the $\dfrac{\pi}{4}$ direction, see figure 3.7.

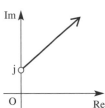

Figure 3.7

(iii) $0 \leqslant \arg(z - j) \leqslant \dfrac{\pi}{4}$

    $\Leftrightarrow$ the vector $z - j$ from the point j to the point z has

        direction between 0 and $\dfrac{\pi}{4}$ (inclusive)

    $\Leftrightarrow$ z lies in the one-eighth plane shown in figure 3.8.

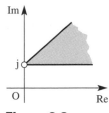

Figure 3.8

(iv) $\arg(z - j) = \arg(z - 2 + j)$

    $\Leftrightarrow$ the vectors from points j and $2 - j$ to

        the point z are in the same direction
        and sense

    $\Leftrightarrow$ z lies on the line joining points j and
        $2 - j$, but does not lie between these
        points or at either of them, see
        figure 3.9.

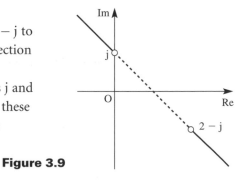

Figure 3.9

In Questions 1–6, draw an Argand diagram showing the set of points z for which the given condition is true.

1 $\arg z = -\dfrac{\pi}{3}$

2 $\arg(z - 4j) = 0$

3 $\arg(z + 3) \geqslant \dfrac{\pi}{2}$

4 $\arg(z + 1 + 2j) = \dfrac{3\pi}{4}$

5 $\arg(z - 3 + j) \leqslant -\dfrac{\pi}{6}$

6 $-\dfrac{\pi}{4} \leqslant \arg(z + 5 - 3j) \leqslant \dfrac{\pi}{3}$

7 Find the least and greatest possible values of $\arg z$ if $|z - 8j| \leqslant 4$.

8 If k is positive and $|z| \leqslant k$, prove that $0 \leqslant |z + k| \leqslant 2k$ and

$$-\dfrac{\pi}{2} < \arg(z + k) < \dfrac{\pi}{2}.$$

Find the least and greatest values of $|z + 2k|$ and $\arg(z + 2k)$.

In Questions 9–11, draw an Argand diagram showing the set of points z for which the condition is true.

9 $\arg z = \arg(z + 2)$

10 $\arg(z - 2 - 5j) = \arg(z + 4 - 2j)$

11 $\arg(z + j) = \arg(z - 3) + \pi$

12 Prove that the set of points for which $\arg(z - 1) = \arg(z + 1) + \dfrac{\pi}{4}$ is part of the set of points for which $|z - j| = \sqrt{2}$, and show which part clearly in a diagram.

Multiplication in the Argand diagram

The polar form quickly leads to an elegant geometrical interpretation of the multiplication of complex numbers. For if

$$z_1 = r_1(\cos\theta_1 + j\sin\theta_1) \text{ and } z_2 = r_2(\cos\theta_2 + j\sin\theta_2)$$

then $\quad z_1 z_2 = r_1 r_2(\cos\theta_1 + j\sin\theta_1)(\cos\theta_2 + j\sin\theta_2)$

$$= r_1 r_2[\cos\theta_1\cos\theta_2 - \sin\theta_1\sin\theta_2 + j(\sin\theta_1\cos\theta_2 + \cos\theta_1\sin\theta_2)].$$

Using the compound angle formulae gives

$$z_1 z_2 = r_1 r_2[\cos(\theta_1 + \theta_2) + j\sin(\theta_1 + \theta_2)].$$

This is the complex number with modulus $r_1 r_2$ and argument $(\theta_1 + \theta_2)$, so we have the beautiful result that

$$|z_1 z_2| = |z_1||z_2|$$

and

$$\arg(z_1 z_2) = \arg z_1 + \arg z_2 \ (\pm 2\pi \text{ if necessary, to give the principal argument}).$$

So to multiply complex numbers in polar form you *multiply* their moduli and *add* their arguments.

ACTIVITY 3.4   Using this interpretation, investigate
(i) multiplication by j
(ii) multiplication by -1.

This gives the following simple geometrical
interpretation of multiplication.

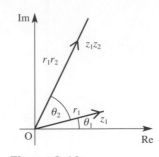

To obtain the vector $z_1 z_2$, enlarge the vector z_1
by the scale factor $|z_2|$ and rotate it through
$\arg z_2$ anticlockwise about O (figure 3.10).

This combination of an enlargement followed
by a rotation is called a *spiral dilatation*.

Figure 3.10

ACTIVITY 3.5   Check this by accurate drawing and measurement for the case
$z_1 = 2 + j$, $z_2 = 3 + 4j$. Then do the same with z_1 and z_2 interchanged.

The corresponding results for division are easily obtained by letting
$\dfrac{z_1}{z_2} = w$. Then $z_1 = wz_2$ so that

$$|z_1| = |w||z_2| \text{ and } \arg z_1 = \arg w + \arg z_2 \ (\pm 2\pi \text{ if necessary}).$$

Therefore $|w| = \left|\dfrac{z_1}{z_2}\right| = \dfrac{|z_1|}{|z_2|}$

and $\quad \arg w = \arg \dfrac{z_1}{z_2}$

$$= \arg z_1 - \arg z_2 \ (\pm 2\pi \text{ if necessary, to give the principal argument}).$$

So to divide complex numbers in polar form you *divide* their moduli and
subtract their arguments.

EXERCISE 3C   In Questions 1–9, given that $z = 2\left(\cos\dfrac{\pi}{4} + j\sin\dfrac{\pi}{4}\right)$ and

$w = 3\left(\cos\dfrac{\pi}{3} + j\sin\dfrac{\pi}{3}\right)$, find the following in polar form.

1 wz **2** $\dfrac{w}{z}$ **3** $\dfrac{z}{w}$

4 $\dfrac{1}{z}$ **5** w^2 **6** z^5

7 $w^3 z^4$ **8** $5jz$ **9** $(1+j)w$

10 Prove that, in general, $\arg\dfrac{1}{z} = -\arg z$, and deal with the exceptions.

11 Given the points 1 and z on an Argand diagram, explain how to find the
following points by geometrical construction:

    (i) $3z$ **(ii)** $2jz$ **(iii)** $(3 + 2j)z$
    (iv) z^* **(v)** $|z|$ **(vi)** z^2

12 Describe the motion of each of the points in Question 11 as the point z moves

(a) along the imaginary axis from $-j$ to j;

(b) once anticlockwise around the circle $|z| = 1$, starting at $z = 1$.

13 By considering powers of $2 + j$, show that the position vector $\begin{pmatrix} 3 \\ 4 \end{pmatrix}$ bisects the angle formed by the position vectors $\begin{pmatrix} 2 \\ 1 \end{pmatrix}$ and $\begin{pmatrix} 2 \\ 11 \end{pmatrix}$. Check this by vector methods, using the scalar product.

14 Find the real and imaginary parts of $\dfrac{-1 + j}{1 + \sqrt{3}j}$.

Express $-1 + j$ and $1 + \sqrt{3}j$ in polar form.

Hence show that $\cos\dfrac{5\pi}{12} = \dfrac{\sqrt{3} - 1}{2\sqrt{2}}$, and find an exact expression for $\sin\dfrac{5\pi}{12}$.

15 The complex numbers α and β are given by $\dfrac{\alpha + 4}{\alpha} = 2 - j$ and $\beta = -\sqrt{6} + \sqrt{2}j$.

(i) Show that $\alpha = 2 + 2j$.

(ii) Show that $|\alpha| = |\beta|$. Find $\arg \alpha$ and $\arg \beta$.

(iii) Find the modulus and argument of $\alpha\beta$. Illustrate the complex numbers α, β and $\alpha\beta$ on an Argand diagram.

(iv) Describe the locus of points in the Argand diagram representing complex numbers z for which $|z - \alpha| = |z - \beta|$. Draw this locus on your diagram.

(v) Show that $z = \alpha + \beta$ satisfies $|z - \alpha| = |z - \beta|$. Mark the point representing $\alpha + \beta$ on your diagram, and find the exact value of $\arg(\alpha + \beta)$.

[**MEI**]

16 The right-hand diagram below shows what happens to the character drawn on the Argand diagram on the left when each point representing z is replaced by the point representing z^2. Explain why

(i) the knife has moved nearer the origin, but got longer;

(ii) his forearm has moved from vertical to horizontal;

(iii) his boots have grown more than his head;

(iv) he has stabbed himself in the stomach.

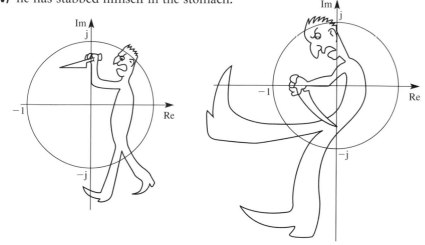

de Moivre's theorem

When you multiply two complex numbers (in polar form) you *multiply* their moduli and *add* their arguments: the product of

$$z_1 = r_1(\cos\theta_1 + j\sin\theta_1) \quad \text{and} \quad z_2 = r_2(\cos\theta_2 + j\sin\theta_2)$$

is

$$z_1 z_2 = r_1 r_2(\cos(\theta_1 + \theta_2) + j\sin(\theta_1 + \theta_2)).$$

Much can be done by using this result repeatedly with just a single complex number z, of modulus 1. This allows you to concentrate on what happens to the argument.

For if $\quad z = \cos\theta + j\sin\theta$

then $\quad z^2 = \cos(\theta + \theta) + j\sin(\theta + \theta) = \cos 2\theta + j\sin 2\theta,$

$$z^3 = z^2 z = \cos(2\theta + \theta) + j\sin(2\theta + \theta) = \cos 3\theta + j\sin 3\theta,$$

and so on. This suggests the following general result.

de Moivre's theorem

If n is any integer then
$$(\cos\theta + j\sin\theta)^n = \cos n\theta + j\sin n\theta.$$

Proof

The proof is in three parts, in which n is **(i)** positive **(ii)** zero or **(iii)** negative.

(i) When n is a positive integer the proof is by induction.

The theorem is obviously true when $n = 1$, and if
$$(\cos\theta + j\sin\theta)^k = \cos k\theta + j\sin k\theta$$

then $\quad (\cos\theta + j\sin\theta)^{k+1} = (\cos k\theta + j\sin k\theta)(\cos\theta + j\sin\theta)$

$$= \cos(k\theta + \theta) + j\sin(k\theta + \theta)$$

$$= \cos(k+1)\theta + j\sin(k+1)\theta$$

so by induction the theorem is true for all positive integers n.

(ii) By definition, $z^0 = 1$ for all complex numbers $z \neq 0$. Therefore
$$(\cos\theta + j\sin)^0 = 1 = \cos 0 + j\sin 0.$$

(iii) For negative n the proof starts with the case $n = -1$. Since
$$(\cos\theta + j\sin\theta)(\cos(-\theta) + j\sin(-\theta)) = \cos(\theta - \theta) + j\sin(\theta - \theta) = 1$$

it follows that $(\cos\theta + j\sin\theta)^{-1} = \cos(-\theta) + j\sin(-\theta).$ ①

If n is a negative integer, let $n = -m$. Then

$$(\cos\theta + j\sin\theta)^n = (\cos\theta + j\sin\theta)^{-m}$$

$$= [(\cos\theta + j\sin\theta)^m]^{-1}$$

$$= (\cos m\theta + j\sin m\theta)^{-1} \quad \text{using (i) for } m, \text{ which is positive}$$

$$= \cos(-m\theta) + j\sin(-m\theta) \quad \text{using ① with } m\theta \text{ in place of } \theta$$

$$= \cos n\theta + j\sin n\theta.$$

de Moivre's theorem is also useful for simplifying powers of complex numbers when the modulus is not 1. For if $z = r(\cos\theta + j\sin\theta)$ then

$$z^n = [r(\cos\theta + j\sin\theta)]^n = r^n(\cos\theta + j\sin\theta)^n = r^n(\cos n\theta + j\sin n\theta).$$

EXAMPLE 3.2

Evaluate   **(i)** $\left(\cos\dfrac{\pi}{8} + j\sin\dfrac{\pi}{8}\right)^{12}$ **(ii)** $\left(\sqrt{3} + j\right)^5.$

SOLUTION

(i) By de Moivre's theorem

$$\left(\cos\frac{\pi}{8} + j\sin\frac{\pi}{8}\right)^{12} = \cos\left(12 \times \frac{\pi}{8}\right) + j\sin\left(12 \times \frac{\pi}{8}\right)$$

$$= \cos\left(\frac{3\pi}{2}\right) + j\sin\left(\frac{3\pi}{2}\right) = -j.$$

(ii) First convert to polar form:

$$z = \sqrt{3} + j \Rightarrow |z| = \sqrt{3+1} = 2,\ \arg z = \arctan\left(\frac{1}{\sqrt{3}}\right) = \frac{\pi}{6}.$$

So $\left(\sqrt{3} + j\right)^5 = 2^5\left(\cos\dfrac{\pi}{6} + j\sin\dfrac{\pi}{6}\right)^5$

$$= 32\left(\cos\frac{5\pi}{6} + j\sin\frac{5\pi}{6}\right)$$

$$= 32\left(-\frac{\sqrt{3}}{2} + \frac{j}{2}\right)$$

$$= -16\sqrt{3} + 16j.$$

Historical note

Abraham de Moivre (1667–1754) came to England from France as a Huguenot refugee at the age of eighteen and spent the rest of his long life in London. In papers from 1707 onwards he made use of 'his' theorem, though he never published it explicitly.

EXERCISE 3D

1 Use de Moivre's theorem to evaluate the following.

(i) $\left(\cos\dfrac{\pi}{4} + j\sin\dfrac{\pi}{4}\right)^{15}$ **(ii)** $\left(\cos\dfrac{\pi}{3} + j\sin\dfrac{\pi}{3}\right)^{-8}$

(iii) $\left(\cos\left(-\dfrac{\pi}{12}\right) + j\sin\left(-\dfrac{\pi}{12}\right)\right)^{10}$ **(iv)** $\left(\cos\dfrac{7\pi}{8} - j\sin\dfrac{7\pi}{8}\right)^6$

[Hint for **(iv)**: $\cos\theta - j\sin\theta = \cos(-\theta) + j\sin(-\theta)$]

2 By converting to polar form and using de Moivre's theorem, find the following in the form $x + jy$, giving x and y as exact expressions or correct to 3 decimal places.

(i) $(1 - \sqrt{3}j)^4$ **(ii)** $(-2 + 2j)^7$

(iii) $(0.6 + 0.8j)^{-5}$ **(iv)** $(\sqrt{27} + 3j)^6$

3 Simplify the following.

(i) $(\cos(-\alpha) + j\sin(-\alpha))^8$

(ii) $\dfrac{(\cos\beta + j\sin\beta)^3}{(\cos\beta - j\sin\beta)^{-5}}$

(iii) $(\cos^2\gamma + j\sin\gamma\cos\gamma)^{10}$

(iv) $(1 + \cos 2\delta + j\sin 2\delta)^{-4}$

4 Deduce from de Moivre's theorem that $(\cos\theta - j\sin\theta)^n = \cos n\theta - j\sin n\theta$

(i) by putting $\theta = -\phi$ **(ii)** by using conjugates.

Using de Moivre's theorem

One of the reasons for the general acceptance of complex numbers during the eighteenth century was their usefulness in producing results involving only *real* numbers; these results could also be obtained without using complex numbers, but often only with considerably greater trouble; de Moivre's theorem is a good source of such examples.

EXAMPLE 3.3   Express $\cos 5\theta$ in terms of $\cos\theta$.

SOLUTION

By de Moivre's theorem

$$\cos 5\theta + j\sin 5\theta = (\cos\theta + j\sin\theta)^5$$
$$= c^5 + 5jc^4s - 10c^3s^2 - 10jc^2s^3 + 5cs^4 + js^5$$

(where c and s are used as abbreviations for $\cos\theta$ and $\sin\theta$ respectively).

Equating real parts:

$$\cos 5\theta = c^5 - 10c^3s^2 + 5cs^4.$$

But $s^2 = 1 - c^2$

so $\cos 5\theta = c^5 - 10c^3(1 - c^2) + 5c(1 - c^2)^2$
$$= c^5 - 10c^3 + 10c^5 + 5c - 10c^3 + 5c^5.$$

Therefore $\cos 5\theta = 16\cos^5\theta - 20\cos^3\theta + 5\cos\theta$.

ACTIVITY 3.6

(i) Check that the above expression for $\cos 5\theta$ gives the correct results when $\theta = 0$ and when $\theta = \pi$.

(ii) By equating imaginary parts find $\sin 5\theta$ in terms of $\sin \theta$.

Notice that de Moivre not only gives a straightforward solution of the original problem, but also gives the expression for $\sin 5\theta$ with very little extra work – two for the price of one!

Example 3.3 gave a multiple-angle formula in terms of powers; it is sometimes useful (e.g. when integrating) to do the reverse. For this you need the following deduction from the main theorem:

if $\qquad z = \cos \theta + j \sin \theta$

then $\qquad z^n = \cos n\theta + j \sin n\theta$

and $\qquad z^{-n} = \cos (-n\theta) + j \sin (-n\theta) = \cos n\theta - j \sin n\theta.$

Therefore $\quad \cos n\theta = \dfrac{z^n + z^{-n}}{2}$

and $\qquad \sin n\theta = \dfrac{z^n - z^{-n}}{2j}.$

EXAMPLE 3.4

Express $\cos^5 \theta$ in terms of multiple angles.

SOLUTION

Let $z = \cos \theta + j \sin \theta$.

Then $\qquad 2 \cos \theta = z + z^{-1}$

$\Rightarrow \quad 2^5 \cos^5 \theta = (z + z^{-1})^5$

$\qquad\qquad = z^5 + 5z^3 + 10z + 10z^{-1} + 5z^{-3} + z^{-5}$

$\qquad\qquad = (z^5 + z^{-5}) + 5(z^3 + z^{-3}) + 10(z + z^{-1})$

$\qquad\qquad = 2 \cos 5\theta + 10 \cos 3\theta + 20 \cos \theta$

$\Rightarrow \qquad \cos^5 \theta = \dfrac{\cos 5\theta + 5 \cos 3\theta + 10 \cos \theta}{16}$

ACTIVITY 3.7

Use a similar method to express $\sin^5 \theta$ in terms of multiple angles.

1 Prove that $\cos 4\theta = c^4 - 6c^2s^2 + s^4$ and $\sin 4\theta = 4c^3s - 4cs^3$, where $c = \cos\theta$, $s = \sin\theta$.

Use these results to find $\tan 4\theta$ as a rational function of $\tan\theta$.

[**Hint:** Put $\tan 4\theta = \dfrac{\sin 4\theta}{\cos 4\theta}$ and divide throughout by c^4.]

2 Find the expressions for $\cos 3\theta$ and $\sin 3\theta$ given by de Moivre's theorem. Hence express
   (i) $\cos 3\theta$ in terms of $\cos\theta$
   (ii) $\sin 3\theta$ in terms of $\sin\theta$
   (iii) $\tan 3\theta$ in terms of $\tan\theta$.

3 Find $\cos 6\theta$ and $\dfrac{\sin 6\theta}{\sin\theta}$ in terms of $\cos\theta$.

4 If $c = \cos\theta$, $s = \sin\theta$, $t = \tan\theta$ show that
$$\cos n\theta = c^n - {}^nC_2 c^{n-2}s^2 + {}^nC_4 c^{n-4}s^4 - \cdots$$
$$= c^n(1 - {}^nC_2 t^2 + {}^nC_4 t^4 - \cdots)$$
and $\sin n\theta = {}^nC_1 c^{n-1}s - {}^nC_3 c^{n-3}s^3 + \cdots$
$$= c^n({}^nC_1 t - {}^nC_3 t^3 + \cdots).$$

Hence find $\tan n\theta$ in terms of t.

5 Express each of the following in terms of multiple angles.
   (i) $\cos^4\theta$ (ii) $\sin^5\theta$ (iii) $\sin^6\theta$
   (iv) $\cos^3\theta\sin^4\theta$ (v) $\cos^4\theta\sin^3\theta$

6 Prove that $\cos^m\theta\sin^n\theta$ can be expressed in terms of the cosines of multiple angles if n is even, and in terms of the sines of multiple angles if n is odd.

7 Use your previous results to find these integrals.
   (i) $\displaystyle\int \sin^6\theta\, d\theta$ (ii) $\displaystyle\int_0^{\pi/2} \cos^3\theta\sin^4\theta\, d\theta$ (iii) $\displaystyle\int_0^{\pi} \cos^4\theta\sin^3\theta\, d\theta$

8 Use $\cos n\theta = \dfrac{z^n + z^{-n}}{2}$ to express
$$\cos\theta + \cos 3\theta + \cos 5\theta + \cdots + \cos(2n-1)\theta$$
as a geometric series in terms of z. Hence find this sum in terms of θ.

9 (i)   Given that $z = \cos\theta + j\sin\theta$, write down z^n and $\dfrac{1}{z^n}$ in the form $a + jb$.
         Simplify $z^n + \dfrac{1}{z^n}$ and $z^n - \dfrac{1}{z^n}$.

   (ii) By considering z^5, show that $\tan 5\theta = \dfrac{5\tan\theta - 10\tan^3\theta + \tan^5\theta}{1 - 10\tan^2\theta + 5\tan^4\theta}$.

   (iii) By considering $\left(z - \dfrac{1}{z}\right)^2 \left(z + \dfrac{1}{z}\right)^4$ find the constants p, q, r and s such that $\sin^2\theta\cos^4\theta = p + q\cos 2\theta + r\cos 4\theta + s\cos 6\theta$.

[MEI]

10 (i) Given that $z = \cos\theta + j\sin\theta$, write down z^n and $\dfrac{1}{z^n}$ in the form $a + jb$.

Simplify $z^n + \dfrac{1}{z^n}$ and $z^n - \dfrac{1}{z^n}$.

(ii) Expand $\left(z - \dfrac{1}{z}\right)^4 \left(z + \dfrac{1}{z}\right)^2$, and hence find the constants p, q, r and s such that $\sin^4\theta\cos^2\theta = p + q\cos 2\theta + r\cos 4\theta + s\cos 6\theta$.

(iii) Using a suitable substitution, and your answer to part **(ii)**, show that

$$\int_1^2 x^4\sqrt{4 - x^2}\,\mathrm{d}x = \frac{4\pi}{3} + \sqrt{3}.$$

[MEI]

11 By expressing $\cos^{2n}\theta$ in terms of cosines of multiple angles, prove that

$$\int_0^\pi \cos^{2n}\theta\,\mathrm{d}\theta = \frac{(2n)!\pi}{2^{2n}(n!)^2}.$$

What is $\displaystyle\int_0^\pi \cos^{2n+1}\theta\,\mathrm{d}\theta$?

Complex exponents

When multiplying complex numbers in polar form you add the arguments, and when multiplying powers of the same base you add the exponents. This suggests that there may be a link between the familiar expression $\cos\theta + j\sin\theta$ and the seemingly remote territory of the exponential function. This was first noticed in 1714 by the young Englishman Roger Cotes, two years before his death at the age of 28 (when Newton remarked 'If Cotes had lived we might have known something'), and made widely known through an influential book published by Euler in 1748.

Let $z = \cos\theta + j\sin\theta$. Since j behaves like any other constant in algebraic manipulation, to differentiate z with respect to θ you simply differentiate the real and imaginary parts separately. This gives

$$\begin{aligned}
\frac{\mathrm{d}z}{\mathrm{d}\theta} &= -\sin\theta + j\cos\theta \\
&= j^2\sin\theta + j\cos\theta \\
&= j(\cos\theta + j\sin\theta) \\
&= jz.
\end{aligned}$$

So $z = \cos\theta + j\sin\theta$ is a solution of the differential equation $\dfrac{\mathrm{d}z}{\mathrm{d}\theta} = jz$.

If j continues to behave like any other constant when it is used as an index, then the general solution of $\dfrac{\mathrm{d}z}{\mathrm{d}\theta} = jz$ is $z = \mathrm{e}^{j\theta+c}$, where c is a constant, just as $x = \mathrm{e}^{kt+c}$ is the general solution of $\dfrac{\mathrm{d}x}{\mathrm{d}t} = kx$.

Therefore $\cos\theta + j\sin\theta = \mathrm{e}^{j\theta+c}$.

Putting $\theta = 0$ gives

$$\cos 0 + j \sin 0 = e^{0+c}$$

$$\Rightarrow \qquad 1 = e^c$$

$$\Rightarrow \qquad c = 0$$

and it follows that

$$\cos \theta + j \sin \theta = e^{j\theta}.$$

The problem with this argument is that you have no way of knowing how j behaves as an index. But this does not matter. Since no meaning has yet been given to e^z when z is complex, the following *definition* can be made, suggested by this work with differential equations but not dependent on it:

$$e^{j\theta} = \cos \theta + j \sin \theta.$$

Note

The particular case when $\theta = \pi$ gives $e^{j\pi} = \cos \pi + j \sin \pi = -1$, so that

$$e^{j\pi} + 1 = 0.$$

This remarkable statement, linking the five fundamental numbers 0, 1, j, e, π, the three fundamental operations of addition, multiplication and exponentiation, and the fundamental relation of equality, has been described as a 'mathematical poem'.

The first use of $e^{j\theta}$ is simply as a more compact way of writing familiar expressions. For example, the polar form $r(\cos \theta + j \sin \theta)$ can now be abbreviated to $re^{j\theta}$, and de Moivre's theorem becomes the seemingly obvious statement

$$(e^{j\theta})^n = e^{jn\theta} \text{ for all rational } n.$$

The definition of e^z for any complex number z is now fairly obvious. Since you naturally want to preserve the basic property $e^{a+b} = e^a \times e^b$, it follows that if $z = x + jy$ then $e^z = e^x \times e^{jy}$.

This suggests the *definition*

$$e^z = e^x(\cos y + j \sin y).$$

Notice that, when $y = 0$, $e^z = e^x$, so that when z is real this definition of e^z gives the exponential function you have used until now. Also, taking $x = 0$, $e^{jy} = \cos y + j \sin y$, agreeing with the definition suggested by the differential equation.

ACTIVITY 3.8   Prove that $e^{z+2\pi nj} = e^z$. This means that the exponential function is periodic, with the imaginary period $2\pi j$.

EXAMPLE 3.5

Given two complex numbers, z and w, prove from the definition that

$$e^{z+w} = e^z \times e^w.$$

SOLUTION

Let $z = x + jy$ and $w = u + jv$. Then

$$
\begin{aligned}
e^z \times e^w &= e^x(\cos y + j\sin y) \times e^u(\cos v + j\sin v) \\
&= e^x e^u(\cos y + j\sin y)(\cos v + j\sin v) \\
&= e^{x+u}(\cos(y+v) + j\sin(y+v)) \\
&= e^{x+u+j(y+v)} \\
&= e^{z+w}.
\end{aligned}
$$

Since $e^{j\theta} = \cos\theta + j\sin\theta$ and $e^{-j\theta} = \cos(-\theta) + j\sin(-\theta) = \cos\theta - j\sin\theta$, it follows that

$$\cos\theta = \frac{e^{j\theta} + e^{-j\theta}}{2} \quad \text{and} \quad \sin\theta = \frac{e^{j\theta} - e^{-j\theta}}{2j}.$$

These are essentially the same as the results which were used in Example 3.4.

EXAMPLE 3.6

Prove that $1 + e^{j\theta} = 2\cos\dfrac{\theta}{2} e^{j\theta/2}$.

SOLUTION

The factor $e^{j\theta/2}$ on the right-hand side suggests writing each term on the left-hand side as a multiple of $e^{j\theta/2}$.

$$1 = e^{j\theta/2} \times e^{-j\theta/2} \quad \text{and} \quad e^{j\theta} = e^{j\theta/2} \times e^{j\theta/2}.$$

Therefore $\quad 1 + e^{j\theta} = e^{j\theta/2}(e^{-j\theta/2} + e^{j\theta/2})$

$$= e^{j\theta/2} \times 2\cos\frac{\theta}{2}, \text{ as required.}$$

Note

You should remember the result of Example 3.6 as it will be useful in the work of the next section. See Question 6 of Exercise 3F for an alternative method.

1 Express e^z in the form $x + jy$, where z is the given complex number.

(i) $-j\pi$ (ii) $\dfrac{j\pi}{4}$ (iii) $\dfrac{2 + 5j\pi}{6}$ (iv) $3 - 4j$

2 Find all the solutions of $e^z = e^3$, and plot some of them on an Argand diagram.

3 Find all the solutions of $e^z = \dfrac{1 - \sqrt{3}j}{2e^4}$, and plot some of them on an Argand diagram.

4 Find all the values of z for which $e^{z*} = (e^z)^*$.

5 Prove that $1 - e^{j\theta} = -2j\sin\dfrac{\theta}{2}e^{j\theta/2}$.

6 Plot the points 0, 1, $e^{j\theta}$, $1 + e^{j\theta}$ on an Argand diagram.

   What sort of quadrilateral do these points form?

   Use the geometry of this quadrilateral to prove again the results of Example 3.6 and Question 5.

7 Prove that $(1 + e^{2j\theta})^n = 2^n \cos^n \theta\, e^{jn\theta}$.

8 If $z = f(p) + jg(p)$, where p is a real parameter, then the derivative and integral of z with respect to p are defined by $\dfrac{dz}{dp} = f'(p) + jg'(p)$ and

$$\int z\,dp = \int f(p)\,dp + j\int g(p)\,dp.$$

Prove that if $z = e^{\alpha p}$ where α is a fixed complex number, then $\dfrac{dz}{dp} = \alpha e^{\alpha p}$ and $\int z\,dp = \dfrac{e^{\alpha p}}{\alpha} + c$.

9 The position at time t of a point Z moving in an Argand diagram is given by $z = re^{j\theta}$, where r and θ depend on t.

   Find $\dfrac{dz}{dt}$ and $\dfrac{d^2z}{dt^2}$, and deduce the radial and transverse components of the velocity and acceleration of Z. (The *radial* and *transverse* directions are respectively parallel and perpendicular to $\overrightarrow{OZ}$.)

10 Let $C = \int e^{3x} \cos 2x\,dx$ and $S = \int e^{3x} \sin 2x\,dx$.

   Show that $C + jS = \dfrac{e^{(3+2j)x}}{3 + 2j} + A$, where A is a constant. Hence find C and S.

11 Find $\int e^{ax} \cos bx\,dx$ and $\int e^{ax} \sin bx\,dx$

(i) by using integration by parts twice
(ii) by using the method of Question 10.

   Which method do you prefer?

Summations using complex numbers

This section shows how complex numbers can be used to evaluate certain real sums. It may be possible to do these summations without using complex numbers (e.g. by induction, once you know the answer), but this is considerably more awkward. Sometimes it is worth setting out to do *more* than is required, as in the next example.

EXAMPLE 3.7

Find a simplified expression for the sum of the series

$$1 + {}^nC_1 \cos \theta + {}^nC_2 \cos 2\theta + {}^nC_3 \cos 3\theta + \cdots + \cos n\theta.$$

SOLUTION

At first sight this series suggests the binomial expansion $(1 + \cos \theta)^n$: the coefficients $1(= {}^nC_0)$, ${}^nC_1$, ${}^nC_2, \ldots, 1(= {}^nC_n)$ are right, but there are multiple angles, $\cos r\theta$, instead of powers of cosines, $\cos^r \theta$. This indicates that de Moivre's theorem can be used. The trick is to introduce the corresponding sine series too.

Let $\quad C = 1 + {}^n C_1 \cos \theta + {}^n C_2 \cos 2\theta + {}^nC_3 \cos 3\theta + \cdots + \cos n\theta$

and $\quad S = {}^n C_1 \sin \theta + {}^n C_2 \sin 2\theta + {}^n C_3 \sin 3\theta + \cdots + \sin n\theta.$

Then $C + jS = 1 + {}^nC_1(\cos \theta + j \sin \theta) + {}^nC_2(\cos 2\theta + j \sin 2\theta) + \cdots$

$$+ (\cos n\theta + j \sin n\theta)$$

$$= 1 + {}^n C_1 e^{j\theta} + {}^n C_2 e^{j2\theta} + \cdots + e^{jn\theta}$$

$$= 1 + {}^n C_1 e^{j\theta} + {}^n C_2 (e^{j\theta})^2 + \cdots + (e^{j\theta})^n.$$

> Using de Moivre's theorem: $e^{jr\theta} = (e^{j\theta})^r$.

This is now recognisable as a binomial expansion, so that

$$C + jS = (1 + e^{j\theta})^n.$$

To find C you need to find the real part of $(1 + e^{j\theta})^n$, and here Example 3.6 is useful:

$$(1 + e^{j\theta})^n = \left(2 \cos \frac{\theta}{2} e^{j\theta/2}\right)^n = 2^n \cos^n \frac{\theta}{2} e^{jn\theta/2}$$

$$= 2^n \cos^n \frac{\theta}{2} \left(\cos \frac{n\theta}{2} + j \sin \frac{n\theta}{2}\right).$$

Taking the real part, $C = 2^n \cos^n \frac{\theta}{2} \cos \frac{n\theta}{2}.$

ACTIVITY 3.9

State the result obtained by equating imaginary parts.

⚠ Remember there are alternative notations for binomial coefficients, ${}^nC_r$ or $\binom{n}{r}$.

1 Let $C = 1 + \cos\theta + \cos 2\theta + \cdots + \cos(n-1)\theta$
   and $S = \sin\theta + \sin 2\theta + \cdots + \sin(n-1)\theta$.

   Show that $C + jS$ is a geometric progression with common ratio $e^{j\theta}$ and

   sum $\dfrac{1 - e^{jn\theta}}{1 - e^{j\theta}}$. By multiplying the numerator and denominator of this sum

   by $1 - e^{-j\theta}$, show that $C = \dfrac{1 - \cos\theta + \cos(n-1)\theta - \cos n\theta}{2 - 2\cos\theta}$ and find S.

2 (ii) Show the points 2 and $2 + \cos\dfrac{2\pi}{3} + j\sin\dfrac{2\pi}{3}$ on an Argand diagram, and

   hence show that $2 + \cos\dfrac{2\pi}{3} + j\sin\dfrac{2\pi}{3} = \sqrt{3}e^{j\pi/6}$.

   (ii) Deduce that $\displaystyle\sum_{r=0}^{n} {}^{n}C_r 2^{n-r} \cos\dfrac{2r\pi}{3} = 3^{n/2} \cos\dfrac{n\pi}{6}$.

   (iii) State the corresponding result for sines.

3 You are given that $w = 1 - e^{j\theta}\cos\theta$, where $0 < \theta < \frac{1}{2}\pi$.

   (i) Express $e^{jk\theta}$ and $e^{-jk\theta}$ in the form $a + jb$, and show that $w = -je^{j\theta}\sin\theta$.
   (ii) Find $|w|$ and $\arg w$.
   Hence write down the modulus and argument of each of the two square
   roots of w.

   Series C and S are defined by

   $C = \cos\theta\cos\theta + \cos 2\theta\cos^2\theta + \cos 3\theta\cos^3\theta + \cdots + \cos n\theta\cos^n\theta$
   $S = \sin\theta\cos\theta + \sin 2\theta\cos^2\theta + \sin 3\theta\cos^3\theta + \cdots + \sin n\theta\cos^n\theta$.

   (iii) Show that $C + jS$ is a geometric series, and write down the sum of this
   series.

   (iv) Using the results in part (i), or otherwise, show that $C = \dfrac{\sin n\theta\cos^{n+1}\theta}{\sin\theta}$,

   and find a similar expression for S.

   [MEI]

4 (i) Given that $z = \cos\theta + j\sin\theta$, express z^2, z^3 and z^n in the form $a + jb$.

   The infinite series C and S are defined as follows:

   $C = 1 + \dfrac{1}{3}\cos\theta + \dfrac{1}{9}\cos 2\theta + \dfrac{1}{27}\cos 3\theta + \cdots + \dfrac{1}{3^n}\cos n\theta + \cdots$

   $S = \dfrac{1}{3}\sin\theta + \dfrac{1}{9}\sin 2\theta + \dfrac{1}{27}\sin 3\theta + \cdots + \dfrac{1}{3^n}\sin n\theta + \cdots$.

   (ii) Express $C + jS$ in terms of z, and show that it is a geometric series.
   (iii) Write down, in terms of z, the sum to infinity of this geometric series.
   (iv) Express, in terms of θ, the sum to infinity of   (a) C (b) S.

   (v) Show that $|C + jS| = \dfrac{3}{\sqrt{10 - 6\cos\theta}}$.

   [MEI]

5 **(i)** Write down, in the form $a + jb$, the following complex numbers:
$e^{j\theta}$, $e^{jn\theta}$ and $e^{-jn\theta}$.

(ii) Show that $(1 - \frac{1}{2}e^{2j\theta})(1 - \frac{1}{2}e^{-2j\theta}) = \frac{5}{4} - \cos 2\theta$.

The infinite series C and S are defined as follows:

$$C = \cos\theta + \frac{1}{2}\cos 3\theta + \frac{1}{4}\cos 5\theta + \frac{1}{8}\cos 7\theta + \cdots + \frac{1}{2^{r-1}}\cos(2r-1)\theta + \cdots$$

$$S = \sin\theta + \frac{1}{2}\sin 3\theta + \frac{1}{4}\sin 5\theta + \frac{1}{8}\sin 7\theta + \cdots + \frac{1}{2^{r-1}}\sin(2r-1)\theta + \cdots.$$

(iii) Show that $C + jS = \dfrac{4e^{j\theta} - 2e^{-j\theta}}{5 - 4\cos 2\theta}$.

(iv) Hence find expressions for C and S in terms of $\cos\theta$, $\sin\theta$ and $\cos 2\theta$ only.

[MEI]

6 **(i)** Express the complex number $e^{jn\theta}$ in the form $a + bj$.

(ii) Simplify $\frac{1}{2}(e^{j\theta} + e^{-j\theta})$ and $(1 + \frac{1}{2}e^{j\theta})(1 + \frac{1}{2}e^{-j\theta})$.

Infinite series C and S are defined as follows:

$$C = \frac{\cos\theta}{2} - \frac{\cos 2\theta}{4} + \frac{\cos 3\theta}{8} - \frac{\cos 4\theta}{16} + \cdots$$

$$S = \frac{\sin\theta}{2} - \frac{\sin 2\theta}{4} + \frac{\sin 3\theta}{8} - \frac{\sin 4\theta}{16} + \cdots.$$

(iii) Show that $C + jS = \dfrac{2e^{j\theta} + 1}{5 + 4\cos\theta}$.

(iv) Hence find expressions for C and S in terms of $\cos\theta$ and $\sin\theta$.

[MEI]

7 Sum the series $\displaystyle\sum_{r=0}^{n} {}^nC_r \sin(\alpha + r\beta)$.

Complex roots: the roots of unity

As early as 1629 Albert Girard stated that every polynomial equation of degree n has exactly n roots (including repetitions); this was first proved by the 18-year-old Carl Friedrich Gauss 170 years later.

Therefore even the simple equation $z^n = 1$ has n roots. Of course one of these is $z = 1$, and if n is even then $z = -1$ is another. But where are the rest?

ACTIVITY 3.10 **(i)** Write down the two roots of $z^2 = 1$, and show them in an Argand diagram.

(ii) Use $z^3 - 1 = (z - 1)(z^2 + z + 1)$ to find the three roots of $z^3 = 1$. Show them in an Argand diagram.

(iii) Find the four roots of $z^4 = 1$, and show them in an Argand diagram.

Every root of the equation $z^n = 1$ must have unit modulus, since otherwise the modulus of z^n would not be 1. So every root is of the form $z = \cos\theta + j\sin\theta$,

and $\quad z^n = 1 \quad \Leftrightarrow \quad (\cos\theta + j\sin\theta)^n = 1$

$\qquad\qquad\qquad \Leftrightarrow \quad \cos n\theta + j\sin n\theta = 1$ (by de Moivre)

$\qquad\qquad\qquad \Leftrightarrow \quad n\theta = 2k\pi$, where k is any integer,

since, in polar form, 1 is $(1, 0)$ or $(1, 2\pi)$ or $(1, 4\pi)$ or $\ldots$.

As k takes the values $0, 1, 2, \ldots, n-1$ the corresponding values of θ are

$$0, \ \frac{2\pi}{n}, \ \frac{4\pi}{n}, \ \ldots, \ \frac{2(n-1)\pi}{n},$$

giving n distinct values of z. But when $k = n$ then $\theta = 2\pi$, which gives the same z as $\theta = 0$. Similarly any integer value of k larger than n differs from one of $0, 1, 2, \ldots, n-1$ by a multiple of n, and so gives a value of θ differing by a multiple of 2π from one already listed; the same applies when k is any negative integer.

Therefore the equation $z^n = 1$ has precisely n roots. These are

$$z = \cos\frac{2k\pi}{n} + j\sin\frac{2k\pi}{n}, \quad k = 0, 1, 2, \ldots, n-1.$$

These n complex numbers are called the nth *roots of unity*. They include $z = 1$ when $k = 0$ and, if n is even, $z = -1$ when $k = \frac{n}{2}$. It is customary to use ω (the Greek letter omega) for the root with the smallest positive argument:

$$\omega = \cos\frac{2\pi}{n} + j\sin\frac{2\pi}{n}.$$

Then, by de Moivre's theorem,

$$\omega^k = \cos\frac{2k\pi}{n} + j\sin\frac{2k\pi}{n},$$

so that the nth roots of unity may be written as

$$1, \omega, \omega^2, \ldots, \omega^{n-1}.$$

The complex numbers $1, \omega, \omega^2, \ldots,$ ω^{n-1} are represented on an Argand diagram by the vertices of a regular n-sided polygon inscribed in the unit circle with one vertex at the point 1.

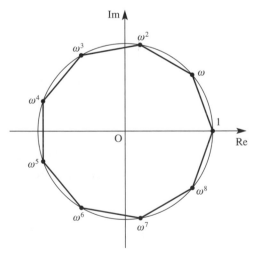

Figure 3.11 *The nine ninth roots of unity*

| ACTIVITY 3.11   Prove that $(\omega^r)^* = \omega^{n-r}$.

The sum of all the nth roots of unity is a geometric series with common ratio ω:

$$1 + \omega + \omega^2 + \ldots + \omega^{n-1} = \frac{1 - \omega^n}{1 - \omega} = 0.$$

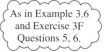 since $\omega^n = 1$

Therefore the sum of all n of the nth roots of unity is zero.

EXAMPLE 3.8

Solve the equation $(1 + jz)^n = (1 - jz)^n$, where n is odd.

SOLUTION

The equation can be rearranged as $\left(\dfrac{1 + jz}{1 - jz}\right)^n = 1$.

By taking the nth root of both sides you have, $\dfrac{1 + jz}{1 - jz} = \alpha$, where $\alpha = e^{j\theta}$ is an nth root of unity.

Solving this for z gives $z = \dfrac{\alpha - 1}{j(\alpha + 1)}$, where since n is odd $\alpha + 1 \neq 0$.

But

$$\alpha - 1 = 2j \sin\frac{\theta}{2} e^{j\theta/2}$$

and

$$\alpha + 1 = 2 \cos\frac{\theta}{2} e^{j\theta/2}.$$

As in Example 3.6 and Exercise 3F Questions 5, 6.

Substituting these in the expression for z and simplifying gives

$$z = \frac{\sin\dfrac{\theta}{2}}{\cos\dfrac{\theta}{2}} = \tan\frac{\theta}{2}$$

Since α is a nth root of unity, $\theta = \dfrac{2k\pi}{n}$, and so the roots are $z = \tan\dfrac{k\pi}{n}$, $k = 0, 1, 2, \ldots, n - 1$.

ACTIVITY 3.12

Work through Example 3.8 in the case when n is even. (Be careful: what is the degree of the equation now?)

EXERCISE 3H

1 Explain geometrically why the set of tenth roots of unity is the same as the set of fifth roots of unity together with their negatives.

2 If ω is a complex cube root of unity, $\omega \neq 1$, prove that

   (i) $(1 + \omega)(1 + \omega^2) = 1$
   (ii) $1 + \omega$ and $1 + \omega^2$ are complex cube roots of -1
   (iii) $(a + b)(a + \omega b)(a + \omega^2 b) = a^3 + b^3$
   (iv) $(a + b + c)(a + \omega b + \omega^2 c)(a + \omega^2 b + \omega c) = a^3 + b^3 + c^3 - 3abc.$

3 A regular hexagon is inscribed in the unit circle. One vertex is α. Give the other vertices in terms of α and ω, where ω is a complex cube root of unity.

4 The complex numbers $1, \omega, \omega^2, \ldots, \omega^{n-1}$ are represented as *vectors* in an Argand diagram, following 'nose to tail' in order. Explain geometrically why these form a regular polygon. Hence prove again that the sum of all the nth roots of unity is zero.

5 (i) (a) Draw an Argand diagram showing the points $1, \omega, \omega^2, \omega^3, \omega^4$,

where $\omega = \cos\dfrac{2\pi}{5} + j\sin\dfrac{2\pi}{5}$.

   (b) If $\alpha = \omega^2$ show that the points $1, \alpha, \alpha^2, \alpha^3, \alpha^4$ are the same as the points in **(a)**, but in a different order. Indicate this order by joining successive points on your diagram.

   (c) Repeat **(b)** with α replaced by β, where $\beta = \omega^3$.

   (ii) Repeat the whole of **(i)** taking $\omega = \cos\dfrac{2\pi}{6} + j\sin\dfrac{2\pi}{6}$ and considering the points $1, \omega, \ldots, \omega^5; 1, \alpha, \ldots, \alpha^5; 1, \beta, \ldots, \beta^5$.

   (iii) Do likewise for the seventh and eighth roots of unity.

   (iv) If $\omega = \cos\dfrac{2\pi}{n} + j\sin\dfrac{2\pi}{n}$ and $\alpha = \omega^m$, form a conjecture about when

$$\{1, \omega, \omega^2, \ldots, \omega^{n-1}\} = \{1, \alpha, \alpha^2, \ldots, \alpha^{n-1}\}.$$

6 Solve the equation $z^3 = (j - z)^3$.

7 Solve the equation $z^5 + z^4 + z^3 + z^2 + z + 1 = 0$.

8 Prove that all the roots of $(z - 1)^n = z^n$ have real part $\frac{1}{2}$.

9 Solve the equation $(j - z)^n = (jz - 1)^n$.

10 Solve the equation $(z + j)^n + (z - j)^n = 0$.

Complex roots: the general case

To find the nth roots of any given non-zero complex number w you have to find z such that $z^n = w$. The pattern of argument is the same as in the previous section on nth roots of unity, but adjusted to take account of the modulus s and argument ϕ of w. So let

$$z = r(\cos\theta + j\sin\theta) \text{ and } w = s(\cos\phi + j\sin\phi).$$

Then

$$z^n = w \Leftrightarrow r^n(\cos\theta + j\sin\theta)^n = s(\cos\phi + j\sin\phi)$$
$$\Leftrightarrow r^n(\cos n\theta + j\sin n\theta) = s(\cos\phi + j\sin\phi).$$

Two complex numbers in polar form are equal only if they have the same moduli and their arguments are equal or differ by a multiple of 2π. Therefore

$$r^n = s \text{ and } n\theta = \phi + 2k\pi, \text{ where } k \text{ is an integer.}$$

Since r and s are positive real numbers the equation $r^n = s$ gives the *unique* value $r = s^{1/n}$, so all the roots lie on the circle $|z| = s^{1/n}$.

The argument of z is $\theta = \dfrac{\phi + 2k\pi}{n}$. As k can take the values $0, 1, 2, \ldots, n-1$, this gives n distinct complex numbers z, and (by the same argument as for the roots of unity) there are no others.

Therefore the non-zero complex number $w = s(\cos\phi + j\sin\phi)$ has precisely n different nth roots. These are

$$s^{1/n}\left(\cos\left(\frac{\phi + 2k\pi}{n}\right) + j\sin\left(\frac{\phi + 2k\pi}{n}\right)\right) \text{ where } k = 0, 1, 2, \ldots, n-1.$$

You may also express these n roots as $\alpha, \alpha\omega, \alpha\omega^2, \ldots, \alpha\omega^{n-1}$ where

$$\alpha = s^{1/n}\left(\cos\frac{\phi}{n} + j\sin\frac{\phi}{n}\right) \text{ and } \omega = \cos\frac{2\pi}{n} + j\sin\frac{2\pi}{n}.$$

Then the sum of these n nth roots of w is

$$\alpha + \alpha\omega + \alpha\omega^2 + \cdots + \alpha\omega^{n-1} = \frac{\alpha(1 - \omega^n)}{1 - \omega} = 0, \text{ since } \omega^n = 1.$$

You may prove the same result by considering the 'nose to tail' addition of the vectors representing the n nth roots.

EXAMPLE 3.9 Represent $2 - 2j$ and its five fifth roots on an Argand diagram.

SOLUTION

Since $2 - 2j = 8^{1/2}\left(\cos\left(-\dfrac{\pi}{4}\right) + j\sin\left(-\dfrac{\pi}{4}\right)\right)$, the fifth roots all have modulus $8^{1/10} \approx 1.23$.

Their arguments are

$$-\frac{\pi}{20}, \quad -\frac{\pi}{20} + \frac{2\pi}{5}, \quad -\frac{\pi}{20} + \frac{4\pi}{5}, \quad -\frac{\pi}{20} + \frac{6\pi}{5}, \quad -\frac{\pi}{20} + \frac{8\pi}{5},$$

or (taking principal arguments in degrees) $-9°, 63°, 135°, -153°, -81°$.

The fifth roots are the vertices of a regular pentagon inscribed in the circle $|z| = 8^{1/10}$, as in figure 3.12. The sum of these five fifth roots is 0.

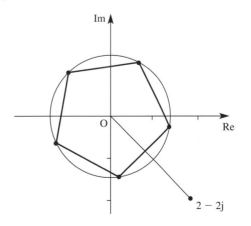

Figure 3.12

ACTIVITY 3.13 Express $8^{1/10}\left(\cos\left(-\dfrac{\pi}{20}\right)+j\sin\left(-\dfrac{\pi}{20}\right)\right)$ in the form $x+yj$, giving x and y correct to 2 decimal places.

Figure 3.12 is typical of the general case: the n nth roots of z are represented by the vertices of a regular n-gon inscribed in the circle with centre O and radius $|z|^{1/n}$. This can be useful when dealing with the geometry of regular polygons.

EXAMPLE 3.10 The vertices A_0, A_1, ..., A_{n-1} of a regular n-gon lie on a circle of unit radius with centre O. The point P is such that $\overrightarrow{OP}=3\overrightarrow{OA_0}$.

Prove that $(PA_0)^2+(PA_1)^2+\cdots+(PA_{n-1})^2=10n$.

SOLUTION

Let $\omega=\cos\dfrac{2\pi}{n}+j\sin\dfrac{2\pi}{n}$, an nth root of unity. Then the vertices A_r represent the complex numbers ω^r for $r=0,1,\ldots,n-1$, and P represents 3. Therefore

$$(PA_r)^2=|\omega^r-3|^2=(\omega^r-3)(\omega^r-3)^*=(\omega^r-3)(\omega^{n-r}-3)$$
$$=\omega^n-3\omega^r-3\omega^{n-r}+9$$
$$=10-3\omega^r-3\omega^{n-r},\text{ since }\omega^n=1.$$

When this expression is summed from $r=0$ to $r=n-1$ the first term gives $10n$ and each of the two sums involving ω is zero, since $1+\omega+\omega^2+\cdots+\omega^{n-1}=0$. This proves the required result.

If $w=s(\cos\phi+j\sin\phi)$ then $w^m=s^m(\cos m\phi+j\sin m\phi)$ for all integers m by de Moivre's theorem.

The complex number w^m has the n nth roots

$$s^{m/n}\left(\cos\left(\frac{m\phi+2k\pi}{n}\right)+j\sin\left(\frac{m\phi+2k\pi}{n}\right)\right).$$

One of these is $s^{m/n}\left(\cos\dfrac{m\phi}{n}+j\sin\dfrac{m\phi}{n}\right)$, and the notation $w^{m/n}$ is used to mean *this* nth root of w^m. This definition ensures that de Moivre's theorem is also true for rational powers, since

$$(\cos\theta+j\sin\theta)^{m/n}=\left(\cos\frac{m\theta}{n}+j\sin\frac{m\theta}{n}\right).$$

? Explain the fallacy in the following argument:

$$j=\sqrt{(-1)}=\sqrt{\frac{1}{-1}}=\frac{\sqrt{1}}{\sqrt{(-1)}}=\frac{1}{j},\text{ so }j^2=1.$$

But $j^2=-1$. Therefore $1=-1$.

1 Find both square roots of $-7 + 5j$, giving your answers in the form $x + yj$ with x and y correct to 2 decimal places.

2 Find the four fourth roots of -4, giving your answers in the form $x + yj$, and show them on an Argand diagram.

3 One fourth root of w is $2 + 3j$. Find w and its other fourth roots, and represent all five points on an Argand diagram.

4 Represent the five solutions of the equation $(z - 3j)^5 = 32$ on an Argand diagram.

5 A regular heptagon (seven sides) on an Argand diagram has centre $-1 + 3j$ and one vertex at $2 + 3j$. Write down the equation whose solutions are represented by the vertices of this heptagon.

6 One of the nth roots of w is α. Prove that the other roots are $\alpha\omega$, $\alpha\omega^2$, ..., $\alpha\omega^{n-1}$ where $\omega = \cos\dfrac{2\pi}{n} + j\sin\dfrac{2\pi}{n}$. Deduce that the sum of all the nth roots of w is zero.

7 The nth roots of w are represented by vectors on an Argand diagram, with $w^{1/n}$ as a position vector and with each subsequent vector added to its predecessor. Describe the figure which is formed, and deduce again that the sum of all the nth roots is zero.

8 The vertices A_1, A_2, A_3, A_4, A_5 of a regular pentagon lie on a circle of unit radius with centre at the point O. A_1 is the mid-point of OP. Prove that

   (i) $PA_1 \times PA_2 \times PA_3 \times PA_4 \times PA_5 = 31$

   (ii) $\displaystyle\sum_{n=1}^{5} (PA_n)^2 = 25$

   (iii) $A_1A_2 \times A_1A_3 \times A_1A_4 \times A_1A_5 = 5$.

9 The fourth roots of -64 are α_1, α_2, α_3, α_4, and these complex numbers are represented by points A_1, A_2, A_3, A_4 on an Argand diagram.

   (i) Express α_1, α_2, α_3, α_4, in the form $a + bj$.
   (ii) Draw $A_1A_2A_3A_4$ on an Argand diagram.

   With $\beta = \sqrt{3} + j$, the complex numbers $\alpha_1\beta$, $\alpha_2\beta$, $\alpha_3\beta$, $\alpha_4\beta$ are represented by points B_1, B_2, B_3, B_4 on the Argand diagram.

   (iii) Describe in detail how $A_1A_2A_3A_4$ may be transformed geometrically into $B_1B_2B_3B_4$. Hence show that $B_1B_2B_3B_4$ is a square, and state the length of a side of this square. Draw the square $B_1B_2B_3B_4$ on your diagram.
   (iv) The complex numbers $\alpha_1\beta$, $\alpha_2\beta$, $\alpha_3\beta$, $\alpha_4\beta$ are the fourth roots of a complex number w. Find w in the form $a + bj$.

[MEI, part]

10 (i) Express $e^{j\theta}$ and $e^{-j\theta}$ in the form $a + jb$, and show that

$$\frac{1}{1 + e^{2j\theta}} = \frac{1}{2}(1 - j\tan\theta).$$

(ii) Solve the equation $z^5 + 32 = 0$, giving the roots in the form $re^{j\alpha}$ (where $r > 0$ and $-\pi < \alpha \leqslant \pi$). Illustrate the roots on an Argand diagram.

(iii) If $\left(\dfrac{1 - 2w}{w}\right)^5 + 32 = 0$, show that w has the form $\frac{1}{4}(1 - j\tan\beta)$, and

state the four possible values of β in the interval $-\frac{1}{2}\pi < \beta < \frac{1}{2}\pi$.

On a separate Argand diagram, illustrate the four possible values of w.

[MEI]

11 (i) Express $e^{jk\theta}$ and $e^{-jk\theta}$ in the form $a + jb$, and show that

$$\frac{1}{1 - e^{j\theta}} = \frac{1}{2}(1 + j\cot\frac{1}{2}\theta).$$

(ii) Find the sixth roots of $8j$ in the form $re^{j\theta}$, where $r > 0$ and $-\pi < \theta \leqslant \pi$. Illustrate these roots on an Argand diagram.

(iii) Show that two of these sixth roots have the form $m + jn$, where m and n are integers.

(iv) Given that $\left(\sqrt{2} - \dfrac{1}{w}\right)^6 = 8j$, show that $w = p(1 + j\cot\alpha)$, stating the value of the real number p and the six possible values of α satisfying $-\frac{1}{2}\pi < \alpha < \frac{1}{2}\pi$.

[MEI]

12 (i) By considering the solutions of the equation $z^n - 1 = 0$ prove that

$$(z - \omega)(z - \omega^2)(z - \omega^3)\ldots(z - \omega^{n-1}) = z^{n-1} + z^{n-2} + \cdots + z + 1,$$

where $\omega = \cos\dfrac{2\pi}{n} + j\sin\dfrac{2\pi}{n}$.

(ii) There are n points equally spaced around the circumference of a unit circle. Prove that the product of the distances from one of these points to each of the others is n. (Question 8 part **(iii)** is the case $n = 5$.)

(iii) By finding expressions for the distances in **(ii)**, deduce that

$$\sin\frac{\pi}{n}\sin\frac{2\pi}{n}\sin\frac{3\pi}{n}\ldots\sin\frac{(n-1)\pi}{n} = \frac{n}{2^{n-1}}.$$

13 Find the following in polar form.

(i) $\left[32\left(\cos\dfrac{\pi}{6} + j\sin\dfrac{\pi}{6}\right)\right]^{3/5}$

(ii) $\left[343\left(\cos\dfrac{3\pi}{8} + j\sin\dfrac{3\pi}{8}\right)\right]^{-2/3}$

(iii) $\left[81\left(\cos\left(-\dfrac{\pi}{3}\right) + j\sin\left(-\dfrac{\pi}{3}\right)\right)\right]^{-1.75}$

14 (i) Find $(j^{1/2})^3$ and $(j^3)^{1/2}$. Which of these is $j^{3/2}$?

(ii) Find $(j^{1/3})^2$ and $(j^2)^{1/3}$.

(iii) Find a condition involving m and arg w which ensures that $(w^{1/n})^m = (w^m)^{1/n}$.

15 (i) Express $e^{jk\theta}$ and $e^{-jk\theta}$ in the form $a + jb$, and show that

$$e^{2j\theta} - 1 = 2je^{j\theta}\sin\theta.$$

Series C and S are defined by

$$C = \cos\theta + \cos 3\theta + \cos 5\theta + \cdots + \cos(2n-1)\theta$$
$$S = \sin\theta + \sin 3\theta + \sin 5\theta + \cdots + \sin(2n-1)\theta$$

where n is a positive integer and $0 < \theta < \dfrac{\pi}{n}$.

(ii) Show that $C + jS$ is a geometric series, and write down the sum of this series.

(iii) Show that $|C + jS| = \dfrac{\sin n\theta}{\sin\theta}$, and find $\arg(C + jS)$.

(iv) Find C and S.

The points $A_0, A_1, A_2, A_3, A_4, A_5, A_6$ in the Argand diagram correspond to complex numbers $z_0, z_1, z_2, z_3, z_4, z_5, z_6$ where $z_0 = 0$ and $z_1 = \cos\frac{1}{7}\pi + j\sin\frac{1}{7}\pi$. The points are the vertices of a regular heptagon with sides of length 1, as shown in the diagram below.

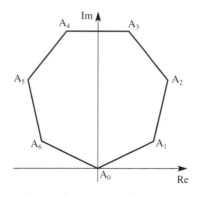

(v) Explain why $z_n = e^{\frac{1}{7}j\pi} + e^{\frac{3}{7}j\pi} + \cdots + e^{\frac{1}{7}(2n-1)j\pi}$ for $n = 1, 2, 3, 4, 5, 6$. Hence, or otherwise, show that $\arg(z_n) = \frac{1}{7}n\pi$ for $n = 1, 2, 3, 4, 5, 6$.

[MEI]

16 The Polish mathematician Hoëné Wronski (1778–1853) once wrote that

$$\pi = \frac{2\infty}{\sqrt{-1}}\{(1 + \sqrt{-1})^{1/\infty} - (1 - \sqrt{-1})^{1/\infty}\}.$$

Was Wronski wrong?

Geometrical uses of complex numbers

Your study of complex numbers started in *AS Further Pure Mathematics* (*FP1*) with their origin in algebra, in connection with the solution of polynomial equations. Then the simple idea of representing a complex number as a point or a vector in the Argand diagram soon made it possible for you to use complex numbers in geometry too. Some of these geometrical applications, such as the use of mid-points, other points of subdivision, centroids, and enlargements, can be handled equally well by two-dimensional vector methods. But with other problems, especially those involving rotations or similarity, complex number methods are especially effective. For example, you have seen in the previous section some fruitful links between regular polygons and the complex roots of unity.

Much of the geometrical power of complex numbers comes from the crucial result about the multiplication of complex numbers in polar form: 'multiply the moduli, add the arguments'. This means that the effect of multiplying a complex number z by a complex number λ is to turn the vector z in an Argand diagram through the angle $\arg \lambda$ anticlockwise and stretch it by the scale factor $|\lambda|$ to give the vector λz.

In particular, if A, B, C represent the numbers a, b, c in an Argand diagram, then $\overrightarrow{BA}$ represents the complex number $a - b$, while $\overrightarrow{BC}$ represents $c - b$ (see figure 3.13). Therefore

$$\text{if} \quad \frac{a - b}{c - b} = \lambda \quad \text{then} \quad \text{angle ABC} = \arg \lambda = \arg\left(\frac{a - b}{c - b}\right).$$

Angle ABC here means the *anticlockwise* angle through which $\overrightarrow{BC}$ has to be turned to bring it into line with $\overrightarrow{BA}$.

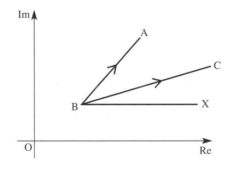

Figure 3.13

ACTIVITY 3.14   Prove the same result by starting with $\arg\left(\dfrac{a - b}{c - b}\right) = \arg\left(a - b\right) - \arg\left(c - b\right)$.

EXAMPLE 3.11

Find the locus of points z for which $\arg\left(\dfrac{z-2j}{z+3}\right) = \dfrac{\pi}{3}$.

SOLUTION

Let A, B, P be the points representing $2j$, -3, z respectively.

The given condition shows that the direction of $\overrightarrow{AP}\,(=z-2j)$ is $\dfrac{\pi}{3}$ ahead of the direction of $\overrightarrow{BP}\,(=z+3)$, in the anticlockwise sense. Therefore $\angle APB = \dfrac{\pi}{3}$, and so (using the converse of the 'angles in the same segment' circle property) P lies on the arc of the circle with end points A and B as shown.

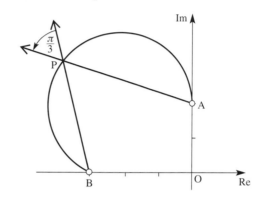

Figure 3.14

ACTIVITY 3.15 Find in a similar form the condition for P to lie on the other arc of this circle.

EXAMPLE 3.12

Two similar figures are *directly* similar if corresponding points moving round the two figures go in the same sense, either both clockwise or both anticlockwise. Find a condition for two triangles in an Argand diagram to be directly similar.

SOLUTION

Let A, B, C, D, E, F be the points representing a, b, c, d, e, f (see figure 3.15).

Then triangles ABC, DEF are directly similar if and only if

$$\frac{AB}{BC} = \frac{DE}{EF} \quad \text{and} \quad \text{angle ABC} = \text{angle DEF},$$

both angles being in the same sense because the similarity is direct.

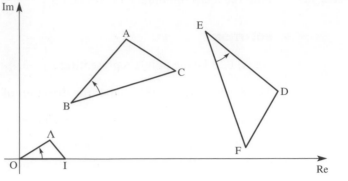

Figure 3.15

Therefore $\dfrac{|a-b|}{|c-b|} = \dfrac{|d-e|}{|f-e|}$ and $\arg\left(\dfrac{a-b}{c-b}\right) = \arg\left(\dfrac{d-e}{f-e}\right)$, and so

$$\dfrac{a-b}{c-b} = \dfrac{d-e}{f-e}.$$

Note

The shape of these triangles is determined by the single complex number

$\lambda = \dfrac{a-b}{c-b} = \dfrac{d-e}{f-e}$, and both triangles are similar to the triangle ΛOI with vertices

λ, 0, 1 (see figure 3.15). When dealing with a set of similar triangles it can be helpful to make use of ΛOI as the 'standard representative' of the whole family of triangles with this shape.

ACTIVITY 3.16   Prove that the condition for two triangles ABC, DEF to have opposite similarity (where corresponding points move in opposite senses round the two triangles) is

$$\dfrac{a-b}{c-b} = \left(\dfrac{d-e}{f-e}\right)^{*}.$$

EXAMPLE 3.13   Squares whose centres are P, Q, R are drawn outwards on the sides BC, CA, AB respectively of a triangle ABC. Prove that AP and QR are equal and mutually perpendicular.

SOLUTION

Working on an Argand diagram, let the points A, B, ... correspond to the complex numbers a, b, ... as usual (see figure 3.16).

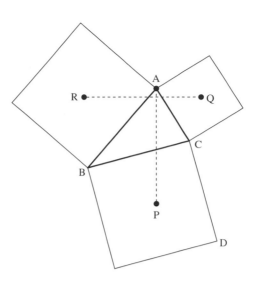

Figure 3.16

The first step is to find p in terms of b and c: two ways of doing this are given.

(i)   If D is the vertex opposite B in the square with centre P then $\overrightarrow{CD}$ is obtained by turning $\overrightarrow{CB}$ through a right angle anticlockwise, and so $d - c = j(b - c)$. Therefore, since P is the mid-point of BD,

$$p = \frac{b + d}{2} = \frac{b + c + j(b - c)}{2}.$$

(ii) Alternatively, triangles BCP, CAQ, ABR are all right-angled isosceles triangles, and therefore all similar to the 'standard representative' triangle ΛOI with vertices $\dfrac{1 + j}{2}$, 0, 1.

Hence $\dfrac{p - c}{b - c} = \dfrac{q - a}{c - a} = \dfrac{r - b}{a - b} = \dfrac{1 + j}{2}$,

from which

$$p = c + \frac{(1 + j)(b - c)}{2} = \frac{b + c + j(b - c)}{2}, \qquad \text{as before.}$$

Similarly

$$q = \frac{c + a + j(c - a)}{2} \quad \text{and} \quad r = \frac{a + b + j(a - b)}{2}.$$

It is now easy to complete the proof:

$$\begin{aligned}
2(q - r) &= c + a + j(c - a) - a - b - j(a - b) \\
&= c - b + j(b + c) - 2ja \\
&= j(b + c + j(b - c) - 2a) \\
&= 2j(p - a).
\end{aligned}$$

Therefore $\overrightarrow{RQ}$ is obtained by turning $\overrightarrow{AP}$ through a right angle.

1 Explain the following construction for multiplication of given numbers z_1 and z_2 in an Argand diagram.

Draw the triangle with vertices 0, 1, z_1. Then construct the directly similar triangle which has vertices 0 and z_2 corresponding to vertices 0 and 1 of the original triangle. The third vertex of the constructed triangle is $z_1 z_2$.

Illustrate this by doing the construction for $z_1 = 2 + j$, $z_2 = 3 + 4j$. Then do the same with z_1 and z_2 interchanged.

2 Find the locus of points z for which

$$\arg\left(\frac{z - 2j}{z + 3}\right) = -\frac{\pi}{3}.$$

(Compare this with Example 3.11.)

3 On a single diagram draw and identify the locus of points z for which

$$\arg\left(\frac{z - 3 - 2j}{z - 1}\right) = \alpha \text{ where } \alpha \text{ is}$$

(i) $\dfrac{\pi}{4}$ **(ii)** $-\dfrac{\pi}{4}$ **(iii)** $\dfrac{3\pi}{4}$ **(iv)** $-\dfrac{3\pi}{4}$.

4 Prove that $\arg\left(\dfrac{z - 5}{z + 5j}\right) = \dfrac{\pi}{4} \Rightarrow |z| = 5$.

Investigate whether the converse is true.

5 Given that $z_1 = 3 + 4j$, and $z_2 = -3 + 2j$, illustrate the following loci or regions on separate Argand diagrams. For parts **(i)** to **(v)** you are not required to give the cartesian equation of the loci.

(i) $|z - z_1| = 2$

(ii) $|z - z_2| \leqslant 2$

(iii) $0 \leqslant \arg(z - z_1) \leqslant \pi$ and $|z - z_1| \leqslant 1$

(iv) $|z - z_1| = |z - z_2|$

(v) $\arg(z - z_1) - \arg(z - z_2) = \dfrac{\pi}{2}$

(vi) Find the cartesian equation of the locus given by $|z - z_1| = 2|z - z_2|$ and draw a sketch to illustrate it.

[MEI]

6 Let A, B, C, D, E, F be the points representing a, b, c, d, e, f in an Argand diagram. Prove that triangles ABC, DEF are directly similar if and only if

$$ae + bf + cd = af + bd + ce.$$

Find in a similar form the condition for these triangles to have opposite similarity.

7 The points A, B, C in an Argand diagram represent the complex numbers a, b, c, and $a = (1 - \lambda)b + \lambda c$. Prove that if λ is real then A lies on BC and divides BC in the ratio $\lambda : 1 - \lambda$, but if λ is complex then, in triangle ABC, AB : BC $= |\lambda| : 1$ and angle ABC $= \arg \lambda$.

8 (i) If $\omega = \cos\dfrac{2\pi}{3} + j\sin\dfrac{2\pi}{3}$ and z is any vector, how are the vectors z and ωz related geometrically?

   (ii) If $2 + 3j$ and $4 + 7j$ are two vertices of an equilateral triangle, find both possible positions for the third vertex.

9 (i) If the points a and b are two vertices of an equilateral triangle, prove that the third vertex is either $b + \omega(b - a)$ or $b + \omega^2(b - a)$, where ω is as in Question 8.

   (ii) Show that these expressions can be written as $-\omega a - \omega^2 b$ and $-\omega^2 a - \omega b$ respectively.

   (iii) Deduce that the triangle with vertices z_1, z_2, z_3 is equilateral if and only if

$$z_1 + \omega z_2 + \omega^2 z_3 = 0 \quad \text{or} \quad z_1 + \omega^2 z_2 + \omega z_3 = 0.$$

   (iv) Deduce that a necessary and sufficient condition for the points z_1, z_2, z_3 to form an equilateral triangle is

$$z_1^2 + z_2^2 + z_3^2 = z_2 z_3 + z_3 z_1 + z_1 z_2.$$

10 The points A, B, C in an Argand diagram represent the complex numbers a, b, c; M is the mid-point of AB, and G is the point dividing the median AM in the ratio 2 : 1. Show that G represents the number $\dfrac{a + b + c}{3}$, and deduce from the symmetry of this expression that G also lies on the median through B and the median through C. (A *median* of a triangle is a line joining a vertex to the mid-point of the opposite side; the point G at which the medians meet is called the *centroid* of the triangle.)

11 Directly similar triangles BCL, CAM, ABN are drawn on the sides of a triangle ABC. Prove that triangles ABC, LMN have the same centroid.

12 (i) On the sides of any triangle, equilateral triangles are drawn, pointing outward. Using Question 9 part (ii), prove that the centroids of these equilateral triangles form another equilateral triangle. This is *Napoleon's theorem*; it was attributed to the Emperor within a few years of his death, and he was a good enough mathematician to have discovered it.

  (ii) Prove that the theorem is still true if the equilateral triangles are drawn inward rather than outward.

  (iii) Prove that the triangle of centroids in part (i), the corresponding triangle in part (ii), and the original triangle all have the same centroid.

13 (i) Squares whose centres are P, Q, R, S are drawn outwards on the sides AB, BC, CD, DA of a general quadrilateral ABCD. Prove that PR and QS are equal and mutually perpendicular.

  (ii) What difference does it make if all the squares are drawn inwards?

  (iii) Explain how the result of Example 3.13 can be deduced from part (i).

INVESTIGATION

Roberts' theorem

Figure 3.17 shows four rods AB, BC, CD, DA which are flexibly linked. Rod AD is fixed (sometimes the points A and D are just fixed without being joined by a rod), and a triangle BCP is attached to rod BC.

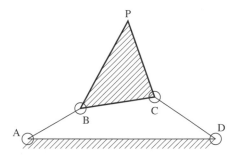

Figure 3.17

This mechanism is called a *four-bar linkage*: by adjusting the lengths of the rods and the shape of the triangle it is possible to achieve many different paths for the point P as the mechanism moves. Four-bar linkages are used to control the motion of parts of many machines (a good collection of examples is given in *Mathematics Meets Technology* by Brian Bolt, CUP, 1991). In 1878 the English engineer Richard Roberts proved that any motion of P which can be produced by a particular four-bar linkage can also be produced by two other linkages; this is useful since the other linkages may be more convenient to fit into the machine.

To prove Roberts' theorem you complete the parallelograms ABPE, DCPF, then construct triangles EPG, PFH directly similar to triangle BCP, and finally complete parallelogram GPHK (see figure 3.18).

Putting the figure on an Argand diagram, let $\overrightarrow{AB}$, $\overrightarrow{BC}$, $\overrightarrow{CD}$ represent the complex numbers u, v, w respectively, and let the shape of triangle BCP be defined by the complex number λ, so that $\overrightarrow{BP} = \lambda v$.

Copy figure 3.18 and mark on each edge the complex number it represents.

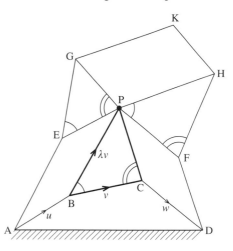

Figure 3.18

Deduce that $\overrightarrow{AK}$ represents $\lambda(u + v + w)$, and hence that K is a fixed point. This shows that the linkage AEGK with triangle EGP and linkage DFHK with triangle FHP also give the same motion for P.

1 The *principal argument* of z is the angle θ, $-\pi < \theta \leqslant \pi$, such that $\cos\theta : \sin\theta : 1 = x : y : r$, where $r = |z|$.

2 The *polar form* of z is $z = r(\cos\theta + j\sin\theta)$.

3 Multiplication in polar form – multiply the moduli, add the arguments:

$$z_1 z_2 = r_1 r_2 [\cos(\theta_1 + \theta_2) + j\sin(\theta_1 + \theta_2)]$$

4 Division in polar form – divide the moduli, subtract the arguments:

$$\frac{z_1}{z_2} = \frac{r_1}{r_2}[\cos(\theta_1 - \theta_2) + j\sin(\theta_1 - \theta_2)]$$

5 de Moivre's theorem: $(\cos\theta + j\sin\theta)^n = \cos n\theta + j\sin n\theta$, where n is rational.

6 If $z = \cos\theta + j\sin\theta$ then

$$\frac{1}{z} = \cos\theta - j\sin\theta, \quad \cos n\theta = \frac{z^n + z^{-n}}{2}, \quad \sin n\theta = \frac{z^n - z^{-n}}{2j}.$$

7 $e^{j\theta} = \cos\theta + j\sin\theta, \quad \cos n\theta = \dfrac{e^{jn\theta} + e^{-jn\theta}}{2}, \quad \sin n\theta = \dfrac{e^{jn\theta} - e^{-jn\theta}}{2j}.$

8 The equation $z^n = 1$ has precisely n roots. These are

$$\omega^k = \cos\frac{2k\pi}{n} + j\sin\frac{2k\pi}{n}, \quad k = 0, 1, 2, \ldots, n-1.$$

The sum of all these nth roots of unity is zero.

9 The non-zero complex number $s(\cos\phi + j\sin\phi)$ has precisely n different nth roots. These are

$$s^{1/n}\left(\cos\left(\frac{\phi + 2k\pi}{n}\right) + j\sin\left(\frac{\phi + 2k\pi}{n}\right)\right), \text{ where } k = 0, 1, 2, \ldots, n-1.$$

The sum of these n roots is zero, and in an Argand diagram they are the vertices of a regular n-gon with centre O.

10 In an Argand diagram if $\dfrac{a-b}{c-b} = \lambda$ then

$$\text{angle ABC} = \arg\lambda = \arg\left(\frac{a-b}{c-b}\right),$$

and triangle ABC is similar to triangle ΛOI with vertices λ, 0, 1.

4

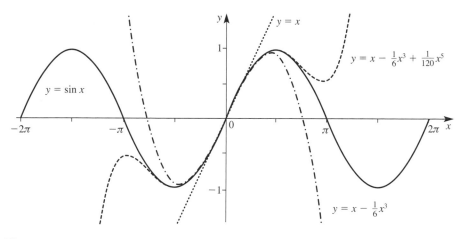

Power series

If I feel unhappy, I do mathematics to become happy.
If I am happy, I do mathematics to keep happy.

Alfréd Rényi, 1921–1970

Figure 4.1

What do you notice about the graphs shown in figure 4.1? What questions do the graphs provoke?

Polynomial approximations

Since polynomial functions are easy to evaluate, to differentiate or to integrate they can be useful as approximations to more complicated functions. Here is one way of finding such approximations, using the exponential function as an example.

If you want to use a straight line to approximate the curve with equation $y = e^x$, there are many straight lines you could choose. Even restricting your choice to those which are tangents, there are infinitely many lines you could choose. The most obvious straight line to use is the tangent to the curve at the point where $x = 0$, as illustrated in figure 4.2. Suppose the tangent has equation $y = a_0 + a_1 x$; then:

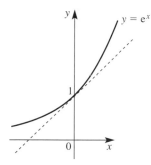

Figure 4.2

① line and curve cut the y axis at the same point $\Rightarrow a_0 = e^0 = 1$
② line and curve have the same gradient when $x = 0 \Rightarrow a_1 = 1$ since

$$\frac{\mathrm{d}}{\mathrm{d}x}(e^x) = e^x, \text{ which is 1 when } x = 0.$$

So the linear approximation for e^x is $1 + x$.

But straight lines are straight, and are not really suitable for approximating to curves over any distance. Using the quadratic equation,

$$y = a_0 + a_1 x + a_2 x^2$$

to approximate to $y = e^x$, as shown in figure 4.3, requires as before, that:

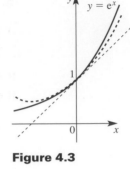

Figure 4.3

① both curves cut the y axis at the same point $\Rightarrow a_0 = e^0 = 1$

② both curves have the same gradient when $x = 0 \Rightarrow a_1 = e^0 = 1$

but now: ③ both curves must have the same second derivative when $x = 0$.

Since $\dfrac{d^2}{dx^2}(e^x) = e^x$, which is 1 when $x = 0$, and $\dfrac{d^2}{dx^2}(a_0 + a_1 x + a_2 x^2) = 2a_2$,

③ $\Rightarrow 2a_2 = 1 \Rightarrow a_2 = \frac{1}{2}$. So the quadratic approximation for e^x is $1 + x + \frac{1}{2}x^2$.

Extending this to finding the cubic $a_0 + a_1 x + a_2 x^2 + a_3 x^3$ that approximates to e^x brings in the additional requirement that the cubic and e^x have the same third derivative at $x = 0$. Now $\dfrac{d^3}{dx^3}(a_0 + a_1 x + a_2 x^2 + a_3 x^3) = 3 \times 2a_3 = 3!a_3$ and $\dfrac{d^3}{dx^3}(e^x) = e^x = 1$ when $x = 0$ so you require $a_3 = \dfrac{1}{3!}$. The cubic approximation for e^x is $1 + x + \dfrac{1}{2!}x^2 + \dfrac{1}{3!}x^3$.

Figure 4.4 shows the graph of $y = e^x$ together with the graphs of the linear, quadratic and cubic approximations you have just constructed. The graph shows that, for positive x, the accuracy of the approximation improves as more terms are used. Using more terms also improves the accuracy when x is negative, though the diagram alone does not justify that claim.

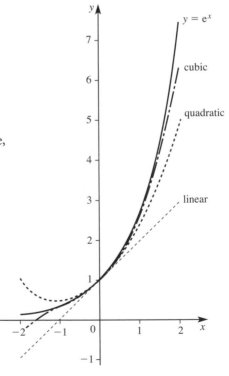

Figure 4.4

ACTIVITY 4.1 The cubic approximation for e^x is $1 + x + \dfrac{x^2}{2} + \dfrac{x^3}{6}$. Write down a cubic approximation for e^{-x}. Multiply the two approximations together and comment on your answer.

ACTIVITY 4.2 Show that the next (i.e. the fourth degree) approximation for e^x is $1 + x + \dfrac{x^2}{2!} + \dfrac{x^3}{3!} + \dfrac{x^4}{4!}$. Hence show that $e \approx 1 + 1 + \dfrac{1}{2!} + \dfrac{1}{3!} + \dfrac{1}{4!}$ and evaluate this approximation correct to 3 decimal places.

This is typical of the general case. Suppose $f(x)$ is a function, that its first n derivatives exist at $x = 0$, and that you want to find a polynomial $p(x)$ of degree n which has the same values as $f(x)$ and its first n derivatives at $x = 0$. Then

$$p(0) = f(0), \ p'(0) = f'(0), \ p''(0) = f''(0), \ldots, \ p^{(n)}(0) = f^{(n)}(0).$$

Solving these $n + 1$ equations gives the $n + 1$ coefficients needed for a polynomial of degree n.

> Note the symbol for the nth derivative of $p(x)$, evaluated here at $x = 0$.

If $p(x) \equiv a_0 + a_1 x + a_2 x^2 + a_3 x^3 + \cdots + a_r x^r + \cdots + a_n x^n$ then $p(0) = a_0 = f(0)$ and

$p'(x) \equiv a_1 + 2a_2 x + 3a_3 x^2 + \cdots + ra_r x^{r-1} + \cdots + na_n x^{n-1}$ $\Rightarrow p'(0) = a_1 = f'(0)$;

$p''(x) \equiv 2a_2 + 6a_3 x + \cdots + r(r-1)a_r x^{r-2} + \cdots + n(n-1)a_n x^{n-2} \Rightarrow p''(0) = 2a_2 = f''(0)$;

$p^{(3)}(x) \equiv 6a_3 + \cdots + r(r-1)(r-2)a_r x^{r-3} + \cdots + n(n-1)(n-2)a_n x^{n-3}$

$\Rightarrow p^{(3)}(0) = 6a_3 = f^{(3)}(0)$;

and so on. Generalising:

$p^{(r)}(x) \equiv r!a_r + \cdots + n(n-1)(n-2)\cdots(n-r+1)a_n x^{n-r}$ $\Rightarrow p^{(r)}(0) = r!a_r = f^{(r)}(0)$;

and $p^{(n)}(x) \equiv n!a_n$ $\Rightarrow p^{(n)}(0) = n!a_n = f^{(n)}(0)$.

The last equality on each line gives

$$a_0 = f(0), \ a_1 = f'(0), \ a_2 = \frac{1}{2}f''(0), \ a_3 = \frac{1}{6}f^{(3)}(0),$$

$$\cdots, \ a_r = \frac{1}{r!}f^{(r)}(0), \cdots, \ a_n = \frac{1}{n!}f^{(n)}(0).$$

Putting all these together produces the approximation

$$f(x) \approx f(0) + xf'(0) + \frac{x^2}{2!}f''(0) + \frac{x^3}{3!}f^{(3)}(0) + \cdots + \frac{x^r}{r!}f^{(r)}(0) + \cdots + \frac{x^n}{n!}f^{(n)}(0).$$

This is known as the *Maclaurin expansion* for $f(x)$ as far as the term in x^n, or the nth *Maclaurin approximation* for $f(x)$.

EXAMPLE 4.1

Find the Maclaurin expansion for $(1 - x)^{-1}$ as far as x^n.

SOLUTION

Let $f(x) \equiv (1 - x)^{-1}$.

$f(x) \equiv (1 - x)^{-1}$	$f(0) = 1$
$f'(x) \equiv (1 - x)^{-2}$	$f'(0) = 1$
$f''(x) \equiv 2(1 - x)^{-3}$	$f''(0) = 2$
$f^{(3)}(x) \equiv 6(1 - x)^{-4}$	$f^{(3)}(0) = 6$
$f^{(4)}(x) \equiv 24(1 - x)^{-5}$	$f^{(4)}(0) = 24$
$\vdots$	$\vdots$
$f^{(n)}(x) \equiv n!(1 - x)^{-(n+1)}$	$f^{(n)}(0) = n!$

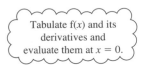

Tabulate $f(x)$ and its derivatives and evaluate them at $x = 0$.

Then $(1 - x)^{-1} \approx 1 + x + x^2 + x^3 + x^4 + \cdots + x^n$.

EXERCISE 4A

1 Find the Maclaurin expansion up to the term in x^4 for each of these functions.
   (i) $\sin x$ **(ii)** $\cos x$ **(iii)** $\tan x$

2 These spreadsheet entries show the start of a method for calculating e^x.

	A	**B**
1	1	$= A1 + 1$
2	0.5	$= A2$
3	1	$= A3 * B2/A1$
4		
5	$= SUM(A3:K3)$	

Copy them into the first two columns of a spreadsheet. Then drag the formulae in cells B1 to B3 to cells C1 to C3, D1 to D3, . . ., K1 to K3. The number in cell A2 is the value of x: try changing it. Cell A5 contains the sum of the numbers in cells A3 to K3. Explain why this is an approximation to e^x.

3 Use a Maclaurin approximation to calculate $\dfrac{1}{\sqrt{e}}$ to 5 decimal places.

4 Use the cubic approximation to $\sin x$ to show that the positive root of $\sin x = x^2$ is approximately $\sqrt{15} - 3$.

5 The third Maclaurin approximation to $f(x)$ is $1 - \frac{3}{2}x^2 + \frac{5}{2}x^3$. Write down the values of $f'(0)$, $f''(0)$, $f^{(3)}(0)$. Sketch the graph of $y = f(x)$ near $x = 0$.

6 If $E_n(x) = \displaystyle\sum_{r=0}^{n} \frac{x^r}{r!}$ show that

(i) $E'_n(x) = E_{n-1}(x)$

(ii) $\int E_n(x)\mathrm{d}x = E_{n+1}(x) + c.$

Explain how these results are linked to properties of e^x.

7 An approximate rule used by builders to find the length, c, of a circular arc ABC is

$$c = \frac{8b - a}{3},$$

where a and b are as shown in the diagram.

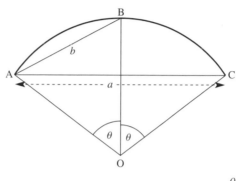

(i) If O is the centre of the circle, show that $b = 2r\sin\dfrac{\theta}{2}$ and $a = 2r\sin\theta$.

(ii) Using the cubic approximation to $\sin x$, show that $8b - a = 6r\theta$. Hence verify the rule.

(iii) Find the percentage error caused by using this rule when $\theta = \dfrac{\pi}{3}$.

8 A surveyor measures a length AB on sloping ground. Before he plots A and B on the map he must find the horizontal distance AC between them.

An approximate rule used by surveyors for reducing a sloping length of 100 metres to its horizontal equivalent is 'Square the number of degrees in the slope, multiply by $1\frac{1}{2}$ and obtain the *correction* in centimetres.'

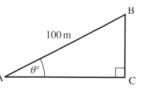

If the slope $\theta°$ equals α radians, show that the correction is about $5000\alpha^2$ centimetres. Show that the rule is approximately correct for gentle slopes.

9 Write down the Maclaurin series for $e^{-\frac{1}{2}x^2}$

  (i) as far as x^6

  (ii) as far as x^8.

It can be shown that $e^{-\frac{1}{2}x^2}$ always lies between these two approximations.

Use them to estimate $\int_0^1 e^{-\frac{1}{2}x^2}\,dx$ and to establish error bounds for your

answer. (It is not possible to find $\int e^{-\frac{1}{2}x^2}\,dx$ explicitly, but finding good

approximations for integrals such as $\int_a^b e^{-\frac{1}{2}x^2}\,dx$ was an essential part of the

construction of the Normal distribution tables, a key tool in statistics.)

Maclaurin series

At this stage it is not possible to say much about the accuracy of these Maclaurin approximations. But the nth Maclaurin expansion for $(1-x)^{-1}$, obtained in Example 4.1, is the geometric progression $1 + x + x^2 + x^3 + x^4 + \cdots + x^n$; if you let n tend to infinity you obtain the infinite geometric series

$1 + x + x^2 + x^3 + x^4 + \cdots$ which, if $|x| < 1$, converges to $\dfrac{1}{1-x} \equiv (1-x)^{-1}$,

known as its *sum to infinity*.

This means that, provided $|x| < 1$, by taking sufficiently many terms you can make the Maclaurin expansion of $(1-x)^{-1}$ as close to $(1-x)^{-1}$ as you like. But the geometric series $1 + x + x^2 + x^3 + x^4 + \cdots$ does not converge if $|x| \geqslant 1$.

Generalising these ideas: if the function $f(x)$ and all its derivatives exist at $x = 0$, then the infinite series

$$f(0) + xf'(0) + \frac{x^2}{2!}f''(0) + \frac{x^3}{3!}f^{(3)}(0) + \cdots + \frac{x^r}{r!}f^{(r)}(0) + \cdots$$

is known as the *Maclaurin series* for $f(x)$. If the sum of this series up to and including the term in x^n (i.e. the sum of the first $n+1$ terms) tends to a limit as n tends to infinity, and this limit is $f(x)$, you say that the expansion *converges* to $f(x)$. For some functions, for example $(1-x)^{-1}$, the series only converges for a limited range of values of x; these are described as the values for which the series is *valid*. A more detailed examination of the validity of the Maclaurin series is beyond the scope of this book; for now the values of x for which the common Maclaurin series are valid are merely stated, without proof.

This chapter started by developing Maclaurin expansions for e^x. Since e^x and all its derivatives are identical, and $e^x = 1$ when $x = 0$, the Maclaurin series for e^x is

$$1 + x + \frac{x^2}{2!} + \frac{x^3}{3!} + \cdots + \frac{x^r}{r!} + \cdots.$$

This series is valid for all x.

EXAMPLE 4.2

Find the Maclaurin series for $\sin x$.

SOLUTION

Let $f(x) \equiv \sin x$.

$f(x) \equiv \sin x$	$f(0) = 0$
$f'(x) \equiv \cos x$	$f'(0) = 1$
$f''(x) \equiv -\sin x$	$f''(0) = 0$
$f^{(3)}(x) \equiv -\cos x$	$f^{(3)}(0) = -1$
$f^{(4)}(x) \equiv \sin x$	$f^{(4)}(0) = 0$
$f^{(2r+1)}(x) \equiv (-1)^r \cos x$	$f^{(2r+1)}(0) = (-1)^r$
$f^{(2r+2)}(x) \equiv (-1)^{r+1} \sin x$	$f^{(2r+2)}(0) = 0$
$f^{(2r+3)}(x) \equiv (-1)^{r+1} \cos x$	$f^{(2r+3)}(0) = (-1)^{r+1}$
$f^{(2r+4)}(x) \equiv (-1)^{r+2} \sin x$	$f^{(2r+4)}(0) = 0$

Tabulate $f(x)$ and its derivatives and evaluate them at $x = 0$.

Then $\sin x = x - \dfrac{x^3}{3!} + \dfrac{x^5}{5!} - \dfrac{x^7}{7!} + \cdots + \dfrac{(-1)^r x^{2r+1}}{(2r+1)!} + \cdots$.

(This series is valid for all values of x.)

Note the connection between these terms and the fact that $\sin x$ is an odd function.

ACTIVITY 4.3

Show that the Maclaurin series for $\cos x$ is

$$1 - \frac{x^2}{2!} + \frac{x^4}{4!} - \frac{x^6}{6!} + \cdots + \frac{(-1)^r x^{2r}}{(2r)!} + \cdots.$$

(This series is also valid for all x. Notice that the first two terms here form the familiar approximation for $\cos x$ when x is small, and that, as you might expect, the series for $\cos x$ is the same as the series obtained by differentiating the $\sin x$ series term by term.)

ACTIVITY 4.4

Show that the Maclaurin series for $(1 + x)^n$ is

$$1 + nx + \frac{n(n-1)}{2!} x^2 + \cdots + \frac{n(n-1)\ldots(n-r+1)}{r!} x^r + \cdots$$

i.e. the familiar binomial series for $(1 + x)^n$.

If n is a positive integer: the series terminates after $n + 1$ terms, and is valid for all x.

If n is not a positive integer: the series is valid for $|x| < 1$, but not valid for $|x| > 1$; the series is also valid for $x = 1$ if $n > -1$, and for $x = -1$ if $n > 0$.

Figure 4.5 shows the graph of the function $(1 + x)^{-\frac{1}{2}}$ and several successive Maclaurin approximations. It illustrates the fact that the approximations converge on $(1 + x)^{-\frac{1}{2}}$ if $|x| < 1$, but not if $x > 1$. At first sight the graph may appear to show that successive approximations also converge when $x < -1$; but they cannot be converging on $(1 + x)^{-\frac{1}{2}}$, which is undefined for $x \leqslant -1$.

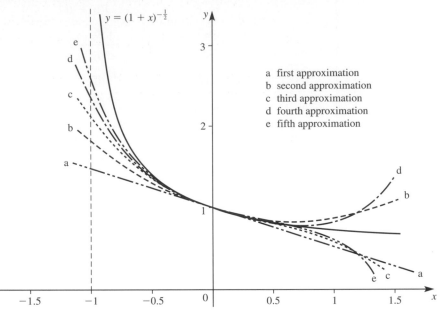

Figure 4.5

1 (i) Explain why it is not possible to find Maclaurin expansions for $\ln x$.

(ii) (a) Show that the Maclaurin series for $\ln(1 + x)$ is

$$x - \frac{x^2}{2} + \frac{x^3}{3} - \cdots + \frac{(-1)^{n+1}x^n}{n} + \cdots.$$

(b) This series is valid for $-1 < x \leqslant 1$ only; by drawing graphs of $y = \ln(1 + x)$ and several successive approximations show that this is plausible.

(This series was first found by Nicolaus Mercator (1620–87), who lived for many years in London, though he was born in Denmark.)

2 A graphic calculator or graph-drawing software will be useful in this question.

(i) Draw a graph of $y = \sin x$. On the same axes draw graphs of the first few Maclaurin approximations to $\sin x$.

(ii) Repeat (i) for (a) $\cos x$ (b) $(1 + x)^{-1}$ (c) $(1 + x)^{0.5}$.

3 Find the Maclaurin expansion of $f(x) = \dfrac{e^x}{e^x + 1}$ as far as the term in x^3.

Show that no even powers of x can occur in the full expansion.

[**Hint for the last part**: Show that $f(x) - f(0)$ is an odd function.]

4 In this question give all numerical answers to 4 decimal places.

(i) Put $x = 1$ in the expansion

$$\ln(1 + x) \approx x - \frac{x^2}{2} + \frac{x^3}{3} - \cdots - \frac{x^{10}}{10}$$

and calculate an estimate of $\ln 2$. (Approximately 1000 terms would be needed to obtain $\ln 2$ correct to 3 decimal places by this method.)

(ii) Show that $\ln 2 = -\ln(1 - \frac{1}{2})$ and hence estimate $\ln 2$ by summing six terms.

(iii) Write down the series for $\ln(1 + x) - \ln(1 - x)$ as far as the first three non-zero terms and estimate $\ln 2$ by summing these terms using a suitable value of x.

5 **(i)** Given that $f(x) = \arctan(1 + x)$, find $f'(x)$ and $f''(x)$.

(ii) Find the Maclaurin series for $\arctan(1 + x)$ as far as the term in x^2.

(iii) Use this Maclaurin series to find an approximate value of

$$\int_0^{0.4} \arctan(1 + x^2)\,dx,$$ giving your answer to 3 decimal places.

[MEI, part]

6 A curve passes through the point $(0, 2)$; its gradient is given by the differential equation $\frac{dy}{dx} = 1 - xy$. Assume that the equation of this curve can be expressed as the Maclaurin series

$$y = a_0 + a_1 x + a_2 x^2 + a_3 x^3 + a_4 x^4 + \cdots.$$

(i) Find a_0 and show that

$$a_1 + 2a_2 x + 3a_3 x^2 + 4a_4 x^3 + \cdots = 1 - 2x - a_1 x^2 - a_2 x^3 - a_3 x^4 - \cdots.$$

(ii) Equate coefficients to find the first seven terms of the Maclaurin series.

(iii) Draw graphs to compare the solution given by these seven terms with a solution generated (step by step) on a computer.

7 **(i)** Write down the Maclaurin expansions of

(a) $\cos\theta$ **(b)** $\sin\theta$ **(c)** $\cos\theta + j\sin\theta$,

giving series **(c)** in ascending powers of θ.

(ii) Substitute $x = j\theta$ in the Maclaurin series for e^x and simplify the terms.

(iii) Show that the series in parts **(i)(c)** and **(ii)** are the same.

(This confirms that the definition $e^{j\theta} = \cos\theta + j\sin\theta$ given on page 46 is consistent with the Maclaurin series of the functions involved.)

8 In this question y_n and a_n are used to denote $f^{(n)}(x)$ and $f^{(n)}(0)$ respectively.

(i) Let $f(x) = \arcsin x$. Show that $(1 - x^2)y_1{}^2 = 1$ and $(1 - x^2)y_2 - xy_1 = 0$.

(ii) Find a_1 and a_2.

(iii) Prove by induction that $(1 - x^2)y_{n+2} - (2n + 1)xy_{n+1} - n^2 y_n = 0$, and deduce that $a_{n+2} = n^2 a_n$.

(iv) Find the Maclaurin expansion of $\arcsin x$, giving the first three non-zero terms and the general term.

Alternative approaches

Sometimes finding the coefficients of a Maclaurin series by repeated differentiation can be very laborious. As shown in the next example, the problem can be eased if you can express a derivative in terms of earlier derivatives, or the original function.

EXAMPLE 4.3

Find the first four non-zero terms of the Maclaurin series for $e^{2x} \sin 3x$.

SOLUTION

Let $\quad f(x) \quad \equiv e^{2x} \sin 3x \qquad\qquad\qquad\qquad f(0) = 0.$

Then $\quad f'(x) \quad \equiv 2e^{2x} \sin 3x + 3e^{2x} \cos 3x$

$\qquad\qquad\qquad \equiv 2f(x) + 3e^{2x} \cos 3x \qquad\qquad f'(0) = 3$

and $\quad f''(x) \quad \equiv 2f'(x) + 6e^{2x} \cos 3x - 9e^{2x} \sin 3x$

> Expressing $f''(x)$ in terms of $f'(x)$ and $f(x)$ simplifies further differentiation.

$\qquad\qquad\qquad \equiv 2f'(x) + 2(f'(x) - 2f(x)) - 9f(x)$

$\qquad\qquad\qquad \equiv 4f'(x) - 13f(x) \qquad\qquad\qquad f''(0) = 12.$

Then $\quad f^{(3)}(x) \quad \equiv 4f''(x) - 13f'(x) \qquad\qquad f^{(3)}(0) = 48 - 39 = 9$

and $\quad f^{(4)}(x) \quad \equiv 4f^{(3)}(x) - 13f''(x),$ etc. $\qquad f^{(4)}(0) = 36 - 156 = -120.$

Thus $\quad e^{2x} \sin 3x = 3x + \dfrac{x^2}{2!} \times 12 + \dfrac{x^3}{3!} \times 9 - \dfrac{x^4}{4!} \times 120 + \cdots$

$\qquad\qquad\qquad\qquad = 3x + 6x^2 + \tfrac{3}{2}x^3 - 5x^4 + \cdots.$

Sometimes a Maclaurin series can be found by adapting one or more known Maclaurin series. Some such methods are indicated in the next activity. You may well wonder whether the processes used are justifiable. Is it legitimate (for example) to integrate (or differentiate) an infinite series term by term? Can you form the product of two infinite series by multiplying terms? Is the series obtained identical to the series that would have been obtained by evaluating the derivatives? Answering these important questions in detail is beyond the scope of this book, though generally the answer is 'Yes, subject to certain conditions'.

ACTIVITY 4.5

Try out the following methods and explain why they work. How would you obtain further terms of the required series?

(i) The Maclaurin series for $\ln(1 + x)$ can be found by integrating the terms of the binomial series for $(1 + x)^{-1}$. Why is the integration constant zero?

(ii) The start of the Maclaurin series for $\dfrac{e^x}{1 + x}$ can be found by multiplying together the first four terms of the Maclaurin series for e^x and $(1 + x)^{-1}$ and discarding all terms in x^4 and higher powers.

(iii) The first few terms of the Maclaurin series for $\sec x$ can be found from the first three terms of the Maclaurin series for $(1+y)^{-1}$ where

$$y = -\frac{x^2}{2!} + \frac{x^4}{4!}$$

Taylor approximations

All Maclaurin expansions are 'centred' on $x = 0$. But it is possible to form expansions centred elsewhere:

let $g(h) \equiv f(a + h)$ where a is the constant $x - h$;

then $g'(h) \equiv f'(a + h)$, $g''(h) \equiv f''(a + h)$, etc.,

and $g(0) = f(a)$, $g'(0) = f'(a)$, $g''(0) = f''(a)$, etc. so that

$$f(a + h) \equiv g(h) \approx g(0) + hg'(0) + \frac{h^2}{2!}g''(0) + \frac{h^3}{3!}g^{(3)}(0) + \cdots + \frac{h^n}{n!}g^{(n)}(0).$$

This may be expressed in either of the following two ways:

$$f(a + h) \approx f(a) + hf'(a) + \frac{h^2}{2!}f''(a) + \frac{h^3}{3!}f^{(3)}(a) + \cdots + \frac{h^n}{n!}f^{(n)}(a)$$

or equivalently

$$f(x) \approx f(a) + (x - a)f'(a) + \frac{(x - a)^2}{2!}f''(a) + \frac{(x - a)^3}{3!}f^{(3)}(a) + \cdots + \frac{(x - a)^n}{n!}f^{(n)}(a).$$

These two formulae are alternative versions of the nth *Taylor approximation* for $f(x)$ centred on $x = a$. They are also known as *Taylor polynomials*. (A Maclaurin approximation is a special case of a Taylor approximation, obtained by putting $a = 0$.)

ACTIVITY 4.6 Explain the connection between the first Taylor approximation for $f(x)$ and the Newton–Raphson method of approximating to the root of the equation $f(x) = 0$.

Historical note

The Taylor approximations were discovered or rediscovered in various forms by several mathematicians in the seventeenth and eighteenth centuries. They were familiar to Scotsman James Gregory (1638–1675), though Englishman Brook Taylor (1685–1731) was the first to publish an account of them, in 1715. In 1742 Colin Maclaurin (1698–1745), Gregory's successor as professor at Edinburgh, published his expansion, stating that it occurred as a special case of Taylor's result; for some reason it has been credited to him as a separate theorem.

1 Use known Maclaurin series to find the Maclaurin series for each of the following functions as far as the term in x^4.

   (i) $\sin 3x$ **(ii)** $\cos 2x$

   (iii) $\sin^2 x$ **(iv)** $\ln(1 + \sin x)$

   (v) $e^{-x} \sin x$ **(vi)** $e^{\sin x}$

2 **(i)** Find $\displaystyle\int \frac{1}{\sqrt{1 - 4x^2}}\, dx$.

   (ii) By expanding $(1 - 4x^2)^{-\frac{1}{2}}$ and integrating term by term, or otherwise, find the series expansion for $\arcsin(2x)$, when $|x| < \frac{1}{2}$, as far as the term in x^7.

[MEI, part]

3 **(i)** By integrating $\dfrac{1}{1 + x^2}$ and its Maclaurin expansion, show that the Maclaurin series for $\arctan x$ is

$$x - \frac{x^3}{3} + \frac{x^5}{5} - \frac{x^7}{7} + \cdots.$$

(This is known as Gregory's series, after the Scottish mathematician James Gregory, who published it in 1668, well before Newton or Leibniz introduced calculus. The series is valid for $|x| \leqslant 1$.)

   (ii) By putting $x = 1$ show that

$$\frac{\pi}{4} = 1 - \frac{1}{3} + \frac{1}{5} - \frac{1}{7} + \cdots.$$

(This is known as Leibniz's series. It converges very slowly.)

   (iii) Show that

      (a) $\dfrac{\pi}{4} = \arctan\dfrac{1}{2} + \arctan\dfrac{1}{3}$ (known as Euler's formula for π)

      (b) $\dfrac{\pi}{4} = 4\arctan\dfrac{1}{5} - \arctan\dfrac{1}{239}$ (known as Machin's formula).

   (iv) Use Machin's formula together with Gregory's series to find the value of π to 5 decimal places. (In 1873 William Shanks used this method to calculate π to 707 decimal places, but he made a mistake in the 528th place, not discovered until 1946!)

4 **(i)** Sketch the graph of $y = \arccos(2x)$.

   (ii) Differentiate $\arccos(2x)$ with respect to x.

   (iii) Use integration by parts to find $\int \arccos(2x)\, dx$.

   (iv) By first expanding $(1 - 4x^2)^{-\frac{1}{2}}$, find the series expansion of $\arccos(2x)$ as far as the term in x^5.

[MEI, part]

5 (i) Prove by induction that

$$f(x) = e^x \sin x \Rightarrow f^{(n)}(x) = 2^{n/2} e^x \sin\left(x + \frac{n\pi}{4}\right).$$

Use this result to obtain the Maclaurin series for $e^x \sin x$ as far as x^6.

(ii) Multiply the third Maclaurin approximation for e^x by the third Maclaurin approximation for $\sin x$, and comment on your answer.

(iii) Find a Maclaurin approximation for $e^x \cos x$ by multiplying the third Maclaurin approximation for e^x by the fourth Maclaurin approximation for $\cos x$, giving as many terms in your answer as you think justifiable.

6 Let $y = \arctan x$, so that $x = \tan y$.

(i) Using $\cos y = \frac{1}{2}(e^{jy} + e^{-jy})$ and $\sin y = \frac{1}{2j}(e^{jy} - e^{-jy})$, prove that
$$x = \frac{e^{2jy} - 1}{j(e^{2jy} + 1)}.$$

(ii) By solving **(i)** for y, deduce that $y = \frac{1}{2j}(\ln(1 + jx) - \ln(1 - jx))$.

(iii) Use the Maclaurin series for $\ln(1 \pm t)$ in **(ii)** to obtain again Gregory's series for $\arctan x$.

7 A projectile is launched from O with initial velocity $\begin{pmatrix} u \\ v \end{pmatrix}$ relative to horizontal and vertical axes through O. The path of the projectile may be modelled in various ways. The table below shows the position (x, y) of the projectile at time t after launch, as given by two different models. Both models assume that g (gravitational acceleration) is constant. Use the Maclaurin expansion for e^{-kt}, where k is constant, to show that the results given by Model 1 are a special case of the results from Model 2, with $k = 0$.

	Assumptions about air resistance	Position at time t
Model 1	There is no air resistance.	$x = ut$ $y = vt - \frac{1}{2}gt^2$
Model 2	Air resistance is proportional to the velocity (with proportionality constant k).	$x = \frac{u}{k}(1 - e^{-kt})$ $y = \frac{g + kv}{k^2}(1 - e^{-kt}) - \frac{gt}{k}$

8 The diagram illustrates a Maclaurin expansion. Find it.
   (You may assume that $0 < r < 1$.)

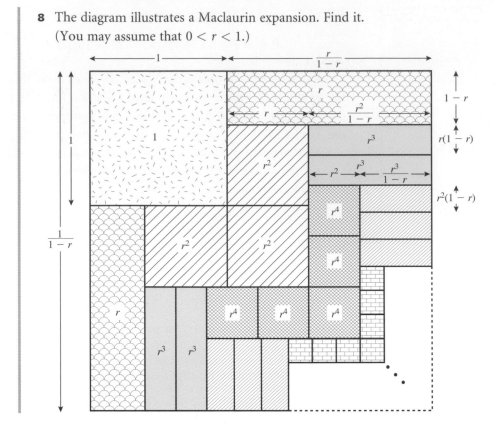

INVESTIGATION

There are many ways of obtaining sequences of polynomial approximations for
$f(x) \equiv \sin x$, for $0 \leqslant x \leqslant \dfrac{\pi}{2}$. Investigate alternative methods such as the following.

(i)   Use **(a)** the linear function which passes through $(0, 0)$ and $\left(\dfrac{\pi}{2}, 1\right)$

    (b) the quadratic function which passes through $(0, 0)$, $\left(\dfrac{\pi}{4}, \dfrac{1}{\sqrt{2}}\right)$ and
    $\left(\dfrac{\pi}{2}, 1\right)$

    (c) the cubic function which passes through four points on $y = f(x)$;
    and so on.

(ii) Use polynomials $P(x)$ which minimise

    (a) $\displaystyle\int_0^{\frac{\pi}{2}} (f(x) - P(x))\,dx$

    (b) the maximum value of $|f(x) - P(x)|$ in $0 \leqslant x \leqslant \dfrac{\pi}{2}$

    (c) $\displaystyle\int_0^{\frac{\pi}{2}} |f(x) - P(x)|\,dx$

    (d) $\displaystyle\int_0^{\frac{\pi}{2}} (f(x) - P(x))^2\,dx$.

Maclaurin series (You will meet other Maclaurin series in Chapter 6.)

1 General form:

$$f(x) = f(0) + xf'(0) + \frac{x^2}{2!}f''(0) + \frac{x^3}{3!}f^{(3)}(0) + \cdots + \frac{x^r}{r!}f^{(r)}(0) + \cdots$$

2 Valid for all x:

$$e^x = 1 + x + \frac{x^2}{2!} + \frac{x^3}{3!} + \cdots + \frac{x^r}{r!} + \cdots$$

$$\sin x = x - \frac{x^3}{3!} + \frac{x^5}{5!} - \frac{x^7}{7!} + \cdots + \frac{(-1)^r x^{2r+1}}{(2r+1)!} + \cdots$$

$$\cos x = 1 - \frac{x^2}{2!} + \frac{x^4}{4!} - \frac{x^6}{6!} + \cdots + \frac{(-1)^r x^{2r}}{(2r)!} + \cdots$$

3 Valid for $|x| \leqslant 1$:

$$\arctan x = x - \frac{x^3}{3} + \frac{x^5}{5} - \frac{x^7}{7} + \cdots + \frac{(-1)^{r-1} x^{2r-1}}{2r-1} + \cdots$$

4 Valid for $-1 < x \leqslant 1$:

$$\ln(1+x) = x - \frac{x^2}{2} + \frac{x^3}{3} - \cdots + \frac{(-1)^{r-1} x^r}{r} + \cdots$$

5 Validity depends on n:

$$(1+x)^n = 1 + nx + \frac{n(n-1)}{2!}x^2 + \cdots + \frac{n(n-1)\ldots(n-r+1)}{r!}x^r + \cdots$$

If n is a positive integer: the series terminates after $n+1$ terms, and is valid for all x.

If n is not a positive integer: the series is valid for $|x| < 1$; also for $|x| = 1$ if $n \geqslant -1$; and for $x = -1$ if $n > 0$.

Matrices

By relieving the brain of all unnecessary work, a good notation sets it free to concentrate on more advanced problems.

A.N. Whitehead, 1861–1947

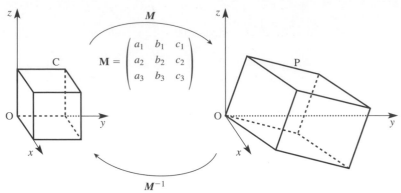

Figure 5.1

Transformation *M* with matrix **M** maps the cube, C, to the parallelepiped, P. Is there a transformation that maps P to C? If so, what is its matrix? These are some of the questions dealt with in this chapter.

In your work on matrices in *AS Further Pure Mathematics* (*FP1*) you learnt
- to represent a transformation by a matrix
- to multiply matrices
- that matrix multiplication is associative: $(\mathbf{PQ})\mathbf{R} = \mathbf{P}(\mathbf{QR})$
- that $\begin{pmatrix} 1 & 0 \\ 0 & 1 \end{pmatrix}$ and $\begin{pmatrix} 1 & 0 & 0 \\ 0 & 1 & 0 \\ 0 & 0 & 1 \end{pmatrix}$ are the 2×2 and 3×3 identity matrices respectively
- to evaluate the determinant of the 2×2 matrix $\mathbf{M} = \begin{pmatrix} a & c \\ b & d \end{pmatrix}$:

$$\det\mathbf{M} = \begin{vmatrix} a & c \\ b & d \end{vmatrix} = ad - bc$$

- that $\det\mathbf{M}$ is the (signed) area scale factor of the transformation represented by **M**
- that a *non-singular* matrix is a matrix with non-zero determinant
- to find the inverse of a non-singular 2×2 matrix **M**:

$$\mathbf{M}^{-1} = \frac{1}{\det\mathbf{M}} \begin{pmatrix} d & -c \\ -b & a \end{pmatrix}$$

- to use matrices to solve simultaneous equations in two unknowns.

In this chapter you will extend your knowledge of matrices so that you can also work with 3×3 matrices and interpret the results. Some of this work was hinted at in *FP1*.

The determinant of a 3×3 matrix

If $\mathbf{M}$ is the 3×3 matrix $\begin{pmatrix} a_1 & b_1 & c_1 \\ a_2 & b_2 & c_2 \\ a_3 & b_3 & c_3 \end{pmatrix}$ then the *determinant* of $\mathbf{M}$ is defined by

$$\det\mathbf{M} = a_1 \begin{vmatrix} b_2 & c_2 \\ b_3 & c_3 \end{vmatrix} - a_2 \begin{vmatrix} b_1 & c_1 \\ b_3 & c_3 \end{vmatrix} + a_3 \begin{vmatrix} b_1 & c_1 \\ b_2 & c_2 \end{vmatrix},$$

known as the *expansion of the determinant by the first column*. Notice that a_1 is multiplied by what is known as its *minor*, the 2×2 determinant $\begin{vmatrix} b_2 & c_2 \\ b_3 & c_3 \end{vmatrix}$

obtained by deleting the row and column containing a_1: $\begin{vmatrix} a_1 & b_1 & c_1 \\ a_2 & b_2 & c_2 \\ a_3 & b_3 & c_3 \end{vmatrix}$. Other

minors are defined similarly: the minor of a_2 is

$$\begin{vmatrix} a_1 & b_1 & c_1 \\ a_2 & b_2 & c_2 \\ a_3 & b_3 & c_3 \end{vmatrix} = \begin{vmatrix} b_1 & c_1 \\ b_3 & c_3 \end{vmatrix} = b_1 c_3 - b_3 c_1.$$

Alternatively you may expand the determinant by the second column:

$$\det\mathbf{M} = -b_1 \begin{vmatrix} a_2 & c_2 \\ a_3 & c_3 \end{vmatrix} + b_2 \begin{vmatrix} a_1 & c_1 \\ a_3 & c_3 \end{vmatrix} - b_3 \begin{vmatrix} a_1 & c_1 \\ a_2 & c_2 \end{vmatrix},$$

or by the third column:

$$\det\mathbf{M} = c_1 \begin{vmatrix} a_2 & b_2 \\ a_3 & b_3 \end{vmatrix} - c_2 \begin{vmatrix} a_1 & b_1 \\ a_3 & b_3 \end{vmatrix} + c_3 \begin{vmatrix} a_1 & b_1 \\ a_2 & b_2 \end{vmatrix}.$$

The signs attached to the minors alternate as shown: $\begin{vmatrix} + & - & + \\ - & + & - \\ + & - & + \end{vmatrix}$.

A minor together with its correct sign is known as a *cofactor* and is denoted by the corresponding capital letter; for example the cofactor of a_3 is A_3. This means that the expansion by the first column, say, can be written as $a_1 A_1 + a_2 A_2 + a_3 A_3$.

It is a fairly easy but somewhat tedious task to show that all three expressions simplify to

$$a_1 b_2 c_3 + a_2 b_3 c_1 + a_3 b_1 c_2 - a_3 b_2 c_1 - a_1 b_3 c_2 - a_2 b_1 c_3.$$

The following are alternative symbols for $\det\mathbf{M}$: $\begin{vmatrix} a_1 & b_1 & c_1 \\ a_2 & b_2 & c_2 \\ a_3 & b_3 & c_3 \end{vmatrix}$, $|\mathbf{a}\ \mathbf{b}\ \mathbf{c}|$ or $|\mathbf{M}|$ or Δ.

You will see later that you may also expand by the first row:

$$\det\mathbf{M} = a_1 \begin{vmatrix} b_2 & c_2 \\ b_3 & c_3 \end{vmatrix} - b_1 \begin{vmatrix} a_2 & c_2 \\ a_3 & c_3 \end{vmatrix} + c_1 \begin{vmatrix} a_2 & b_2 \\ a_3 & b_3 \end{vmatrix}$$

$$= a_1 A_1 + b_1 B_1 + c_1 C_1,$$

or by the second or third row.

EXAMPLE 5.1

Evaluate the determinant $\begin{vmatrix} 2 & 3 & -1 \\ 7 & 2 & 3 \\ 4 & 5 & -2 \end{vmatrix}$.

SOLUTION

Expanding by the first column gives

$$2 \times \begin{vmatrix} 2 & 3 \\ 5 & -2 \end{vmatrix} - 7 \times \begin{vmatrix} 3 & -1 \\ 5 & -2 \end{vmatrix} + 4 \times \begin{vmatrix} 3 & -1 \\ 2 & 3 \end{vmatrix}$$

$$= 2 \times (2 \times (-2) - 3 \times 5) - 7 \times (3 \times (-2) - (-1) \times 5)$$
$$\quad + 4 \times (3 \times 3 - (-1) \times 2)$$

$$= 2 \times (-19) - 7 \times (-1) + 4 \times 11$$

$$= 13.$$

The following method of expanding the 3×3 determinant

$\det\mathbf{M} = \begin{vmatrix} a_1 & b_1 & c_1 \\ a_2 & b_2 & c_2 \\ a_3 & b_3 & c_3 \end{vmatrix}$ was devised by P.F. Sarrus, 1798–1861. Copy the first and

second rows below the third row; form diagonal products and sum them, as shown.

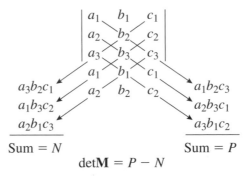

ACTIVITY 5.1

Justify Sarrus' method and use it to evaluate $\begin{vmatrix} 2 & 3 & -1 \\ 7 & 2 & 3 \\ 4 & 5 & -2 \end{vmatrix}$.

Historical note

Although the early work on determinants was done by Vandermonde around 1776, the word 'determinant' was coined by Cauchy in 1815, and the vertical line notation was introduced in 1841 by Arthur Cayley, a pioneer in the study of matrices.

Some properties of determinants are suggested in Questions 2 to 5 of Exercise 5A. These properties will be developed in the next section.

1 Evaluate these determinants.

(i) $\begin{vmatrix} 1 & 3 & 2 \\ 5 & 1 & 4 \\ 6 & 2 & 3 \end{vmatrix}$

(ii) $\begin{vmatrix} 5 & -1 & -2 \\ -2 & 2 & 3 \\ 3 & 4 & 1 \end{vmatrix}$

(iii) $\begin{vmatrix} 5 & 6 & 4 \\ -4 & 0 & 1 \\ 7 & -3 & -5 \end{vmatrix}$

(iv) $\begin{vmatrix} 7 & -6 & -1 \\ -7 & 6 & 0 \\ 2 & -2 & 5 \end{vmatrix}$

2 Evaluate these determinants. What do you notice?

(i) (a) $\begin{vmatrix} 1 & 1 & 3 \\ -1 & 0 & 2 \\ 3 & 1 & 4 \end{vmatrix}$

(b) $\begin{vmatrix} 1 & -1 & 3 \\ 1 & 0 & 1 \\ 3 & 2 & 4 \end{vmatrix}$

(ii) (a) $\begin{vmatrix} 1 & -5 & -4 \\ 2 & 3 & 3 \\ -2 & 1 & 0 \end{vmatrix}$

(b) $\begin{vmatrix} 1 & 2 & -2 \\ -5 & 3 & 1 \\ -4 & 3 & 0 \end{vmatrix}$

3 Evaluate these determinants. What do you notice?

(i) $\begin{vmatrix} 5 & 5 & 3 \\ 7 & 7 & 4 \\ 2 & 2 & 3 \end{vmatrix}$

(ii) $\begin{vmatrix} 3 & 1 & 3 \\ -5 & 4 & 5 \\ -2 & 1 & -2 \end{vmatrix}$

4 Evaluate these determinants. What do you notice?

(i) (a) $\begin{vmatrix} 3 & 2 & 0 \\ -5 & -3 & 7 \\ 6 & 4 & 2 \end{vmatrix}$

(b) $\begin{vmatrix} 2 & 3 & 0 \\ -3 & -5 & 7 \\ 4 & 6 & 2 \end{vmatrix}$

(ii) (a) $\begin{vmatrix} 2 & 4 & 5 \\ 1 & 2 & 2 \\ -5 & 3 & -3 \end{vmatrix}$

(b) $\begin{vmatrix} 2 & 5 & 4 \\ 1 & 2 & 2 \\ -5 & -3 & 3 \end{vmatrix}$

5 Given that $\mathbf{M} = \begin{vmatrix} 1 & 1 & 0 \\ 3 & 3 & 2 \\ 2 & 1 & 1 \end{vmatrix}$ and $\mathbf{N} = \begin{vmatrix} 5 & -2 & -4 \\ 2 & 1 & 3 \\ -4 & 1 & 2 \end{vmatrix}$

evaluate detM and detN, det(**MN**), and comment on your answers.

6 Show that $x = 1$ is one root of the equation $\begin{vmatrix} 2 & 2 & x \\ 1 & x & 1 \\ x & 1 & 4 \end{vmatrix} = 0$, and find

the other roots.

Properties of determinants

1 *Swapping two columns of a determinant reverses its sign.*

Since $\begin{vmatrix} p & r \\ q & s \end{vmatrix} = ps - qr = -\begin{vmatrix} r & p \\ s & q \end{vmatrix}$, and the cofactors of a_1, a_2 and a_3 in

$\begin{vmatrix} a_1 & b_1 & c_1 \\ a_2 & b_2 & c_2 \\ a_3 & b_3 & c_3 \end{vmatrix}$ are 2×2 determinants, swapping the second and third columns

of the 3×3 determinant reverses its sign. Thus $|\mathbf{a} \ \mathbf{b} \ \mathbf{c}| = -|\mathbf{a} \ \mathbf{c} \ \mathbf{b}|$.

A similar argument applies if you swap a different pair of columns.

2 *If two columns of a determinant, Δ, are identical, $\Delta = 0$.*

This follows immediately from Property 1, since swapping those two columns multiplies Δ by -1 but without changing anything: $\Delta = -\Delta \Rightarrow \Delta = 0$.

3 *Cyclic interchange of the columns of a determinant leaves the value of the determinant unchanged.*

Cyclic interchange of the letters p, q, r gives q, r, p or r, p, q; i.e. the same letters, in the same order, but starting in a different place. The proof involves applying Property 1 twice. For example

$$|\mathbf{a}\ \ \mathbf{b}\ \ \mathbf{c}| = -|\mathbf{a}\ \ \mathbf{c}\ \ \mathbf{b}| \quad \text{(swapping the second and third columns)}$$
$$= \ \ |\mathbf{b}\ \ \mathbf{c}\ \ \mathbf{a}| \quad \text{(swapping the first and third columns)}.$$

For the matrix $\mathbf{M} = \begin{pmatrix} a_1 & b_1 & c_1 \\ a_2 & b_2 & c_2 \\ a_3 & b_3 & c_3 \end{pmatrix}$, $\det\mathbf{M} = a_1 A_1 + a_2 A_2 + a_3 A_3$ is the

expansion by the first column. Multiplying the elements of a column by the cofactors of a different column is known as expanding by *alien cofactors*, as in $a_1 B_1 + a_2 B_2 + a_3 B_3$, where the elements of the first column have been multiplied by the cofactors of the second column.

4 *The result of expanding a determinant by alien cofactors is zero.*

Attaching the elements of the first column of $\mathbf{M} = \begin{pmatrix} a_1 & b_1 & c_1 \\ a_2 & b_2 & c_2 \\ a_3 & b_3 & c_3 \end{pmatrix}$, to the

cofactors of the second column gives $a_1 B_1 + a_2 B_2 + a_3 B_3$, which is the first

column expansion of $\begin{vmatrix} a_1 & a_1 & c_1 \\ a_2 & a_2 & c_2 \\ a_3 & a_3 & c_3 \end{vmatrix}$. By Property 2, this is zero, as two columns

are identical. Again, similar arguments apply if you choose different alien cofactors, or a different column.

5 *The determinant of a 3×3 matrix is the volume scale factor of the transformation represented by that matrix.*

This property corresponds to the fact that a 2×2 determinant is the area scale factor of the corresponding transformation. Activity 5.2 guides you towards a proof. Strictly, you should talk about the *signed* scale factors.

6 *The determinant of a product of 3×3 square matrices $\mathbf{M}$ and $\mathbf{N}$ is the product of the determinants of $\mathbf{M}$ and $\mathbf{N}$: $\det(\mathbf{MN}) = \det\mathbf{M} \times \det\mathbf{N}$.*

The transformation M with matrix $\mathbf{M} = \begin{pmatrix} a_1 & b_1 & c_1 \\ a_2 & b_2 & c_2 \\ a_3 & b_3 & c_3 \end{pmatrix}$ maps the unit cube

with edges $\mathbf{i}$, $\mathbf{j}$ and $\mathbf{k}$ to the parallelepiped with edges $\mathbf{a} = \begin{pmatrix} a_1 \\ a_2 \\ a_3 \end{pmatrix}$, $\mathbf{b} = \begin{pmatrix} b_1 \\ b_2 \\ b_3 \end{pmatrix}$

and $\mathbf{c} = \begin{pmatrix} c_1 \\ c_2 \\ c_3 \end{pmatrix}$ and (signed) volume $\det\mathbf{M}$. Transformation M followed by N, as illustrated in figure 5.2, is equivalent to the single transformation *NM* with matrix $\mathbf{NM}$ and volume scale factor $\det(\mathbf{NM})$. It follows that

$$\det(\mathbf{NM}) = \det\mathbf{N} \times \det\mathbf{M} = \det\mathbf{M} \times \det\mathbf{N} = \det(\mathbf{MN}).$$

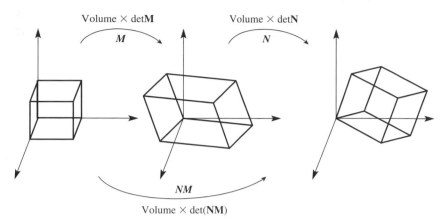

Figure 5.2

The sign of the determinant of a 3×3 matrix $\mathbf{M}$ shows whether the vectors $\mathbf{a}$, $\mathbf{b}$ and $\mathbf{c}$ (in that order) form a left-handed or a right-handed set, as illustrated in figure 5.3.

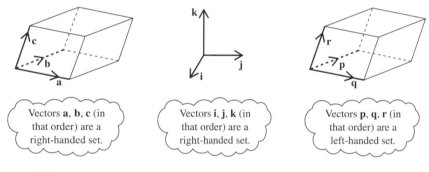

Figure 5.3

EXAMPLE 5.2

Factorise the determinant $\Delta = \begin{vmatrix} 1 & 1 & 1 \\ x & y & z \\ x^3 & y^3 & z^3 \end{vmatrix}$.

SOLUTION

(The obvious approach is to expand the determinant and then to factorise the resulting expression, but this expression consists of six terms of the form yz^3 and factorising this is not easy, so an alternative approach is used here.)

Determinant Δ may be thought of as a polynomial in x (or in y or in z as appropriate).

If y takes the same value as x the first two columns are identical and then $\Delta = 0$. Therefore $(x - y)$ is a factor of Δ by the factor theorem.

Similarly $(y - z)$ and $(z - x)$ are also factors of Δ.

As cyclic interchange of x, y and z leaves both Δ and $(x - y)(y - z)(z - x)$ unchanged, while non-cyclic interchange reverses the signs of both expressions, any further factors of Δ will be symmetrical in x, y and z. Since Δ is of degree 4 in x, y and z, the remaining factor is of degree 1, and so is of the form $k(x + y + z)$ where k is a constant. Considering the coefficient of $x^3 y$ in the expansions of Δ and in $(x - y)(y - z)(z - x)k(x + y + z)$ shows that $k = -1$. Therefore $\Delta = -(x - y)(y - z)(z - x)(x + y + z)$.

e ACTIVITY 5.2

(i) (a) Figure 5.4 illustrates a shear parallel to the y axis; the distance each point moves is p times its x co-ordinate.

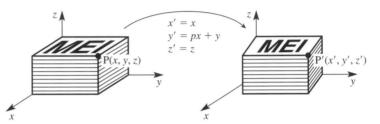

Figure 5.4

Show that $E_1 = \begin{pmatrix} 1 & 0 & 0 \\ p & 1 & 0 \\ 0 & 0 & 1 \end{pmatrix}$ represents this transformation.

(b) Matrix $E_2 = \begin{pmatrix} 1 & 0 & 0 \\ 0 & 1 & 0 \\ q & 0 & 1 \end{pmatrix}$ represents another shear. Describe this shear.

(c) Find E_3, the matrix that represents the shear parallel to the z axis; the distance each point moves is r times its y co-ordinate.

(ii) The transformation with matrix $M = (\mathbf{a}\ \ \mathbf{b}\ \ \mathbf{c}) = \begin{pmatrix} a_1 & b_1 & c_1 \\ a_2 & b_2 & c_2 \\ a_3 & b_3 & c_3 \end{pmatrix}$ maps

the unit cube to the parallelepiped P with edges represented by vectors $\mathbf{a}$, $\mathbf{b}$ and $\mathbf{c}$.

(a) Show that with $p = -\dfrac{a_2}{a_1}$ and $q = -\dfrac{a_3}{a_1}$, $E_2 E_1 M = \begin{pmatrix} a_1 & b_1 & c_1 \\ 0 & b_2' & c_2' \\ 0 & b_3' & c_3' \end{pmatrix}$ where

$$b_2' = b_2 - \frac{a_2}{a_1} b_1, \quad c_2' = c_2 - \frac{a_2}{a_1} c_1, \quad b_3' = b_3 - \frac{a_3}{a_1} b_1, \quad c_3' = c_3 - \frac{a_3}{a_1} c_1,$$

assuming $a_1 \neq 0$.

(b) Show that with $r = -\dfrac{b_3'}{b_2'}$, $E_3 E_2 E_1 M = \begin{pmatrix} a_1 & b_1 & c_1 \\ 0 & b_2' & c_2' \\ 0 & 0 & c_3'' \end{pmatrix}$ where

$c_3'' = c_3' - \dfrac{b_3'}{b_2'} c_2'$, assuming $b_2' \neq 0$.

(c) Explain why parallelepiped P, with sides **a**, **b** and **c** has the same volume as the parallelepiped P′ with sides $\begin{pmatrix} a_1 \\ 0 \\ 0 \end{pmatrix}$, $\begin{pmatrix} b_1 \\ b_2' \\ 0 \end{pmatrix}$ and $\begin{pmatrix} c_1 \\ c_2'' \\ c_3'' \end{pmatrix}$.

(iii) Parallelepiped P′ is illustrated in figure 5.5. Assuming that a_1, b_2' and c_3'' are positive, deduce that the shaded area is $a_1 b_2'$ and that the volume of P′ is $a_1 b_2' c_3''$.

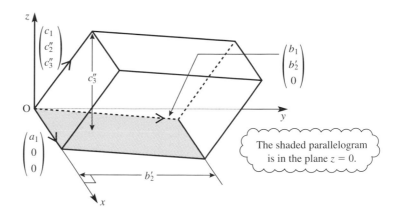

The shaded parallelogram is in the plane $z = 0$.

Figure 5.5

(iv) Show that $a_1 b_2' c_3'' = a_1 b_2 c_3 + a_2 b_3 c_1 + a_3 b_1 c_2 - a_3 b_2 c_1 - a_1 b_3 c_2 - a_2 b_1 c_3$, the same expression as given on page 85 for the value of det**M**.

(If $a_1 = 0$ you may use similar methods to change b_2 or c_2 to 0 instead of a_2 in stage (ii)(a), and then proceed as before. If $b_2' = 0$, $\mathbf{E_2 E_1 M} = \begin{pmatrix} a_1 & b_1 & c_1 \\ 0 & 0 & c_2' \\ 0 & b_3' & c_3' \end{pmatrix}$, and stage (ii)(b) may be omitted. In both cases the volume can still be calculated, much as before.)

1 Explain how you can tell by inspection that the following are true.

(i) $\begin{vmatrix} 3 & 2 & 3 \\ 5 & 1 & 5 \\ 2 & 3 & 2 \end{vmatrix} = 0$

(ii) $\begin{vmatrix} 4 & -3 & 2 \\ 2 & 0 & -3 \\ 7 & 4 & 5 \end{vmatrix} = - \begin{vmatrix} 4 & 2 & -3 \\ 2 & -3 & 0 \\ 7 & 5 & 4 \end{vmatrix}$

(iii) $\begin{vmatrix} 2 & 5 & -7 \\ 3 & 2 & 0 \\ -1 & 4 & 3 \end{vmatrix} = \begin{vmatrix} 5 & -7 & 2 \\ 2 & 0 & 3 \\ 4 & 3 & -1 \end{vmatrix}$

(iv) $(x - 3)$ is a factor of $\begin{vmatrix} x & 3x & 3 \\ x+2 & 8 & 2x-1 \\ 11 & 5-x & x^2+2 \end{vmatrix}$

2 (i) Prove that $|\mathbf{ka} \quad \mathbf{b} \quad \mathbf{c}| = k|\mathbf{a} \quad \mathbf{b} \quad \mathbf{c}|$, where k is constant.

(ii) Explain in terms of volumes why multiplying all the elements in the first column by constant k multiplies the value of the determinant by k.

(iii) What happens if you multiply another column by k?

3 Given that $\begin{vmatrix} 1 & 2 & 3 \\ 6 & 4 & 5 \\ 7 & 5 & 1 \end{vmatrix} = 43$, use the property developed in Question 2 to

evaluate the following without expanding the determinants.

(i) $\begin{vmatrix} 10 & 2 & 3 \\ 60 & 4 & 5 \\ 70 & 5 & 1 \end{vmatrix}$ **(ii)** $\begin{vmatrix} 4 & 10 & -21 \\ 24 & 20 & -35 \\ 28 & 25 & -7 \end{vmatrix}$ **(iii)** $\begin{vmatrix} x^4 & \frac{1}{x} & 12y \\ 6x^4 & \frac{2}{x} & 20y \\ 7x^4 & \frac{5}{2x} & 4y \end{vmatrix}$

4 (i) Prove that $|\mathbf{a} + k\mathbf{b} \quad \mathbf{b} \quad \mathbf{c}| = |\mathbf{a} \quad \mathbf{b} \quad \mathbf{c}|$, where k is constant.

(ii) Interpret this geometrically in terms of volumes.

(iii) Prove that the value of a determinant is unchanged when you add any multiple of one column to any other column.

5 Use the property developed in Question 4 to evaluate the following.

(i) $\begin{vmatrix} 21 & 2 & 3 \\ 46 & 4 & 5 \\ 57 & 5 & 1 \end{vmatrix}$ **(ii)** $\begin{vmatrix} 19 & 14 & 20 \\ 23 & 27 & 25 \\ 15 & 26 & 17 \end{vmatrix}$ **(iii)** $\begin{vmatrix} 25 & 17 & 51 \\ 38 & 33 & 78 \\ 25 & 32 & 52 \end{vmatrix}$

6 In a Fibonacci sequence the third and subsequent terms satisfy $u_{r+2} = u_{r+1} + u_r$. Show that if $u_1, u_2, u_3, \ldots$ is a Fibonacci sequence then

$$\begin{vmatrix} u_1 & u_2 & u_3 \\ u_4 & u_5 & u_6 \\ u_7 & u_8 & u_9 \end{vmatrix} = 0.$$

7 In this question A_1, A_2, etc. represent (as usual) the cofactors of a_1, a_2, etc.

(i) By considering expanding $|\mathbf{b} \quad \mathbf{b} \quad \mathbf{c}|$ by its first column show that $b_1A_1 + b_2A_2 + b_3A_3 = 0$.

(i) Prove that $a_1C_1 + a_2C_2 + a_3C_3 = 0$.

(iii) Write down four other similar expressions which also evaluate to 0.

(Multiplying a column of det$\mathbf{M}$ by cofactors belonging to a different column, and then adding, is known as *expanding by alien cofactors*. The result is always zero.)

8 You will need to use the results of Question 7 in this question.

(i) By multiplying out and simplifying

$$\begin{pmatrix} A_1 & A_2 & A_3 \\ B_1 & B_2 & B_3 \\ C_1 & C_2 & C_3 \end{pmatrix} \begin{pmatrix} a_1 & b_1 & c_1 \\ a_2 & b_2 & c_2 \\ a_3 & b_3 & c_3 \end{pmatrix} \text{ find the inverse of } \begin{pmatrix} a_1 & b_1 & c_1 \\ a_2 & b_2 & c_2 \\ a_3 & b_3 & c_3 \end{pmatrix}.$$

(ii) Will this method always produce the inverse of a 3×3 matrix?

9 Prove that the area of the triangle with vertices at (x_1, y_1), (x_2, y_2), (x_3, y_3) is

$$\pm \frac{1}{2} \begin{vmatrix} x_1 & y_1 & 1 \\ x_2 & y_2 & 1 \\ x_3 & y_3 & 1 \end{vmatrix} \text{ and interpret the equation } \begin{vmatrix} x & y & 1 \\ x_1 & y_1 & 1 \\ x_2 & y_2 & 1 \end{vmatrix} = 0.$$

10 Explain why $\begin{vmatrix} x+1 & 4 & 4 \\ 5 & x+2 & 7 \\ 2 & 2 & x-3 \end{vmatrix} = 0$ can be described as a cubic equation.

Show that $x = 3$ is one root, and find the other two roots.

11 Prove that $\begin{vmatrix} a & b & c \\ c & a & b \\ b & c & a \end{vmatrix} \equiv (a+b+c) \begin{vmatrix} 1 & b & c \\ 1 & a & b \\ 1 & c & a \end{vmatrix}$ and hence deduce that:

$$a^3 + b^3 + c^3 - 3abc = (a+b+c)(a^2 + b^2 + c^2 - bc - ca - ab).$$

12 Factorise these determinants.

(i) $\begin{vmatrix} 1 & a & bc \\ 1 & b & ca \\ 1 & c & ab \end{vmatrix}$ **(ii)** $\begin{vmatrix} 1 & 1 & 1 \\ x & y & z \\ x^2 & y^2 & z^2 \end{vmatrix}$ **(iii)** $\begin{vmatrix} 1 & 1 & 1 \\ x^2 & y^2 & z^2 \\ yz & zx & xy \end{vmatrix}$ **(iv)** $\begin{vmatrix} x & y & z \\ x^2 & y^2 & z^2 \\ yz & zx & xy \end{vmatrix}$

13 Show that x, $(x-1)$, $(x+1)$ are factors of $\Delta = \begin{vmatrix} 1 & 1 & 1 \\ 1 & x & x^2 \\ 1 & x^2 & x^4 \end{vmatrix}$ and factorise Δ completely.

The inverse of a 3×3 matrix

ACTIVITY 5.3 Taking $\mathbf{M} = \begin{pmatrix} a_1 & b_1 & c_1 \\ a_2 & b_2 & c_2 \\ a_3 & b_3 & c_3 \end{pmatrix}$, as usual, and $\det\mathbf{M} = \Delta \neq 0$, use the properties of

determinants to show that $\begin{pmatrix} A_1 & A_2 & A_3 \\ B_1 & B_2 & B_3 \\ C_1 & C_2 & C_3 \end{pmatrix} \begin{pmatrix} a_1 & b_1 & c_1 \\ a_2 & b_2 & c_2 \\ a_3 & b_3 & c_3 \end{pmatrix} = \begin{pmatrix} \Delta & 0 & 0 \\ 0 & \Delta & 0 \\ 0 & 0 & \Delta \end{pmatrix}.$

This result means that $\dfrac{1}{\det\mathbf{M}} \begin{pmatrix} A_1 & A_2 & A_3 \\ B_1 & B_2 & B_3 \\ C_1 & C_2 & C_3 \end{pmatrix} \begin{pmatrix} a_1 & b_1 & c_1 \\ a_2 & b_2 & c_2 \\ a_3 & b_3 & c_3 \end{pmatrix} = \begin{pmatrix} 1 & 0 & 0 \\ 0 & 1 & 0 \\ 0 & 0 & 1 \end{pmatrix}.$

The matrix $\begin{pmatrix} A_1 & A_2 & A_3 \\ B_1 & B_2 & B_3 \\ C_1 & C_2 & C_3 \end{pmatrix}$ is known as the *adjugate* (or *adjoint*) of $\mathbf{M}$,

denoted by adj$\mathbf{M}$. Note that adj$\mathbf{M}$ is formed by replacing each element of $\mathbf{M}$ by its cofactor, and then transposing, i.e. changing rows into columns and columns into rows.

Strictly speaking, the matrix $\mathbf{L} = \dfrac{1}{\det\mathbf{M}} \begin{pmatrix} A_1 & A_2 & A_3 \\ B_1 & B_2 & B_3 \\ C_1 & C_2 & C_3 \end{pmatrix}$ is the *left-inverse* of $\mathbf{M}$

because $\mathbf{LM} = \mathbf{I}$.

But if **R** is a right-inverse (i.e. **MR** = **I**)

$$\mathbf{LM} = \mathbf{I} \implies (\mathbf{LM})\mathbf{R} = \mathbf{IR} = \mathbf{R} \implies \mathbf{L}(\mathbf{MR}) = \mathbf{R} \implies \mathbf{LI} = \mathbf{R} \implies \mathbf{L} = \mathbf{R}$$

so any left-inverse of a matrix is also a right-inverse, and vice versa.

If **L** and **L'** are two left-inverses of **M**, then **L** is also a right-inverse, and

$$\mathbf{L'M} = \mathbf{I} \implies (\mathbf{L'M})\mathbf{L} = \mathbf{IL} = \mathbf{L} \implies \mathbf{L'}(\mathbf{ML}) = \mathbf{L} \implies \mathbf{L'I} = \mathbf{L} \implies \mathbf{L'} = \mathbf{L}.$$

So the inverse of **M** (if it exists) is unique and it is justified to call **L** the inverse of **M**, usually denoted by $\mathbf{M}^{-1}$, where

$$\mathbf{M}^{-1} = \frac{1}{\det\mathbf{M}}\,\mathrm{adj}\mathbf{M} = \frac{1}{\det\mathbf{M}}\begin{pmatrix} A_1 & A_2 & A_3 \\ B_1 & B_2 & B_3 \\ C_1 & C_2 & C_3 \end{pmatrix}, \quad \Delta \neq 0.$$

ACTIVITY 5.4   When you *transpose* a matrix **A** you form a new matrix, denoted by $\mathbf{A}^{\mathrm{T}}$, which has the same elements as **A** except that they are arranged so that the element in the *r*th row and *c*th column of **A** becomes the element in the *c*th row and *r*th column of $\mathbf{A}^{\mathrm{T}}$. This means that the first row of **A** becomes the first column of $\mathbf{A}^{\mathrm{T}}$, and so on.

(i)   Let **A** be an $m \times n$ matrix and **B** be $n \times p$. Taking the *r*th row of **A** to be

$$(r_1 \quad r_2 \quad r_3 \quad \ldots \quad r_n) \text{ and the } c\text{th column of } \mathbf{B} \text{ to be } \begin{pmatrix} c_1 \\ c_2 \\ \vdots \\ c_n \end{pmatrix}, \text{ write down}$$

the element in the *r*th row and *c*th column of **AB**. Show that this is the same as the element in the *c*th row and *r*th column of $\mathbf{B}^{\mathrm{T}}\mathbf{A}^{\mathrm{T}}$. Hence show that $(\mathbf{AB})^{\mathrm{T}} = \mathbf{B}^{\mathrm{T}}\mathbf{A}^{\mathrm{T}}$. (Notice that it is not necessary for **A** and **B** to be square matrices.)

(ii)   By putting $\mathbf{A} = \mathbf{M}$ and $\mathbf{B} = \mathbf{M}^{-1}$, where **M** is a square matrix with $\det\mathbf{M} \neq 0$, use the fact that $\mathbf{I}^{\mathrm{T}} = \mathbf{I}$ to prove that $(\mathbf{M}^{-1})^{\mathrm{T}} = (\mathbf{M}^{\mathrm{T}})^{-1}$.

ACTIVITY 5.5   Use the fact that $\det(\mathbf{NM}) = \det\mathbf{N} \times \det\mathbf{M}$ to prove that if $\det\mathbf{M} = 0$ matrix **M** does not have an inverse. (Such matrices are described as *singular*.)

EXAMPLE 5.3

Find the inverse of the matrix $\mathbf{M} = \begin{pmatrix} 2 & 3 & 4 \\ 2 & -5 & 2 \\ -3 & 6 & -3 \end{pmatrix}$.

SOLUTION

1   Evaluate the three cofactors of the elements of any one column and hence find the determinant. In this example the first column is used.

$$A_1 = \begin{vmatrix} -5 & 2 \\ 6 & -3 \end{vmatrix} = 15 - 12 = 3.$$

$$A_2 = -\begin{vmatrix} 3 & 4 \\ 6 & -3 \end{vmatrix} = -(-9 - 24) = 33.$$

$$A_3 = \begin{vmatrix} 3 & 4 \\ -5 & 2 \end{vmatrix} = 6 - (-20) = 26.$$

$$\Delta = 2A_1 + 2A_2 - 3A_3 = 2 \times 3 + 2 \times 33 - 3 \times 26 = -6.$$

Since $\Delta \neq 0$, $\mathbf{M}^{-1}$ exists.

2 Evaluate the remaining cofactors.

$$B_1 = -\begin{vmatrix} 2 & 2 \\ -3 & -3 \end{vmatrix} = 0. \qquad\qquad B_2 = \begin{vmatrix} 2 & 4 \\ -3 & -3 \end{vmatrix} = -6 - (-12) = 6.$$

$$B_3 = -\begin{vmatrix} 2 & 4 \\ 2 & 2 \end{vmatrix} = -(4 - 8) = 4. \qquad C_1 = \begin{vmatrix} 2 & -5 \\ -3 & 6 \end{vmatrix} = 12 - 15 = -3.$$

$$C_2 = -\begin{vmatrix} 2 & 3 \\ -3 & 6 \end{vmatrix} = -(12 - (-9)) = -21. \quad C_3 = \begin{vmatrix} 2 & 3 \\ 2 & -5 \end{vmatrix} = -10 - 6 = -16.$$

3 Evaluate Δ by other expansions to check your arithmetic.

$$\Delta = 3B_1 - 5B_2 + 6B_3 = 3 \times 0 - 5 \times 6 + 6 \times 4 = -6.$$
$$\Delta = 4C_1 + 2C_2 - 3C_3 = 4 \times (-3) + 2 \times (-21) - 3 \times (-16) = -6.$$

4 Form the matrix of cofactors, transpose it and multiply by $\dfrac{1}{\Delta}$.

$$\mathbf{M}^{-1} = \frac{1}{-6} \begin{pmatrix} 3 & 0 & -3 \\ 33 & 6 & -21 \\ 26 & 4 & -16 \end{pmatrix}^{\mathrm{T}}$$

$$= \frac{1}{-6} \begin{pmatrix} 3 & 33 & 26 \\ 0 & 6 & 4 \\ -3 & -21 & -16 \end{pmatrix}$$

$$= \frac{1}{6} \begin{pmatrix} -3 & -33 & -26 \\ 0 & -6 & -4 \\ 3 & 21 & 16 \end{pmatrix}.$$

The final matrix may be written as $\begin{pmatrix} -\frac{1}{2} & -\frac{11}{2} & -\frac{13}{3} \\ 0 & -1 & -\frac{2}{3} \\ \frac{1}{2} & \frac{7}{2} & \frac{8}{3} \end{pmatrix}.$

The adjugate method illustrated in Example 5.3 is a reasonable way of finding the inverse of a 3 × 3 matrix, though it is important to check your arithmetic as it is very easy to make mistakes. But for larger matrices a routine known as the *row operations method* is used, as it requires far fewer arithmetic steps. For example, it takes about 10^8 steps to invert a 10 × 10 matrix by the adjugate method, but only about 3000 steps by row operations. The row operations method is easy to program for a computer – another major advantage – though care must be exercised to avoid rounding errors, and problems do occur when the determinant is close to zero.

Row properties

You have already seen that if $\det \mathbf{M} = \Delta \neq 0$, $\mathbf{M}^{-1}$ exists and is equal to $\dfrac{1}{\Delta} \text{adj} \mathbf{M}$.

Therefore $\mathbf{M} \text{adj} \mathbf{M} = \Delta \mathbf{I}$, which may be rewritten as

$$\begin{pmatrix} a_1 & b_1 & c_1 \\ a_2 & b_2 & c_2 \\ a_3 & b_3 & c_3 \end{pmatrix} \begin{pmatrix} A_1 & A_2 & A_3 \\ B_1 & B_2 & B_3 \\ C_1 & C_2 & C_3 \end{pmatrix} = \begin{pmatrix} \Delta & 0 & 0 \\ 0 & \Delta & 0 \\ 0 & 0 & \Delta \end{pmatrix}.$$

Inspecting the top left-hand element of the product you have
$a_1 A_1 + b_1 B_1 + c_1 C_1 = \Delta$. But $a_1 A_1 + b_1 B_1 + c_1 C_1$ is the expansion by the first column of $\det(\mathbf{M}^{\mathrm{T}})$. This means that $\det(\mathbf{M}^{\mathrm{T}}) = \det \mathbf{M}$, and it follows that a determinant may be evaluated by expanding by rows as well as by expanding by columns. There are row properties corresponding to all the column properties established earlier.

ACTIVITY 5.6 Some calculators handle matrices. Find out how to use such a calculator to find the determinant and inverse of 3×3 matrices.

EXERCISE 5C

1 By finding the adjugate matrix find the inverses of the following, where possible.

(i) $\begin{pmatrix} 1 & 2 & 4 \\ 2 & 4 & 5 \\ 0 & 1 & 2 \end{pmatrix}$ (ii) $\begin{pmatrix} 3 & 2 & 6 \\ 5 & 3 & 11 \\ 7 & 4 & 16 \end{pmatrix}$

(iii) $\begin{pmatrix} 5 & 5 & -5 \\ -9 & 3 & -5 \\ -4 & -6 & 8 \end{pmatrix}$ (iv) $\begin{pmatrix} 6 & 5 & 6 \\ -5 & 2 & -4 \\ -4 & -6 & -5 \end{pmatrix}$

2 Given $\mathbf{M} = \begin{pmatrix} 1 & 2 & 2 \\ 3 & 2 & 3 \\ 4 & 1 & 1 \end{pmatrix}$ find:

(i) $\text{adj} \mathbf{M}$ (ii) $\mathbf{M}(\text{adj} \mathbf{M})$ (iii) $(\text{adj} \mathbf{M})\mathbf{M}$
(iv) $\det \mathbf{M}$ (v) $\det(\text{adj} \mathbf{M})$ (vi) $\text{adj}(\text{adj} \mathbf{M})$.

Comment on the answer to part (vi).

3 Find the inverse of $\begin{pmatrix} 4 & -5 & 3 \\ 3 & 3 & -4 \\ 5 & 4 & -6 \end{pmatrix}$ and hence solve $\begin{cases} 4x - 5y + 3z = 3 \\ 3x + 3y - 4z = 48 \\ 5x + 4y - 6z = 74. \end{cases}$

4 Given $\mathbf{A} = \begin{pmatrix} 6 & 2 & -3 \\ 2 & 3 & 6 \\ 3 & -6 & 2 \end{pmatrix}$ evaluate $\mathbf{A}\mathbf{A}^{\mathrm{T}}$ and hence, without doing further calculations, write down:

(i) $\mathbf{A}^{-1}$ (ii) $\det \mathbf{A}$ (iii) $\mathbf{A}^{\mathrm{T}}\mathbf{A}$.

5 Given $\mathbf{P} = \begin{pmatrix} -2 & 1 & 0 \\ 3 & 2 & 5 \\ 1 & 2 & 2 \end{pmatrix}$ and $\mathbf{Q} = \begin{pmatrix} 2 & -1 & -2 \\ -1 & 2 & 2 \\ 2 & 3 & 3 \end{pmatrix}$ evaluate:

(i) $\mathbf{PQ}$ and $\det(\mathbf{PQ})$

(ii) $\mathbf{QP}$ and $\det(\mathbf{QP})$

(iii) $\det\mathbf{P}$

(iv) $\det\mathbf{Q}$.

Verify that $\det(\mathbf{PQ}) = \det(\mathbf{QP}) = (\det\mathbf{P}) \times (\det\mathbf{Q})$.

6 Given that the following matrices are singular find the values of x.

(i) $\begin{pmatrix} 5 & 0 & 3 \\ 2 & x & 0 \\ 3 & 4 & 5 \end{pmatrix}$　　**(ii)** $\begin{pmatrix} 4 & 6 & -1 \\ -1 & 2 & -3 \\ 5 & x & 15 \end{pmatrix}$

(iii) $\begin{pmatrix} 6 & 7 & -1 \\ 3 & x & 5 \\ 9 & 11 & x \end{pmatrix}$　　**(iv)** $\begin{pmatrix} 1-x & 1 & -2 \\ -1 & 2-x & 1 \\ 0 & 1 & -1-x \end{pmatrix}$

7 In this question $\mathbf{M}$ and $\mathbf{N}$ are square matrices of the same order.

(i) Prove that if $\mathbf{M}$ and $\mathbf{N}$ are non-singular, then $\mathbf{MN}$ is non-singular.

(ii) By considering $(\mathbf{MN})(\mathbf{N}^{-1}\mathbf{M}^{-1})$, prove that if $\mathbf{MN}$ is non-singular then:

(a) $(\mathbf{MN})^{-1} = \mathbf{N}^{-1}\mathbf{M}^{-1}$

(b) $\mathrm{adj}(\mathbf{MN}) = (\mathrm{adj}\mathbf{N})(\mathrm{adj}\mathbf{M})$.

8 The non-singular matrix $\mathbf{M}$ has the property that $\mathbf{MM}^{\mathrm{T}} = \mathbf{M}^{\mathrm{T}}\mathbf{M}$. Prove that:

(i) $\mathbf{M}^{\mathrm{T}}\mathbf{M}^{-1} = \mathbf{M}^{-1}\mathbf{M}^{\mathrm{T}}$

(ii) $\mathbf{N} = \mathbf{M}^{-1}\mathbf{M}^{\mathrm{T}} \Rightarrow \mathbf{NN}^{\mathrm{T}} = \mathbf{I}$.

9 Let $\mathbf{P} = \begin{pmatrix} a & 0 & b \\ 0 & c & 0 \\ d & 0 & e \end{pmatrix}$ and $\mathbf{Q} = \begin{pmatrix} e & 0 & -b \\ 0 & f & 0 \\ -d & 0 & a \end{pmatrix}$.

(i) Find $\mathbf{PQ}$.

(ii) Given that $\mathbf{PQ}$ is a non-zero multiple of the identity matrix, express f in terms of a, b, c, d and e, and state any necessary conditions on a, b, c, d and e.

(iii) Find $\mathbf{P}^{-1}$, assuming that the conditions you stated in part **(ii)** are satisfied.

$\mathbf{M} = \begin{pmatrix} 3 & 0 & 8 \\ 0 & 2 & 0 \\ 1 & 0 & 4 \end{pmatrix}$ and $\mathbf{N}$ is a 3×3 matrix with inverse

$\mathbf{N}^{-1} = \begin{pmatrix} 1 & -2 & 3 \\ 3 & k & 0 \\ 2 & 4 & k \end{pmatrix}$.

(iv) Find $(\mathbf{MN})^{-1}$.

(v) Given that $\mathbf{MN}\begin{pmatrix} x \\ y \\ z \end{pmatrix} = \begin{pmatrix} 0 \\ 2k \\ 0 \end{pmatrix}$, express x, y and z in terms of k.

[MEI]

10 Prove that if **M** is a non-singular 3×3 matrix then:

☆ **(i)** $\mathbf{M}(\text{adj}\mathbf{M}) = (\det\mathbf{M})\mathbf{I}$

☆ **(ii)** $\det(\text{adj}\mathbf{M}) = (\det\mathbf{M})^2$

☆ **(iii)** $\text{adj}(\text{adj}\mathbf{M}) = (\det\mathbf{M})\mathbf{M}$.

☆ Do these results hold if **M** is singular? Justify your answer.

11 Prove that every matrix of the form $\begin{pmatrix} 1 & p & q \\ 0 & 1 & r \\ 0 & 0 & 1 \end{pmatrix}$ is non-singular, and that

☆

☆ the inverse of such a matrix is of the same form.

12 A square matrix **M** is known as *orthogonal* if $\mathbf{M}^{\mathrm{T}}\mathbf{M} = \mathbf{I}$. Prove that

☆ orthogonal matrices have the following properties.

☆ **(i)** The vectors forming the columns of an orthogonal matrix:

☆ **(a)** have magnitude 1

☆ **(b)** are mutually perpendicular. ('Orthogonal' means 'perpendicular'.)

☆ **(ii)** The determinant of an orthogonal matrix is ± 1.

☆ **(iii)** Transformations represented by orthogonal matrices are *isometric*: i.e.

☆ they preserve length.

Hints:

☆ **1** Let **M** map P to P′ where $\mathbf{p}' = \mathbf{Mp}$.

☆ **2** Use $|\mathbf{q}' - \mathbf{p}'|^2 = (\mathbf{q}' - \mathbf{p}')^{\mathrm{T}}(\mathbf{q}' - \mathbf{p}')$ to show that $(\mathrm{P}'\mathrm{Q}')^2 = (\mathrm{PQ})^2$.

Matrices and simultaneous equations

In *AS Further Pure Mathematics* (*FP1*) you saw how solving simultaneous

equations such as $\begin{cases} ax + cy = e \\ bx + dy = f \end{cases}$ may be regarded as solving the matrix equation

$\mathbf{M}\begin{pmatrix} x \\ y \end{pmatrix} = \begin{pmatrix} e \\ f \end{pmatrix}$, where $\mathbf{M} = \begin{pmatrix} a & c \\ b & d \end{pmatrix}$, leading to two different interpretations,

both of which throw light on the subject.

In *Interpretation A*, the original two equations are regarded as the equations of two lines in a plane. There are three possible situations.

(i) The two lines intersect at a single point, corresponding to the equations having a unique solution.

(ii) The two lines are distinct, parallel lines that do not meet, in which case the equations are described as *inconsistent*.

(iii) The two lines are coincident, with all their points in common, corresponding to the two equations having infinitely many solutions that may all be expressed in terms of a single parameter.

In *Interpretation B* you are dealing with a transformation of the plane, with matrix **M**. You are seeking the co-ordinates of P, knowing that it is mapped to P′ with co-ordinates (e, f). Again there are three possibilities. If $\det \mathbf{M} \neq 0$, the situation is as described in **(i)** below, otherwise it is as in **(ii)** or **(iii)**.

(i) If $\det \mathbf{M} \neq 0$, then **M** is non-singular, $\mathbf{M}^{-1}$ exists, and there is a unique position for P, and a unique solution to the equations.

If $\det \mathbf{M} = 0$, then **M** is singular and $\mathbf{M}^{-1}$ does not exist: in this case the whole of the plane is mapped onto a single line ℓ (through the origin) and P′ is or is not on ℓ.

(ii) If P′ is not on line ℓ then P′ is not the image of any point in the plane, and the equations have no solution: the equations are inconsistent.

(iii) If P′ is on line ℓ then P′ is the image of a whole line of points, so there are infinitely many solutions, which may all be expressed in terms of a single parameter.

It was assumed throughout Interpretation B that $\mathbf{M} \neq \mathbf{O}$, the zero matrix, as that leads to a trivial and obvious situation: all points of the plane are mapped to the origin, and there is no solution if P′ is not at the origin; if P′ is at the origin, P may be anywhere on the plane, meaning that x and y may take any values.

Similarly the three simultaneous equations in three variables

$$a_1 x + b_1 y + c_1 z = d_1$$
$$a_2 x + b_2 y + c_2 z = d_2$$
$$a_3 x + b_3 y + c_3 z = d_3$$

are equivalent to the matrix equation $\mathbf{M} \begin{pmatrix} x \\ y \\ z \end{pmatrix} = \begin{pmatrix} d_1 \\ d_2 \\ d_3 \end{pmatrix}$, where

$$\mathbf{M} = \begin{pmatrix} a_1 & b_1 & c_1 \\ a_2 & b_2 & c_2 \\ a_3 & b_3 & c_3 \end{pmatrix}.$$

The three equations may be regarded as the equations of three planes in three-dimensional space. There are seven possible configurations.

(i) If $\det \mathbf{M} \neq 0$, **M** is non-singular, $\mathbf{M}^{-1}$ exists, and the equations have a unique solution. This corresponds to the three planes having a single common point, figure 5.6.

Figure 5.6

If $\det \mathbf{M} = 0$, **M** is singular and $\mathbf{M}^{-1}$ does not exist: in this case either the equations are inconsistent and have no solutions, see **(ii)** below; or the equations have infinitely many solutions, see **(iii)** below.

(ii) The equations being inconsistent and having no solutions corresponds to the three planes having no common point. When this happens

(a) the three planes form a triangular prism, figure 5.7;

or

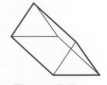

Figure 5.7

(b) two planes are parallel and distinct, and crossed by the third plane, figure 5.8;

or

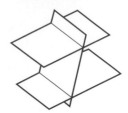

Figure 5.8

(c) two planes are coincident and the third plane is parallel but distinct, figure 5.9;

or

Figure 5.9

(d) all three planes are parallel and distinct, figure 5.10.

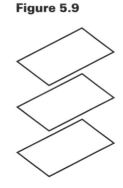

Figure 5.10

(iii) The equations having infinitely many solutions corresponds to the three planes having infinitely many common points. When this happens

either

(a) the three planes have a line of common points: this arrangement is known as a *sheaf* or *pencil* of planes, figure 5.11; the solutions are given in terms of a single parameter;

Figure 5.11

or

(b) the three planes all coincide, figure 5.12: the solutions are given in terms of two parameters.

Figure 5.12

Again the trivial situation where **M** consists entirely of zeros has been ignored. Figure 5.13 summarises the decisions that need to be made.

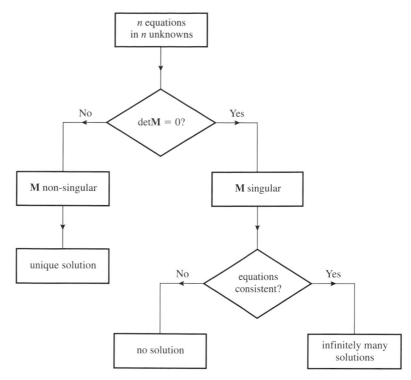

Figure 5.13

EXAMPLE 5.4

Investigate the solution of the equations $\begin{cases} x + 3y - 2z = 7 & \text{A} \\ 2x - 2y + z = 3 & \text{B} \\ 3x + y - z = k & \text{C} \end{cases}$

(i) when $k = 10$ **(ii)** when $k = 12$.

SOLUTION

Start by eliminating one variable (z) to obtain two equations in x, y.

A − 2C: $-5x + y = 7 - 2k$ $\Rightarrow$ $5x - y = -7 + 2k$
B + C: $5x - y = 3 + k$.

Now $5x - y$ can only equal $-7 + 2k$ and $3 + k$ if

$-7 + 2k = 3 + k$
$\Leftrightarrow$ $k = 10$.

(i)   When $k = 10$, equations A − 2C and B + C both reduce to $5x - y = 13$, so you can only solve for x and y (and later z) in terms of a parameter.
If $x = \lambda$, $y = 5\lambda - 13$ and from equation C you get:

$z = 3\lambda + 5\lambda - 13 - 10 = 8\lambda - 23$.

There is a line of solution points, which can be given in terms of a single parameter: $(\lambda, 5\lambda - 13, 8\lambda - 23)$. The three planes are arranged as a sheaf.

(ii) When $k = 12$, equations A − 2C and B + C are inconsistent as $5x - y$ cannot be both 17 and 15.

Equations A and B are the same as in **(i)**, so the corresponding planes have not changed. In equation C the value of k has changed from 10 to 12, causing a translation of the plane.

The original equations are inconsistent. The corresponding planes form a triangular prism.

ALTERNATIVE APPROACHES

A calculator tells you that $\begin{vmatrix} 1 & 3 & -2 \\ 2 & -2 & 1 \\ 3 & 1 & -1 \end{vmatrix} = 0$, so you know that there is not a unique solution, but either no solutions or many solutions.

The normals corresponding to the equations A, B, C are clearly not parallel, so the three planes are not parallel (or identical): you can only be dealing with a sheaf of planes or a triangular prism.

Examination of the equations shows that C = A + B when $k = 10$, so that the equations are not inconsistent in **(i)** and you then have a sheaf of planes, their common line being the line of solution points. (If you want to find expressions for these points you can use algebraic methods, as in the first solution.)

As before, changing the value of k translates the plane represented by C, but does not affect the other two planes so in **(ii)** the three planes form a triangular prism and the equations are inconsistent.

EXERCISE 5D

In Questions 1–10 decide whether the equations are consistent or inconsistent. If they are consistent, solve them, in terms of a parameter if necessary. In each question also describe the configuration of the corresponding lines or planes.

1 $5x + 3y = 31$
$4x + 2y = 25$

2 $3x + 9y = 12$
$2x + 6y = 15$

3 $6x + 3y = 12$
$2x + y = 4$

4 $6x - 3y = 11$
$y = 2x - 4$

5 $x + y + z = 4$
$2x + 3y - 4z = 3$
$5x + 8y - 13z = 8$

6 $2x - y = 1$
$3x + 2z = 13$
$3y + 4z = 23$

7 $x + 2y + 4z = 7$
$3x + 2y + 5z = 21$
$4x + y + 2z = 14$

8 $3x + 2y + z = 2$
$5x + 3y - 4z = 1$
$x + y + 4z = 5$

9 $2x + y - z = 5$
$8x + 4y - 4z = 20$
$-2x - y + z = -5$

10 $5x + 3y - 2z = 6$
$6x + 2y + 3z = 11$
$7x + y + 8z = 12$

11 Find the two values of k for which the equations $\begin{cases} 6x + 3y = 9 \\ kx + 8y = 6 \end{cases}$ do not have have a unique solution. In both cases find the solution set for the equations.

12 Given that $\det \mathbf{M} = 0$, where $\mathbf{M}$ is a 2×2 matrix, explain why $\mathbf{M} \begin{pmatrix} x \\ y \end{pmatrix} = \begin{pmatrix} p \\ q \end{pmatrix}$ has infinitely many solutions if both p and q are zero.

What happens if p and q are not both zero?

13 Solve the equation $\begin{pmatrix} 1 & 3 & -2 \\ -3 & 1 & 1 \\ -3 & 11 & -4 \end{pmatrix} \begin{pmatrix} x \\ y \\ z \end{pmatrix} = \begin{pmatrix} -2 \\ 6 \\ k \end{pmatrix}$ in each of the two cases

(i) $k = 3$

(ii) $k = 6$,

giving x, y and z in terms of a parameter λ if appropriate. In both cases interpret your solution geometrically with reference to three appropriate planes.

14 $\mathbf{A}$ is a 3×3 matrix and $\mathbf{d}$ is a 3×1 column vector. Show that all solutions of the equation

$$\mathbf{Ar} = \mathbf{d} \qquad \qquad \text{①}$$

can be expressed in the form $\mathbf{r} = \mathbf{p} + \mathbf{k}$, where $\mathbf{p}$ is any particular solution of ① and $\mathbf{k}$ is any solution of the related equation $\mathbf{Ar} = \mathbf{0}$. Does it matter if $\mathbf{A}$ is singular or non-singular?

(If you are studying *Differential Equations* compare what you have just done with the method of solving certain differential equations by using a particular integral and a complementary function.)

15 Show that the equations $\begin{cases} 3x + 2y = 4 \\ 2x - 3y = 7 \\ 5x - 4y = k \end{cases}$ are inconsistent unless k takes one particular value. What is that value?

16 You are given the matrix

$$\mathbf{M} = \begin{pmatrix} 3 & 1 & -3 \\ 4 & -2 & 1 \\ 5 & -3 & 2 \end{pmatrix}.$$

(i) Show that $\det \mathbf{M} = 0$.

(ii) Solve the equation $\mathbf{M} \begin{pmatrix} x \\ y \\ z \end{pmatrix} = \begin{pmatrix} 2 \\ 6 \\ k \end{pmatrix}$ in each of the two cases

(a) $k = 3$

(b) $k = 8$,

giving x, y and z in terms of a parameter t if appropriate.

In each case interpret your solution geometrically with reference to the three planes

$$3x + y - 3z = 2$$
$$4x - 2y + z = 6$$
$$5x - 3y + 2z = k.$$

[MEI]

Eigenvalues and eigenvectors

2 × 2 matrices

In a reflection, every point on the mirror line maps to itself. The line may be described as a *line of invariant points*, since every point on the line is itself invariant.

A line of invariant points is a special case of an *invariant line*, where the image of every point on the line is itself on the line but is not necessarily the original point.

As an example, think of the lines through the origin in an enlargement, scale factor 2, centre the origin. Each point on the line in figure 5.14 maps to another point on the line, but the origin maps to itself.

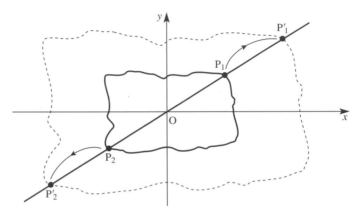

Figure 5.14

This idea is now developed in terms of matrices, but only for lines which pass through the origin.

As an example look at the effect of the transformation with matrix $\mathbf{M} = \begin{pmatrix} 4 & 2 \\ 1 & 3 \end{pmatrix}$. Since $\begin{pmatrix} 4 & 2 \\ 1 & 3 \end{pmatrix} \begin{pmatrix} 1 \\ 1 \end{pmatrix} = \begin{pmatrix} 6 \\ 4 \end{pmatrix}$ the transformation defined by pre-multiplying position vectors by matrix $\mathbf{M}$ maps the vector $\begin{pmatrix} 1 \\ 1 \end{pmatrix}$ to $\begin{pmatrix} 6 \\ 4 \end{pmatrix}$. Similarly the image of $\begin{pmatrix} k \\ k \end{pmatrix}$ is $\begin{pmatrix} 6k \\ 4k \end{pmatrix}$. Each point on the line $y = x$ can be represented by the position vector of the form $\begin{pmatrix} k \\ k \end{pmatrix}$ and the points with position vectors $\begin{pmatrix} 6k \\ 4k \end{pmatrix}$ form the line $y = \frac{2}{3}x$. This means that under the transformation represented by the matrix $\mathbf{M}$ the image of the line $y = x$ is the line $y = \frac{2}{3}x$. Similarly since $\begin{pmatrix} 4 & 2 \\ 1 & 3 \end{pmatrix} \begin{pmatrix} 1 \\ 2 \end{pmatrix} = \begin{pmatrix} 8 \\ 7 \end{pmatrix}$ the image of the line $y = 2x$ is the line $y = \frac{7}{8}x$.

ACTIVITY 5.7

(i) Find the images of the following position vectors under the transformation given by $\mathbf{M} = \begin{pmatrix} 4 & 2 \\ 1 & 3 \end{pmatrix}$.

(a) $\begin{pmatrix} 1 \\ 0 \end{pmatrix}$ **(b)** $\begin{pmatrix} 2 \\ 1 \end{pmatrix}$ **(c)** $\begin{pmatrix} 0 \\ 1 \end{pmatrix}$ **(d)** $\begin{pmatrix} -1 \\ 2 \end{pmatrix}$ **(e)** $\begin{pmatrix} -1 \\ 1 \end{pmatrix}$ **(f)** $\begin{pmatrix} -2 \\ 1 \end{pmatrix}$

(ii) Use your answers to part **(i)** to find the equations of the images of the following lines.

(a) $y = 0$ **(b)** $y = \frac{1}{2}x$ **(c)** $x = 0$

(d) $y = -2x$ **(e)** $y = -x$ **(f)** $y = -\frac{1}{2}x$

The information you have just gathered may be represented as in figure 5.15, where the object lines and their images are shown in separate diagrams.

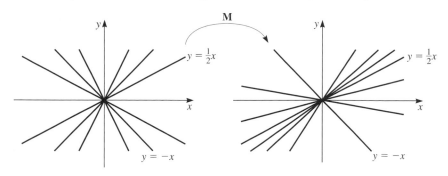

Figure 5.15

However you can show all the information on one diagram, as in figure 5.16, where (parts of) the object lines are shown at the centre of the diagram, and (parts of) their image lines are shown in the outer section of the diagram.

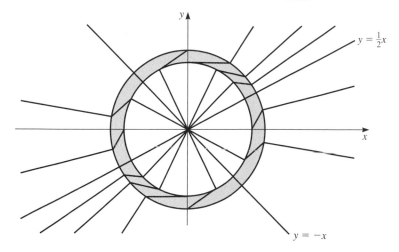

Figure 5.16

The shaded part of the diagram is not directly relevant but shows lines connecting each object line to its image. You will notice that there are two invariant lines, $y = \frac{1}{2}x$ and $y = -x$, which map to themselves under this transformation. The other lines appear to crowd towards $y = \frac{1}{2}x$, moving away from $y = -x$. This diagram prompts several questions.

- Are there other invariant lines?
- Why does $y = \frac{1}{2}x$ attract and $y = -x$ repel?
- Do all transformations behave like this?
- How can such lines be found efficiently?

Terminology

To answer these questions you need suitable terminology.

If **s** is a non-zero vector such that $\mathbf{Ms} = \lambda\mathbf{s}$, where **M** is a matrix and λ is a scalar, then **s** is called an *eigenvector* of **M**. The scalar λ is known as an *eigenvalue*.

Therefore, since
$$\begin{pmatrix} 4 & 2 \\ 1 & 3 \end{pmatrix}\begin{pmatrix} 2 \\ 1 \end{pmatrix} = \begin{pmatrix} 10 \\ 5 \end{pmatrix} = 5\begin{pmatrix} 2 \\ 1 \end{pmatrix}$$

and
$$\begin{pmatrix} 4 & 2 \\ 1 & 3 \end{pmatrix}\begin{pmatrix} -1 \\ 1 \end{pmatrix} = \begin{pmatrix} -2 \\ 2 \end{pmatrix} = 2\begin{pmatrix} -1 \\ 1 \end{pmatrix}$$

$\begin{pmatrix} 2 \\ 1 \end{pmatrix}$ and $\begin{pmatrix} -1 \\ 1 \end{pmatrix}$ are eigenvectors of the matrix $\mathbf{M} = \begin{pmatrix} 4 & 2 \\ 1 & 3 \end{pmatrix}$. The corresponding eigenvalues are 5 and 2 respectively. It will become evident later that these are the only two eigenvalues.

Properties of eigenvectors

Notice the following properties of eigenvectors.

1. All non-zero scalar multiples of $\begin{pmatrix} 2 \\ 1 \end{pmatrix}$ and $\begin{pmatrix} -1 \\ 1 \end{pmatrix}$ are also eigenvectors of **M**, with (respectively) the same eigenvalues.
2. Under the transformation the eigenvector is enlarged by a scale factor equal to its eigenvalue.
3. The direction of an eigenvector is unchanged by the transformation.
   (If the eigenvalue is negative the sense of the eigenvector will be reversed.)

When finding eigenvectors you need to solve the equation $\mathbf{Ms} = \lambda\mathbf{s}$. Now:

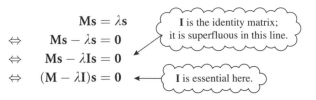

$$\mathbf{Ms} = \lambda\mathbf{s}$$
$$\Leftrightarrow \quad \mathbf{Ms} - \lambda\mathbf{s} = \mathbf{0}$$
$$\Leftrightarrow \quad \mathbf{Ms} - \lambda\mathbf{Is} = \mathbf{0}$$
$$\Leftrightarrow \quad (\mathbf{M} - \lambda\mathbf{I})\mathbf{s} = \mathbf{0}$$

I is the identity matrix; it is superfluous in this line.

I is essential here.

Clearly $\mathbf{s} = \mathbf{0}$ is a solution, but you are seeking a non-zero solution for $\mathbf{s}$. For non-zero solutions you require $\det(\mathbf{M} - \lambda\mathbf{I}) = 0$. The equation $\det(\mathbf{M} - \lambda\mathbf{I}) = 0$ is known as the *characteristic equation* of $\mathbf{M}$. The left-hand side of the characteristic equation is a polynomial in λ; this polynomial is known as the *characteristic polynomial*.

(The German word for 'characteristic' is *eigen*: eigenvectors are also known as *characteristic* vectors; eigenvalues are also known as *characteristic* values.)

Finding eigenvectors

The following are the steps for finding eigenvectors, illustrated in the next example.

1 Form the characteristic equation: $\det(\mathbf{M} - \lambda\mathbf{I}) = 0$.

2 Solve the characteristic equation to find the eigenvalues, λ.

3 For each eigenvalue λ find a corresponding eigenvector $\mathbf{s}$ by solving $(\mathbf{M} - \lambda\mathbf{I})\mathbf{s} = \mathbf{0}$.

EXAMPLE 5.5

Find the eigenvectors of the matrix $\mathbf{M} = \begin{pmatrix} 4 & 2 \\ 1 & 3 \end{pmatrix}$.

SOLUTION

1 Form the characteristic equation, $\det(\mathbf{M} - \lambda\mathbf{I}) = \mathbf{0}$.

$$\mathbf{M} - \lambda\mathbf{I} = \begin{pmatrix} 4 & 2 \\ 1 & 3 \end{pmatrix} - \lambda\begin{pmatrix} 1 & 0 \\ 0 & 1 \end{pmatrix} = \begin{pmatrix} 4 - \lambda & 2 \\ 1 & 3 - \lambda \end{pmatrix}$$

so that $\det(\mathbf{M} - \lambda\mathbf{I}) = 0 \Leftrightarrow \begin{vmatrix} 4 - \lambda & 2 \\ 1 & 3 - \lambda \end{vmatrix} = 0$

$$\Leftrightarrow (4 - \lambda)(3 - \lambda) - 2 = 0$$
$$\Leftrightarrow \lambda^2 - 7\lambda + 10 = 0.$$

2 Solve the characteristic equation to find the eigenvalues, λ.

$$\lambda^2 - 7\lambda + 10 = 0 \quad \Leftrightarrow \quad (\lambda - 2)(\lambda - 5) - 0$$
$$\Leftrightarrow \quad \lambda = 2 \text{ or } 5.$$

3 For each eigenvalue λ find a corresponding eigenvector $\mathbf{s}$ by solving $(\mathbf{M} - \lambda\mathbf{I})\mathbf{s} = \mathbf{0}$.

When $\lambda = 2$: $(\mathbf{M} - \lambda\mathbf{I})\mathbf{s} = \mathbf{0}$ $\Leftrightarrow$ $\begin{pmatrix} 2 & 2 \\ 1 & 1 \end{pmatrix}\begin{pmatrix} x \\ y \end{pmatrix} = \begin{pmatrix} 0 \\ 0 \end{pmatrix}$, where $\mathbf{s} = \begin{pmatrix} x \\ y \end{pmatrix}$

$\Leftrightarrow$ $x + y = 0$ ← This tells you that if y is any number, k say, then x is $-k$.

$\Leftrightarrow$ $\mathbf{s} = \begin{pmatrix} -k \\ k \end{pmatrix} = k\begin{pmatrix} -1 \\ 1 \end{pmatrix}$.

When $\lambda = 5$: $(\mathbf{M} - \lambda\mathbf{I})\mathbf{s} = \mathbf{0}$ $\Leftrightarrow$ $\begin{pmatrix} -1 & 2 \\ 1 & -2 \end{pmatrix}\begin{pmatrix} x \\ y \end{pmatrix} = \begin{pmatrix} 0 \\ 0 \end{pmatrix}$

$\Leftrightarrow$ $-x + 2y = 0$ ← If y is any number, k say, then x is $2k$.

$\Leftrightarrow$ $\mathbf{s} = \begin{pmatrix} 2k \\ k \end{pmatrix} = k\begin{pmatrix} 2 \\ 1 \end{pmatrix}$.

Thus the eigenvectors are $\begin{pmatrix} -1 \\ 1 \end{pmatrix}$ and $\begin{pmatrix} 2 \\ 1 \end{pmatrix}$ or any non-zero scalar multiples of these vectors.

Expressing vectors in terms of the eigenvectors $\mathbf{s}_1 = \begin{pmatrix} -1 \\ 1 \end{pmatrix}$ and $\mathbf{s}_2 = \begin{pmatrix} 2 \\ 1 \end{pmatrix}$ explains why the line $y = \frac{1}{2}x$ attracts and the line $y = -x$ repels under the transformation with matrix $\mathbf{M} = \begin{pmatrix} 4 & 2 \\ 1 & 3 \end{pmatrix}$. Since $\mathbf{s}_1$ and $\mathbf{s}_2$ are non-zero and non-parallel you can express any position vector $\mathbf{p}$ as $\alpha\mathbf{s}_1 + \beta\mathbf{s}_2$. Then:

$$\mathbf{M}\mathbf{p} = \mathbf{M}(\alpha\mathbf{s}_1 + \beta\mathbf{s}_2)$$
$$= \alpha\mathbf{M}\mathbf{s}_1 + \beta\mathbf{M}\mathbf{s}_2$$
$$= 2\alpha\mathbf{s}_1 + 5\beta\mathbf{s}_2$$

showing that the image of $\mathbf{p}$ is attracted towards the eigenvector with the numerically larger eigenvalue.

ACTIVITY 5.8 Express three vectors in terms of $\mathbf{s}_1$ and $\mathbf{s}_2$. Illustrate the above property by drawing an accurate diagram showing your vectors, $\mathbf{s}_1$, $\mathbf{s}_2$, and their images under the transformation given by $\mathbf{M} = \begin{pmatrix} 4 & 2 \\ 1 & 3 \end{pmatrix}$.

3×3 matrices

The definitions of eigenvalue and eigenvector apply to all square matrices. The characteristic equation of matrix $\mathbf{M}$ is $\det(\mathbf{M} - \lambda\mathbf{I}) = 0$. When $\mathbf{M}$ is a 2×2 matrix the characteristic equation is quadratic, and may or may not have real roots. When $\mathbf{M}$ is a 3×3 matrix of real elements the characteristic equation is cubic, with real coefficients; this must have at least one real root. This proves that every real 3×3 matrix has at least one real eigenvector, and so every linear transformation of three-dimensional space has at least one invariant line. You use the same procedure as before for finding the eigenvalues and eigenvectors of a 3×3 matrix, though the work will generally be lengthy.

EXAMPLE 5.6

Find the eigenvectors of the matrix $\mathbf{M} = \begin{pmatrix} 3 & 1 & 1 \\ 1 & 3 & 1 \\ 1 & 1 & 3 \end{pmatrix}$.

SOLUTION

$$\mathbf{M} - \lambda\mathbf{I} = \begin{pmatrix} 3 & 1 & 1 \\ 1 & 3 & 1 \\ 1 & 1 & 3 \end{pmatrix} - \lambda\begin{pmatrix} 1 & 0 & 0 \\ 0 & 1 & 0 \\ 0 & 0 & 1 \end{pmatrix} = \begin{pmatrix} 3-\lambda & 1 & 1 \\ 1 & 3-\lambda & 1 \\ 1 & 1 & 3-\lambda \end{pmatrix};$$

$$\det(\mathbf{M} - \lambda\mathbf{I}) = \begin{vmatrix} 3-\lambda & 1 & 1 \\ 1 & 3-\lambda & 1 \\ 1 & 1 & 3-\lambda \end{vmatrix}$$

$$= (3-\lambda)((3-\lambda)(3-\lambda) - 1) - ((3-\lambda) - 1) + (1 - (3-\lambda))$$

$$= -(\lambda^3 - 9\lambda^2 + 24\lambda - 20)$$

$$= -(\lambda - 5)(\lambda - 2)^2$$

so that $\det(\mathbf{M} - \lambda\mathbf{I}) = 0 \iff \lambda = 5$ or 2 (repeated root).

When $\lambda = 5$: $(\mathbf{M} - \lambda\mathbf{I})\mathbf{s} = \mathbf{0} \iff \begin{pmatrix} -2 & 1 & 1 \\ 1 & -2 & 1 \\ 1 & 1 & -2 \end{pmatrix}\begin{pmatrix} x \\ y \\ z \end{pmatrix} = \begin{pmatrix} 0 \\ 0 \\ 0 \end{pmatrix}$

$$\iff \left.\begin{array}{r} -2x + y + z = 0 \\ x - 2y + z = 0 \\ x + y - 2z = 0 \end{array}\right\} \iff x = y = z = k \text{ say,}$$

so that $\mathbf{s} = \begin{pmatrix} k \\ k \\ k \end{pmatrix} = k\begin{pmatrix} 1 \\ 1 \\ 1 \end{pmatrix}$ is an eigenvector, with eigenvalue 5.

When $\lambda = 2$, a repeated root:

$$(\mathbf{M} - \lambda\mathbf{I})\mathbf{s} = \mathbf{0} \iff \begin{pmatrix} 1 & 1 & 1 \\ 1 & 1 & 1 \\ 1 & 1 & 1 \end{pmatrix}\begin{pmatrix} x \\ y \\ z \end{pmatrix} = \begin{pmatrix} 0 \\ 0 \\ 0 \end{pmatrix}$$

$$\iff x + y + z = 0$$

i.e. any vector in the plane $x + y + z = 0$ is an eigenvector, with eigenvalue 2.

A general vector in that plane is $\mathbf{s} = \begin{pmatrix} p \\ q \\ -p-q \end{pmatrix}$.

Thus the eigenvectors are $k\begin{pmatrix} 1 \\ 1 \\ 1 \end{pmatrix}$ and $\begin{pmatrix} p \\ q \\ -p-q \end{pmatrix}$ where p and q are not both zero.

The ideas above also apply to larger square matrices, but if $\mathbf{M}$ is $n \times n$, its characteristic equation is of degree n, and solving polynomial equations of higher degree is generally not straightforward – Evariste Galois (1811–32) proved that there is no general formula for solving polynomial equations of degree 5 or higher. In practice eigenvalues are not usually found by solving characteristic equations! Numerical methods will usually be applied to matrices, using a computer, with consequent problems caused by approximation and rounding errors.

ACTIVITY 5.9 The 3×3 matrix $\mathbf{M}$ has three eigenvalues $\lambda_1, \lambda_2, \lambda_3$, the roots of the polynomial equation $\det(\mathbf{M} - \lambda\mathbf{I}) = 0$.

(i) Imagine factorising the polynomial $\det(\mathbf{M} - \lambda\mathbf{I})$ into linear factors, and hence show that the product of the three eigenvalues is $\det\mathbf{M}$.

(ii) By considering the coefficient of the term in λ^2 in the polynomial $\det(\mathbf{M} - \lambda\mathbf{I})$ show that the sum of the three eigenvalues is the sum of the elements on the leading diagonal of $\mathbf{M}$. This sum is known as the *trace* of matrix $\mathbf{M}$, $\mathrm{tr}(\mathbf{M})$.

These properties also hold for $n \times n$ matrices.

EXERCISE 5E

1 Find the eigenvalues and corresponding eigenvectors of these 2×2 matrices and check that the sum of the eigenvalues is the trace of the matrix.

(i) $\begin{pmatrix} 5 & 3 \\ 2 & 4 \end{pmatrix}$ (ii) $\begin{pmatrix} 7 & 2 \\ -12 & -4 \end{pmatrix}$ (iii) $\begin{pmatrix} 1 & 2 \\ 1 & 1 \end{pmatrix}$

(iv) $\begin{pmatrix} 1 & -1 \\ 1 & 3 \end{pmatrix}$ (v) $\begin{pmatrix} 1.1 & -0.4 \\ 0.2 & 0.2 \end{pmatrix}$ (vi) $\begin{pmatrix} p & 0 \\ 0 & q \end{pmatrix}, p \neq q$

2 Find the eigenvalues and corresponding eigenvectors of these 3×3 matrices and check that the sum of the eigenvalues is the trace of the matrix.

(i) $\begin{pmatrix} 3 & 0 & 0 \\ 0 & 2 & 1 \\ 0 & 0 & -1 \end{pmatrix}$ (ii) $\begin{pmatrix} 1 & 1 & 2 \\ 4 & 2 & -3 \\ 4 & 2 & 3 \end{pmatrix}$ (iii) $\begin{pmatrix} 1 & 1 & 2 \\ 5 & -2 & 1 \\ 1 & 1 & 2 \end{pmatrix}$

(iv) $\begin{pmatrix} 0 & 1 & -4 \\ -10 & 7 & -20 \\ -2 & 1 & -2 \end{pmatrix}$ (v) $\begin{pmatrix} 0 & 0 & 2 \\ 0 & 3 & 0 \\ 2 & 0 & 0 \end{pmatrix}$ (vi) $\begin{pmatrix} 1 & -3 & -3 \\ -8 & 6 & -3 \\ 8 & -2 & 7 \end{pmatrix}$

3 Matrix $\mathbf{M}$ is 2×2. Find the real eigenvalues of $\mathbf{M}$ and the corresponding eigenvectors when $\mathbf{M}$ represents

(i) reflection in $y = x\tan\theta$

(ii) a rotation through angle θ about the origin.

4 Vector $\mathbf{s}$ is an eigenvector of matrix $\mathbf{A}$, with eigenvalue α, and also an eigenvector of matrix $\mathbf{B}$, with eigenvalue β. Prove that $\mathbf{s}$ is an eigenvector of

(i) $\mathbf{A} + \mathbf{B}$ (ii) $\mathbf{AB}$

and find the corresponding eigenvalues.

[**Hint:** $\mathbf{s}$ is an eigenvector of $\mathbf{M} \Leftrightarrow \mathbf{Ms} = \lambda\mathbf{s}$, $\mathbf{s} \neq \mathbf{0}$.]

5 Matrix $\mathbf{M}$ has eigenvalue λ with corresponding eigenvector $\mathbf{s}$; k is a non-zero scalar. Prove that the matrix $k\mathbf{M}$ has eigenvalue $k\lambda$ and that $\mathbf{s}$ is a corresponding eigenvector.

6 (i) Show that $\mathbf{r} = \begin{pmatrix} -2 \\ 0 \\ 1 \end{pmatrix}$ is an eigenvector of $\mathbf{A} = \begin{pmatrix} 7 & 4 & -4 \\ 4 & 1 & 8 \\ -4 & 8 & 1 \end{pmatrix}$

and determine the corresponding eigenvalue.

(ii) State two other eigenvectors of $\mathbf{A}$ which, together with $\mathbf{r}$, give three mutually perpendicular eigenvectors and state the corresponding eigenvalues.

(iii) What is the value of det$\mathbf{A}$?

[O&C]

7 Matrix $\mathbf{M}$ is $n \times n$. For $n = 2$ and for $n = 3$ prove that if the sum of the elements in each row of $\mathbf{M}$ is 1 then 1 is an eigenvalue of $\mathbf{M}$. (This property holds for all values of n.)

8 Show that if λ is an eigenvalue of the square matrix $\mathbf{M}$ and the corresponding eigenvector is $\mathbf{s}$, then:

$$\lambda^2 \text{ is an eigenvalue of } \mathbf{M}^2$$
$$\lambda^3 \text{ is an eigenvalue of } \mathbf{M}^3$$
$$\lambda^n \text{ is an eigenvalue of } \mathbf{M}^n$$

and even: λ^{-1} is an eigenvalue of $\mathbf{M}^{-1}$.

Show further that $\mathbf{s}$ is the corresponding eigenvector in all cases.

For **(i)** $\mathbf{M} = \begin{pmatrix} 4 & -1 \\ 2 & 1 \end{pmatrix}$ **(ii)** $\mathbf{M} = \begin{pmatrix} 3 & 2 & 2 \\ 1 & 4 & 1 \\ -2 & -4 & -1 \end{pmatrix}$

find the eigenvalues of: **(a)** $\mathbf{M}$ **(b)** $\mathbf{M}^2$ **(c)** $\mathbf{M}^5$ **(d)** $\mathbf{M}^{-1}$.

9 The 2×2 matrix $\mathbf{M}$ has real eigenvalues λ_1, λ_2 and associated eigenvectors $\mathbf{s}_1, \mathbf{s}_2$, where $|\lambda_1| > |\lambda_2|$. By expressing any vector $\mathbf{v}$ in terms of $\mathbf{s}_1$ and $\mathbf{s}_2$, describe the behaviour of $\mathbf{M}^n\mathbf{v}$ as n increases when

(i) $|\lambda_1| < 1$ **(ii)** $|\lambda_1| = 1$ **(iii)** $|\lambda_1| > 1$.

10 Given $\mathbf{M} = -\mathbf{M}^{\mathrm{T}}$, where $\mathbf{M}$ is a 3×3 matrix, prove that

$$\det(\mathbf{M} - k\mathbf{I}) = -\det(\mathbf{M} + k\mathbf{I}).$$

Deduce that if λ is a non-zero eigenvalue of $\mathbf{M}$ then $-\lambda$ is also an eigenvalue of $\mathbf{M}$.

(Such matrices are called *skew-symmetric*.)

11 The self-drive camper-van hire firm DIY has depots at Calgary and Vancouver. The hire period commences on Saturday afternoon, and all vans are returned (to either depot) the following Saturday morning. Each week:

- all DIY's vans are hired out
- of the vans hired in Calgary, 50% are returned there, 50% to Vancouver
- of the vans hired in Vancouver, 70% are returned there, 30% to Calgary.

(i) One Saturday the Calgary depot has c vans and the Vancouver depot has v vans. Form matrix $\mathbf{M}$ so that the product $\mathbf{M}\begin{pmatrix} c \\ v \end{pmatrix}$ gives the number of vans in each depot the following Saturday.

(ii) At the start of the season each depot has 100 vans. Use matrix multiplication to find out how many vans will be at each depot two weeks later.

(iii) Solve the equation $\mathbf{Mx} = \mathbf{x}$ where $\mathbf{x} = \begin{pmatrix} c \\ v \end{pmatrix}$ and explain the connection with eigenvalues.

(iv) How many vans should DIY stock at Calgary and Vancouver if they want the number of vans available at those depots to remain constant?

(The process described above is an example of a *Markov process*. The matrix governing it is a *transition* or *stochastic matrix*. Each column of the transition matrix consists of non-negative elements with a sum of 1.)

⚠ When used in statistics an alternative notation is often used in which a state is represented by a row vector and is post-multiplied by the transition matrix. In that convention the transition matrix is transposed.

---

12 At time t, the rabbit and wolf populations (r and w respectively) on a certain island are described by the differential equations:

$$\begin{cases} \dfrac{dr}{dt} = 5r - 3w \\[2mm] \dfrac{dw}{dt} = r + w \end{cases} \qquad \text{①}$$

Throughout this question $\mathbf{p}$ represents $\begin{pmatrix} r \\ w \end{pmatrix}$ and $\mathbf{M}$ represents $\begin{pmatrix} 5 & -3 \\ 1 & 1 \end{pmatrix}$.

(i) Show that the differential equations may be written as:

$$\frac{d\mathbf{p}}{dt} = \mathbf{Mp}. \qquad \text{②}$$

(ii) Show that if $\mathbf{p} = \mathbf{p}_1(t)$ and $\mathbf{p} = \mathbf{p}_2(t)$ satisfy ② then $\mathbf{p} = a\mathbf{p}_1(t) + b\mathbf{p}_2(t)$ also satisfies ②, where a and b are constants.

(iii) Show that if $\mathbf{p} = e^{\lambda t}\mathbf{k}$ satisfies ②, where $\mathbf{k}$ is constant, then $\mathbf{Mk} = \lambda\mathbf{k}$.

(iv) Find the eigenvalues and eigenvectors of $\mathbf{M}$ and hence solve ① given that there are 1000 rabbits and 50 wolves at $t = 0$.

13 The number k is (numerically) the largest of the eigenvalues of 3×3 matrix
☆ **M**, and **s** is a corresponding eigenvector; $\mathbf{v}_0$ is an arbitrary vector, and
☆ $\mathbf{v}_n = \mathbf{M}^n\mathbf{v}_0$ has components x_n, y_n and z_n.
☆
☆ **(i)** Explain why, as n increases, $\mathbf{v}_n$ generally converges on a multiple of **s**
☆ and identify the occasions when this does not happen.
☆ **(ii)** What do you expect to notice about $\dfrac{x_n}{x_{n-1}}, \dfrac{y_n}{y_{n-1}}$ and $\dfrac{z_n}{z_{n-1}}$ as n increases?

Evaluating powers of square matrices

Pre-multiplying position vector **r** by a matrix **M** gives $\mathbf{r}'$, the position
vector of R′, the image of R under the transformation represented by **M**. If you
apply the same transformation to R′ you get R″, with position vector
$\mathbf{r}'' = \mathbf{M}(\mathbf{Mr}) = \mathbf{M}^2\mathbf{r}$. Higher powers of **M** arise if you continue to apply the
same transformation. In this section you will learn to use eigenvalues and
eigenvectors to evaluate powers of matrices.

The two statements $\begin{pmatrix} 4 & 2 \\ 1 & 3 \end{pmatrix}\begin{pmatrix} -1 \\ 1 \end{pmatrix} = \begin{pmatrix} -2 \\ 2 \end{pmatrix} = 2\begin{pmatrix} -1 \\ 1 \end{pmatrix}$

and $\begin{pmatrix} 4 & 2 \\ 1 & 3 \end{pmatrix}\begin{pmatrix} 2 \\ 1 \end{pmatrix} = \begin{pmatrix} 10 \\ 5 \end{pmatrix} = 5\begin{pmatrix} 2 \\ 1 \end{pmatrix}$

> The eigenvalues and eigenvectors of $\begin{pmatrix} 4 & 2 \\ 1 & 3 \end{pmatrix}$ were found on page 107.

can be combined into the single statement:

$$\begin{pmatrix} 4 & 2 \\ 1 & 3 \end{pmatrix}\begin{pmatrix} -1 & 2 \\ 1 & 1 \end{pmatrix} = \begin{pmatrix} -1 & 2 \\ 1 & 1 \end{pmatrix}\begin{pmatrix} 2 & 0 \\ 0 & 5 \end{pmatrix}$$

which you may write as $\mathbf{MS} = \mathbf{S\Lambda}$

where $\mathbf{M} = \begin{pmatrix} 4 & 2 \\ 1 & 3 \end{pmatrix}, \mathbf{S} = \begin{pmatrix} -1 & 2 \\ 1 & 1 \end{pmatrix}$ and $\mathbf{\Lambda} = \begin{pmatrix} 2 & 0 \\ 0 & 5 \end{pmatrix}$.

$\mathbf{\Lambda}$ is the Greek capital letter lambda.

In just the same way if any 2×2 matrix has eigenvectors $\mathbf{s}_1, \mathbf{s}_2$, corresponding to
eigenvalues λ_1, λ_2, then $\mathbf{Ms}_1 = \lambda_1\mathbf{s}_1$ and $\mathbf{Ms}_2 = \lambda_2\mathbf{s}_2$ so that $\mathbf{MS} = \mathbf{S\Lambda}$, where
$\mathbf{S} = (\mathbf{s}_1 \quad \mathbf{s}_2)$, the 2×2 matrix which has the eigenvectors as columns, and
$\mathbf{\Lambda} = \begin{pmatrix} \lambda_1 & 0 \\ 0 & \lambda_2 \end{pmatrix}$, a matrix with the corresponding eigenvalues on the leading
diagonal and zeros elsewhere.

If **S** is non-singular, $\mathbf{S}^{-1}$ exists, and pre-multiplying $\mathbf{MS} = \mathbf{S\Lambda}$ by $\mathbf{S}^{-1}$ gives
$\mathbf{S}^{-1}\mathbf{MS} = \mathbf{\Lambda}$; you then say that **M** has been *reduced to diagonal form* or that **M**
has been *diagonalised*.

Although there are square matrices which cannot be reduced to diagonal form,
being able to reduce **M** to diagonal form $\mathbf{\Lambda}$ helps if you want to raise **M** to a
power. Post-multiplying $\mathbf{MS} = \mathbf{S\Lambda}$ by $\mathbf{S}^{-1}$ gives $\mathbf{M} = \mathbf{S\Lambda S}^{-1}$

so that

$$\begin{aligned} \mathbf{M}^4 &= (\mathbf{S}\boldsymbol{\Lambda}\mathbf{S}^{-1})(\mathbf{S}\boldsymbol{\Lambda}\mathbf{S}^{-1})(\mathbf{S}\boldsymbol{\Lambda}\mathbf{S}^{-1})(\mathbf{S}\boldsymbol{\Lambda}\mathbf{S}^{-1}) \\ &= \mathbf{S}\boldsymbol{\Lambda}(\mathbf{S}^{-1}\mathbf{S})\boldsymbol{\Lambda}(\mathbf{S}^{-1}\mathbf{S})\boldsymbol{\Lambda}(\mathbf{S}^{-1}\mathbf{S})\boldsymbol{\Lambda}\mathbf{S}^{-1} \\ &= \mathbf{S}\boldsymbol{\Lambda}^4\mathbf{S}^{-1}. \end{aligned}$$

> This simplification makes extensive use of the associate property of matrix multiplication together with properties of inverse identities.

Similarly: $\mathbf{M}^n = \mathbf{S}\boldsymbol{\Lambda}^n\mathbf{S}^{-1}$, which can be proved formally by induction.

Since $\boldsymbol{\Lambda} = \begin{pmatrix} \lambda_1 & 0 \\ 0 & \lambda_2 \end{pmatrix}$, $\boldsymbol{\Lambda}^n = \begin{pmatrix} \lambda_1^n & 0 \\ 0 & \lambda_2^n \end{pmatrix}$ and you can evaluate $\mathbf{M}^n$ readily, doing only two matrix multiplications whatever the value of n.

EXAMPLE 5.7

Find $\mathbf{M}^n$ where $\mathbf{M} = \begin{pmatrix} 4 & 2 \\ 1 & 3 \end{pmatrix}$.

SOLUTION

You have already seen that $\begin{pmatrix} -1 \\ 1 \end{pmatrix}$ and $\begin{pmatrix} 2 \\ 1 \end{pmatrix}$ are eigenvectors, with eigenvalues

2 and 5 respectively, so take $\mathbf{S} = \begin{pmatrix} -1 & 2 \\ 1 & 1 \end{pmatrix}$ and $\boldsymbol{\Lambda} = \begin{pmatrix} 2 & 0 \\ 0 & 5 \end{pmatrix}$.

Then $\mathbf{S}^{-1} = \begin{pmatrix} -\frac{1}{3} & \frac{2}{3} \\ \frac{1}{3} & \frac{1}{3} \end{pmatrix}$ and $\boldsymbol{\Lambda}^n = \begin{pmatrix} 2^n & 0 \\ 0 & 5^n \end{pmatrix}$.

> You could use any non-zero multiples of $\begin{pmatrix} -1 \\ 1 \end{pmatrix}, \begin{pmatrix} 2 \\ 1 \end{pmatrix}$ but these are the simplest.

Therefore $\mathbf{M}^n = \mathbf{S}\boldsymbol{\Lambda}^n\mathbf{S}^{-1} = \begin{pmatrix} -1 & 2 \\ 1 & 1 \end{pmatrix}\begin{pmatrix} 2^n & 0 \\ 0 & 5^n \end{pmatrix}\begin{pmatrix} -\frac{1}{3} & \frac{2}{3} \\ \frac{1}{3} & \frac{1}{3} \end{pmatrix}$

$$= \frac{1}{3}\begin{pmatrix} 2 \times 5^n + 2^n & 2 \times 5^n - 2^{n+1} \\ 5^n - 2^n & 5^n + 2^{n+1} \end{pmatrix}.$$

Again the work with 3×3 and other square matrices follows the same pattern, though the calculations are more complicated.

The Cayley–Hamilton theorem

You have already seen that the characteristic equation for the matrix

$$\mathbf{M} = \begin{pmatrix} 4 & 2 \\ 1 & 3 \end{pmatrix} \text{ is } \det(\mathbf{M} - \lambda\mathbf{I}) = 0 \quad \Leftrightarrow \quad \begin{vmatrix} 4-\lambda & 2 \\ 1 & 3-\lambda \end{vmatrix} = 0$$

$$\Leftrightarrow \quad (4-\lambda)(3-\lambda) - 2 = 0$$

$$\Leftrightarrow \quad 10 - 7\lambda + \lambda^2 = 0.$$

Notice that $\mathbf{M}^2 = \begin{pmatrix} 4 & 2 \\ 1 & 3 \end{pmatrix} \begin{pmatrix} 4 & 2 \\ 1 & 3 \end{pmatrix} = \begin{pmatrix} 18 & 14 \\ 7 & 11 \end{pmatrix}$ and that

$$10\mathbf{I} - 7\mathbf{M} + \mathbf{M}^2 = 10\begin{pmatrix} 1 & 0 \\ 0 & 1 \end{pmatrix} - 7\begin{pmatrix} 4 & 2 \\ 1 & 3 \end{pmatrix} + \begin{pmatrix} 18 & 14 \\ 7 & 11 \end{pmatrix} = \begin{pmatrix} 0 & 0 \\ 0 & 0 \end{pmatrix}$$

so that $10\mathbf{I} - 7\mathbf{M} + \mathbf{M}^2 = \mathbf{O}$, the zero matrix.

This illustrates the *Cayley–Hamilton theorem* which states:

'Every square matrix $\mathbf{M}$ satisfies its own characteristic equation.'

Note that $\mathbf{I}$ and $\mathbf{O}$ have to be inserted appropriately so that the equation makes sense.

You can readily prove this result for the general 2×2 matrix by direct multiplication, but the proof below, though written for 3×3 matrices, shows a style of argument that can be applied to all other square matrices.

When $\mathbf{M}$ is 3×3, notice that $\det(\mathbf{M} - \lambda\mathbf{I}) = \begin{vmatrix} a_1 - \lambda & b_1 & c_1 \\ a_2 & b_2 - \lambda & c_2 \\ a_3 & b_3 & c_3 - \lambda \end{vmatrix}$ which

may be written as $d_0 + d_1\lambda + d_2\lambda^2 - \lambda^3$ where d_0, d_1, d_2 are independent of λ. Then the characteristic equation is

$$d_0 + d_1\lambda + d_2\lambda^2 - \lambda^3 = 0$$

and the Cayley–Hamilton theorem states that

$$d_0\mathbf{I} + d_1\mathbf{M} + d_2\mathbf{M}^2 - \mathbf{M}^3 = \mathbf{O}.$$

Since the elements of the 3×3 matrix $\text{adj}(\mathbf{M} - \lambda\mathbf{I})$ are 2×2 determinants, each element of $\text{adj}(\mathbf{M} - \lambda\mathbf{I})$ is (at most) quadratic in λ. You can therefore write

$$\text{adj}(\mathbf{M} - \lambda\mathbf{I}) = \mathbf{A}_0 + \lambda\mathbf{A}_1 + \lambda^2\mathbf{A}_2$$

where $\mathbf{A}_0, \mathbf{A}_1$ and $\mathbf{A}_2$ are 3×3 matrices with elements that are independent of λ. On page 94 it was proved that $\mathbf{M}^{-1} = \dfrac{1}{\det\mathbf{M}} \text{adj}\mathbf{M}$ for $\det\mathbf{M} \neq 0$, from which it follows that:

$$\mathbf{M}(\text{adj}\mathbf{M}) = (\det\mathbf{M})\mathbf{I}.$$

> This is also true when $\det\mathbf{M} = 0$ (see Exercise 5C, Question 10).

Substituting $(\mathbf{M} - \lambda\mathbf{I})$ for $\mathbf{M}$ gives:

$$(\mathbf{M} - \lambda\mathbf{I})\text{adj}(\mathbf{M} - \lambda\mathbf{I}) = \det(\mathbf{M} - \lambda\mathbf{I})\mathbf{I}$$
$$= (d_0 + d_1\lambda + d_2\lambda^2 - \lambda^3)\mathbf{I};$$

therefore $\quad (\mathbf{M} - \lambda\mathbf{I})(\mathbf{A}_0 + \lambda\mathbf{A}_1 + \lambda^2\mathbf{A}_2) = (d_0 + d_1\lambda + d_2\lambda^2 - \lambda^3)\mathbf{I}$

$\Rightarrow \quad \mathbf{M}\mathbf{A}_0 + \lambda(\mathbf{M}\mathbf{A}_1 - \mathbf{A}_0) + \lambda^2(\mathbf{M}\mathbf{A}_2 - \mathbf{A}_1) - \lambda^3\mathbf{A}_2 = (d_0 + d_1\lambda + d_2\lambda^2 - \lambda^3)\mathbf{I}$

$$\Rightarrow \begin{cases} \mathbf{M}\mathbf{A}_0 = d_0\mathbf{I} \\ \mathbf{M}\mathbf{A}_1 - \mathbf{A}_0 = d_1\mathbf{I} \\ \mathbf{M}\mathbf{A}_2 - \mathbf{A}_1 = d_2\mathbf{I} \\ -\mathbf{A}_2 = -\mathbf{I} \end{cases} \text{so that} \begin{cases} d_0\mathbf{I} = \mathbf{M}\mathbf{A}_0 \\ d_1\mathbf{M} = \mathbf{M}^2\mathbf{A}_1 - \mathbf{M}\mathbf{A}_0 \\ d_2\mathbf{M}^2 = \mathbf{M}^3\mathbf{A}_2 - \mathbf{M}^2\mathbf{A}_1 \\ -\mathbf{M}^3 = -\mathbf{M}^3\mathbf{A}_2 \end{cases}$$

and adding these four results gives $d_0\mathbf{I} + d_1\mathbf{M} + d_2\mathbf{M}^2 - \mathbf{M}^3 = \mathbf{O}$ confirming that $\mathbf{M}$ satisfies its own characteristic equation.

EXAMPLE 5.8

Given $\mathbf{M} = \begin{pmatrix} 4 & 2 \\ 1 & 3 \end{pmatrix}$ use the Cayley–Hamilton theorem to find $\mathbf{M}^8$.

SOLUTION

As before, the characteristic equation is $10 - 7\lambda + \lambda^2 = 0$. By the Cayley–Hamilton theorem:

$$10\mathbf{I} - 7\mathbf{M} + \mathbf{M}^2 = \mathbf{O}$$
$$\Rightarrow \mathbf{M}^2 = 7\mathbf{M} - 10\mathbf{I}$$
$$\Rightarrow \mathbf{M}^4 = (7\mathbf{M} - 10\mathbf{I})^2$$
$$= 49\mathbf{M}^2 - 140\mathbf{M} + 100\mathbf{I}$$
$$= 49(7\mathbf{M} - 10\mathbf{I}) - 140\mathbf{M} + 100\mathbf{I}$$
$$= 203\mathbf{M} - 390\mathbf{I}$$

$$\Rightarrow \mathbf{M}^8 = (203\mathbf{M} - 390\mathbf{I})^2$$
$$= 41\,209\mathbf{M}^2 - 158\,340\mathbf{M} + 152\,100\mathbf{I}$$
$$= 41\,209(7\mathbf{M} - 10\mathbf{I}) - 158\,340\mathbf{M} + 152\,100\mathbf{I}$$
$$= 130\,123\mathbf{M} - 259\,990\mathbf{I}.$$

Thus $\mathbf{M}^8 = 130\,123\begin{pmatrix} 4 & 2 \\ 1 & 3 \end{pmatrix} - 259\,990\begin{pmatrix} 1 & 0 \\ 0 & 1 \end{pmatrix} = \begin{pmatrix} 260\,502 & 260\,246 \\ 130\,123 & 130\,379 \end{pmatrix}$.

(Check this against $\mathbf{M}^n = \dfrac{1}{3}\begin{pmatrix} 2 \times 5^n + 2^n & 2 \times 5^n - 2^{n+1} \\ 5^n - 2^n & 5^n + 2^{n+1} \end{pmatrix}$ with $n = 8$. See Example 5.7.)

ACTIVITY 5.10

Use the Cayley–Hamilton theorem to show that:

$$\mathbf{M} = \begin{pmatrix} 5 & 2 \\ 3 & 3 \end{pmatrix} \quad \Rightarrow \quad \mathbf{M}^{n+2} = 8\mathbf{M}^{n+1} - 9\mathbf{M}^n.$$

This expression, giving $\mathbf{M}^{n+2}$ in terms of $\mathbf{M}^{n+1}$ and $\mathbf{M}^n$, is an example of a *recurrence relation*.

? The Cayley–Hamilton theorem states that a matrix $\mathbf{M}$ satisfies its own characteristic equation. The characteristic equation may be written as $\det(\mathbf{M} - \lambda\mathbf{I}) = 0$. Replacing λ by $\mathbf{M}$ produces a determinant consisting entirely of zeros. Is this sufficient proof of the theorem?

Historical note

The Cayley–Hamilton theorem was first announced by Arthur Cayley in '*A Memoir on the Theory of Matrices*' in 1858, in which he proved the theorem for 2×2 matrices and checked it for 3×3 matrices. Amazingly he went on to say, 'I have not thought it necessary to undertake the labour of a formal proof of the theorem in the general case of a matrix of any degree.' Essentially the same property was contained in Sir William Hamilton's '*Lectures on Quaternions*' in 1853, with a proof covering 4×4 matrices. The name 'characteristic equation' is attributed to Augustin Louis Cauchy (1789–1857), and the first general proof of the theorem was supplied in 1878 by Georg Frobenius (1849–1917), complete with modifications to take account of the problems caused by repeated eigenvalues.

EXERCISE 5F

1 Find matrices **S** and **Λ** such that $\mathbf{M} = \mathbf{S\Lambda S}^{-1}$.

(i) $\mathbf{M} = \begin{pmatrix} 5 & 4 \\ 3 & 6 \end{pmatrix}$

(ii) $\mathbf{M} = \begin{pmatrix} 7 & -10 \\ 3 & -4 \end{pmatrix}$

(iii) $\mathbf{M} = \begin{pmatrix} 0.5 & 0.5 \\ 0.3 & 0.7 \end{pmatrix}$

2 Express $\mathbf{M} = \begin{pmatrix} 1.9 & -1.5 \\ 0.6 & 0 \end{pmatrix}$ in the form $\mathbf{S\Lambda S}^{-1}$ and hence find $\mathbf{M}^4$. What can you say about $\mathbf{M}^n$ when n is very large?

3 Calculate the following.

(i) $\begin{pmatrix} 6 & -6 \\ 2 & -1 \end{pmatrix}^5$

(ii) $\begin{pmatrix} 3 & -1 \\ -1 & 3 \end{pmatrix}^{10}$

(iii) $\begin{pmatrix} 0.7 & 0.3 \\ 0.6 & 0.4 \end{pmatrix}^4$

4 Find examples of 2×2 matrices to illustrate the following.

(i) **M** has repeated eigenvalues and cannot be diagonalised.
(ii) **M** has repeated eigenvalues and can be diagonalised.
(iii) **M** has 0 as an eigenvalue and cannot be diagonalised.
(iv) **M** has 0 as an eigenvalue and can be diagonalised.

5 Demonstrate that $\begin{pmatrix} 1 & 2 \\ -1 & 4 \end{pmatrix}$ satisfies its own characteristic equation.

6 Prove the Cayley–Hamilton theorem for $\mathbf{M} = \begin{pmatrix} a & c \\ b & d \end{pmatrix}$ by calculating $\mathbf{M}^2$ and substituting directly into the characteristic equation.

7 You are given the matrix $\mathbf{M} = \begin{pmatrix} k & 3 \\ 0 & 2 \end{pmatrix}$, where $k \neq 2$.

   (i)   Find the eigenvalues of $\mathbf{M}$, and the corresponding eigenvectors.
   (ii) Write down a matrix $\mathbf{P}$ for which $\mathbf{P}^{-1}\mathbf{MP}$ is a diagonal matrix.
   (iii) Hence find the matrix $\mathbf{M}^n$.
   (iv) For the case $k = 1$, use the Cayley–Hamilton theorem to find integers p and q such that

$$\mathbf{M}^9 = p\mathbf{M}^8 + q\mathbf{M}^7.$$

[MEI]

8 You are given the matrix $\mathbf{M} = \begin{pmatrix} 0 & -1 & 1 \\ 6 & -2 & 6 \\ 4 & 1 & 3 \end{pmatrix}$.

   (i)   Show that -2 and -1 are eigenvalues of $\mathbf{M}$, and find the other eigenvalue.
   (ii) Show that $\begin{pmatrix} 1 \\ 1 \\ -1 \end{pmatrix}$ is an eigenvector corresponding to the eigenvalue -2, and find an eigenvector corresponding to the eigenvalue -1.
   (iii) Using the Cayley–Hamilton theorem, or otherwise:
         (a) show that $\mathbf{M}^4 = 11\mathbf{M}^2 + 18\mathbf{M} + 8\mathbf{I}$
         (b) find the values of p, q and r such that $\mathbf{M}^{-1} = p\mathbf{M}^2 + q\mathbf{M} + r\mathbf{I}$.
   (iv) Evaluate $\mathbf{M}^{-1} \begin{pmatrix} 1 \\ 1 \\ -1 \end{pmatrix}$.

[MEI]

9 Show that $\begin{pmatrix} 1 \\ 1 \\ 0 \end{pmatrix}$ is an eigenvector of $\mathbf{M} = \begin{pmatrix} 1 & 4 & -1 \\ -1 & 6 & -1 \\ 2 & -2 & 4 \end{pmatrix}$ and state the corresponding eigenvalue. By finding the other eigenvalues and their eigenvectors express $\mathbf{M}$ in the form $\mathbf{S\Lambda S}^{-1}$.

10 You are given the matrix $\mathbf{A} = \begin{pmatrix} 3 & 1 & -2 \\ 2 & 4 & -4 \\ 2 & 1 & -1 \end{pmatrix}$.

   (i)   Show that 1 is an eigenvalue of $\mathbf{A}$, and find the other two eigenvalues.
   (ii) Find an eigenvector corresponding to the eigenvalue 1.
   (iii) Using the Cayley–Hamilton theorem, or otherwise, find integers p, q and r such that

$$\mathbf{A}^3 = p\mathbf{A}^2 + q\mathbf{A} + r\mathbf{I},$$

and show that

$$\mathbf{A}^4 = 25\mathbf{A}^2 - 60\mathbf{A} + 36\mathbf{I}.$$

[MEI]

11 A matrix $\mathbf{M}$ is given by $\mathbf{M} = \begin{pmatrix} -1 & -1 & 1 \\ 6 & 2 & k \\ 0 & -2 & 1 \end{pmatrix}$.

(i) Find, in terms of k,

  (a) the determinant of $\mathbf{M}$

  (b) the inverse matrix $\mathbf{M}^{-1}$.

One of the eigenvalues of $\mathbf{M}$ is 2.

(ii) Find the value of k, and show that the other two eigenvalues are 1 and -1.

(iii) Find integers p, q and r such that $\mathbf{M}^2 = p\mathbf{M} + q\mathbf{I} + r\mathbf{M}^{-1}$.

(iv) Show that $\mathbf{M}^4 = 10\mathbf{M} + \mathbf{I} - 10\mathbf{M}^{-1}$.

[MEI]

12 You are given the matrix $\mathbf{M} = \begin{pmatrix} -2 & -5 \\ 3 & 6 \end{pmatrix}$.

(i) Show that 3 is an eigenvalue of $\mathbf{M}$, and find the other eigenvalue.

(ii) For each eigenvalue, find a corresponding eigenvector.

(iii) Write down a matrix $\mathbf{P}$ such that $\mathbf{P}^{-1}\mathbf{M}\mathbf{P}$ is a diagonal matrix.

(iv) Hence show that $\mathbf{M}^n = \dfrac{1}{2}\begin{pmatrix} 5 - 3^{n+1} & 5 - 5 \times 3^n \\ -3 + 3^{n+1} & -3 + 5 \times 3^n \end{pmatrix}$.

[MEI]

13 The Fibonacci sequence $1, 1, 2, 3, \ldots$ is defined by

$$f_1 = f_2 = 1, f_{n+1} = f_n + f_{n-1}. \text{ Let } \mathbf{u}_n = \begin{pmatrix} f_{n+1} \\ f_n \end{pmatrix}.$$

(i) Show that $\mathbf{u}_{n+1} = \mathbf{M}\mathbf{u}_n$ where $\mathbf{M} = \begin{pmatrix} 1 & 1 \\ 1 & 0 \end{pmatrix}$.

(ii) Show that the eigenvalues of $\mathbf{M}$ are $\lambda_1 = \frac{1}{2}(1 + \sqrt{5})$, $\lambda_2 = \frac{1}{2}(1 - \sqrt{5})$, with associated eigenvectors $\begin{pmatrix} \lambda_1 \\ 1 \end{pmatrix}, \begin{pmatrix} \lambda_2 \\ 1 \end{pmatrix}$.

(iii) Deduce that $\mathbf{M} = \dfrac{1}{\lambda_1 - \lambda_2}\begin{pmatrix} \lambda_1 & \lambda_2 \\ 1 & 1 \end{pmatrix}\begin{pmatrix} \lambda_1 & 0 \\ 0 & \lambda_2 \end{pmatrix}\begin{pmatrix} 1 & -\lambda_2 \\ -1 & \lambda_1 \end{pmatrix}$ and

hence show that $f_n = \dfrac{1}{\sqrt{5}}\left(\left(\dfrac{1 + \sqrt{5}}{2}\right)^n - \left(\dfrac{1 - \sqrt{5}}{2}\right)^n\right)$.

14 (i) $\mathbf{A}$ and $\mathbf{B}$ are 2×2 matrices with eigenvalues α_1, α_2 and β_1, β_2 respectively. Are the eigenvalues of the product $\mathbf{AB}$ the products of the eigenvalues of $\mathbf{A}$ and $\mathbf{B}$? Justify your answer.

(ii) Find the fallacy in this 'proof'.

$\mathbf{A}$ has eigenvalue λ and $\mathbf{B}$ has eigenvalue μ

$\Rightarrow \mathbf{ABs} = \mathbf{A}\mu\mathbf{s}$

$\Rightarrow \mathbf{ABs} = \mu\mathbf{As}$

$\Rightarrow \mathbf{ABs} = \mu\lambda\mathbf{s}$

$\Rightarrow \mathbf{AB}$ has eigenvalue $\lambda\mu$.

15 Matrix **M** is $n \times n$. Matrix **S** is such that **MS** = **SD**, where **D** is a diagonal matrix with $\lambda_1, \lambda_2, \dots \lambda_n$ on the leading diagonal and zeros elsewhere. Suppose the first column of **S** is $\mathbf{s}_1$. By considering the first columns of the products **SD** and **MS** show that λ_1 is an eigenvalue of **M** and that $\mathbf{s}_1$ is a corresponding eigenvector.

(Similar arguments apply to the other columns of **S** and $\lambda_2, \lambda_3, \dots \lambda_n$ showing that when searching for **S** and **D** such that $\mathbf{M} = \mathbf{SDS}^{-1}$ where **D** is diagonal, the leading diagonal of **D** is composed of eigenvalues, and **S** is composed of corresponding eigenvectors in the correct order.)

16 As usual $\mathbf{s}_1, \mathbf{s}_2$ and $\mathbf{s}_3$ are eigenvectors corresponding to distinct eigenvalues λ_1, λ_2 and λ_3 of the 3×3 matrix **M**, and **S** is the matrix $(\mathbf{s}_1 \quad \mathbf{s}_2 \quad \mathbf{s}_3)$.

(i) By pre-multiplying $a\mathbf{s}_1 + b\mathbf{s}_2 = \mathbf{0}$ by **M** show that $\mathbf{s}_1$ cannot be parallel to $\mathbf{s}_2$.

(ii) Extend the argument to show that $\mathbf{s}_1, \mathbf{s}_2$ and $\mathbf{s}_3$ cannot be coplanar.

(iii) Show that **S** is non-singular and deduce that **M** can be diagonalised.

(All $n \times n$ matrices with n distinct eigenvalues can be diagonalised.)

17 The 3×3 matrix **A** is said to be *similar* to the 3×3 matrix **B** if a non-singular matrix **P** exists such that $\mathbf{A} = \mathbf{P}^{-1}\mathbf{BP}$.

(i) Prove that every 3×3 matrix is similar to itself.

(ii) Prove that **A** is similar to **B** $\Rightarrow$ **B** is similar to **A**.

(iii) Prove that if **A** is similar to **B** and **B** is similar to **C** then **A** is similar to **C**.

(iv) Prove that similar matrices have the same characteristic equation and deduce that similar matrices have the same eigenvalues.

18 The *trace* of matrix **A** is $\mathrm{tr}(\mathbf{A})$, defined as the sum of the elements on the leading diagonal of **A**. For 3×3 matrices prove that:

(i) $\mathrm{tr}(\mathbf{A} + \mathbf{B}) = \mathrm{tr}(\mathbf{A}) + \mathrm{tr}(\mathbf{B})$

(ii) $\mathrm{tr}(k\mathbf{A}) = k\mathrm{tr}(\mathbf{A})$, where k is a scalar

(iii) $\mathrm{tr}(\mathbf{AB}) = \mathrm{tr}(\mathbf{BA})$

(iv) if there exists a non-singular matrix **P** such that

$$\mathbf{P}^{-1}\mathbf{AP} = \begin{pmatrix} \alpha & 0 & 0 \\ 0 & \beta & 0 \\ 0 & 0 & \gamma \end{pmatrix} \text{ then } \mathrm{tr}(\mathbf{A}) = \alpha + \beta + \gamma$$

(v) $\mathrm{tr}(\mathbf{A})$ is the sum of the three eigenvalues of **A**.

19 Matrices **A** and **B** can be diagonalised. Assuming neither matrix has repeated eigenvalues, show that:

A and **B** share the same eigenvectors $\Leftrightarrow$ **AB** = **BA**.

(This result, useful in quantum mechanics, also holds if eigenvalues are repeated.)

20 A *non-negative* matrix is one which contains no negative elements. In this question, λ_1 is the numerically larger eigenvalue of non-negative 2×2 matrix **M**.

(i) Prove that λ_1 is positive.

(ii) By considering $(\mathbf{I} - \mathbf{M})(\mathbf{I} + \mathbf{M} + \mathbf{M}^2 + \mathbf{M}^3 + \ldots + \mathbf{M}^n)$ show that if $\lambda_1 < 1$ then $(\mathbf{I} - \mathbf{M})^{-1} = \mathbf{I} + \mathbf{M} + \mathbf{M}^2 + \mathbf{M}^3 + \ldots$ and deduce that $(\mathbf{I} - \mathbf{M})^{-1}$ is non-negative.

(All non-negative matrices exhibit similar properties. They are important when applying mathematical models to economics.)

INVESTIGATION

Using a computer, investigate how to find the inverses of matrices.

1 Program a spreadsheet to find the inverses of:

(i) 3×3 matrices without using the spreadsheet's built-in functions
(ii) matrices using the spreadsheet's built-in functions.

2 Find out how to use a computer algebra system to invert matrices.

1 $\mathbf{M} = \begin{pmatrix} a_1 & b_1 & c_1 \\ a_2 & b_2 & c_2 \\ a_3 & b_3 & c_3 \end{pmatrix} \Rightarrow \det\mathbf{M} = \Delta = |\mathbf{M}| = a_1 A_1 + a_2 A_2 + a_3 A_3$

$$\text{adj}\mathbf{M} = \begin{pmatrix} A_1 & A_2 & A_3 \\ B_1 & B_2 & B_3 \\ C_1 & C_2 & C_3 \end{pmatrix}$$

and $\mathbf{M}^{-1} = \dfrac{1}{\det\mathbf{M}}\,\text{adj}\mathbf{M}$, provided $\det\mathbf{M} \neq 0$,

where A_3 = the cofactor of $a_3 = +\begin{vmatrix} b_1 & c_1 \\ b_2 & c_2 \end{vmatrix} = b_1 c_2 - b_2 c_1$,

C_2 = the cofactor of $c_2 = -\begin{vmatrix} a_1 & b_1 \\ a_3 & b_3 \end{vmatrix} = -(a_1 b_3 - a_3 b_1)$, etc.

2 $\det(\mathbf{MN}) = \det\mathbf{M} \times \det\mathbf{N}$ provided $\mathbf{M}$ and $\mathbf{N}$ are both $n \times n$.

3 $(\mathbf{MN})^{-1} = \mathbf{N}^{-1}\mathbf{M}^{-1}$, provided both $\mathbf{M}$ and $\mathbf{N}$ are $n \times n$ and non-singular.

4 $(\mathbf{MN})^{\mathrm{T}} = \mathbf{N}^{\mathrm{T}}\mathbf{M}^{\mathrm{T}}$, provided $\mathbf{M}$ is $m \times n$ and $\mathbf{N}$ is $n \times p$.

5 When solving n simultaneous equations in n unknowns:
   - if $\det\mathbf{M} = 0$, there is a unique solution
   - if $\det\mathbf{M} \neq 0$, either there is no solution or there are infinitely many solutions.

6 An *eigenvector* of square matrix $\mathbf{M}$ is a non-zero vector $\mathbf{s}$ such that $\mathbf{Ms} = \lambda\mathbf{s}$; the scalar λ is the corresponding *eigenvalue*.

7 The characteristic equation of $\mathbf{M}$ is $\det(\mathbf{M} - \lambda\mathbf{I}) = 0$.

8 If $\mathbf{S}$ is the matrix formed of the eigenvectors of $\mathbf{M}$ and $\mathbf{\Lambda}$ is the diagonal matrix formed of the corresponding eigenvalues then

$$\mathbf{MS} = \mathbf{S\Lambda}, \mathbf{\Lambda} = \mathbf{S}^{-1}\mathbf{MS}, \mathbf{M}^n = \mathbf{S\Lambda}^n\mathbf{S}^{-1}.$$

9 The Cayley–Hamilton theorem states:

'Every square matrix $\mathbf{M}$ satisfies its own characteristic equation.'

6 Hyperbolic functions

Just as much as it is easy to find the differential of a given quantity, so it is difficult to find the integral of a given differential. Moreover, sometimes we cannot say with certainty whether the integral of a given quantity can be found or not.

John Bernoulli, 1667–1748

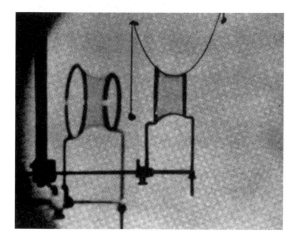

The soap bubble between two rings on the left casts a shadow which coincides with the hanging chain, showing that both form the same curve – a catenary.

The hyperbolic cosine and hyperbolic sine functions

The cosine and sine functions are called *circular functions*, since the parametric equations $x = \cos\theta$, $y = \sin\theta$ give the circle $x^2 + y^2 = 1$. This equation can be rearranged to give $y = \pm\sqrt{1 - x^2}$, which is why the inverse circular functions are useful in finding integrals involving $\sqrt{1 - x^2}$ (and, likewise, $\sqrt{a^2 - x^2}$, as on page 12). In the eighteenth century several mathematicians investigated integrals involving $\sqrt{x^2 - 1}$ in a similar way, noticing that if $y = \sqrt{x^2 - 1}$ then $x^2 - y^2 = 1$ which is the equation of a hyperbola.

Now $\qquad x^2 - y^2 = 1 \Leftrightarrow (x + y)(x - y) = 1$

so that if $\qquad x + y = p$

then $\qquad x - y = \dfrac{1}{p}$

from which $\quad x = \dfrac{1}{2}\left(p + \dfrac{1}{p}\right)$ and $y = \dfrac{1}{2}\left(p - \dfrac{1}{p}\right).$

These are parametric equations for the hyperbola $x^2 - y^2 = 1$ in terms of the parameter p.

These equations turn out to be particularly useful in the case when $p = e^u$,

so that $\dfrac{1}{p} = e^{-u}$.

Then

$$x = \tfrac{1}{2}(e^u + e^{-u}) \text{ and } y = \tfrac{1}{2}(e^u - e^{-u}).$$

By analogy with the circular functions these are called the *hyperbolic cosine* and *hyperbolic sine* functions respectively (names introduced by J. H. Lambert in 1768). These are abbreviated to *cosh* and *sinh* (pronounced 'shine' or 'sine-ch' or 'sinch' or 'sinsh' – take your pick!), so that

$$\cosh u = \tfrac{1}{2}(e^u + e^{-u}) \quad \text{and} \quad \sinh u = \tfrac{1}{2}(e^u - e^{-u}).$$

ACTIVITY 6.1   Prove that $\cosh(-u) = \cosh u$ and that $\sinh(-u) = -\sinh u$ (i.e. that cosh and sinh are respectively even and odd functions). What does this tell you about the symmetries of the graphs of these functions?

The graphs of these hyperbolic functions are easy to sketch. Since $\cosh u = \tfrac{1}{2}(e^u + e^{-u})$ the graph of $v = \cosh u$ lies mid-way between the graphs of $v = e^u$ and $v = e^{-u}$, as shown in figure 6.1. Note that $v = \cosh u$ has a minimum point at $(0, 1)$.

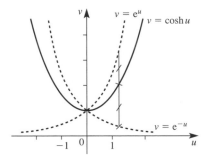

Figure 6.1

Similarly, the graph of $v = \sinh u$ is mid-way between the graphs of $v = e^u$ and $v = -e^{-u}$ (figure 6.2). It passes through the origin where it has a point of inflection.

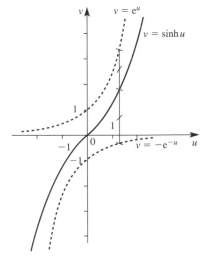

Figure 6.2

These graphs are nothing like the sine or cosine wave graphs, but the definitions of the hyperbolic functions are very similar to the results linking the circular functions with $e^{j\theta}$ which were given on page 47. Compare

$$\cosh u = \frac{1}{2}(e^u + e^{-u}) \quad \text{and} \quad \cos\theta = \frac{1}{2}(e^{j\theta} + e^{-j\theta})$$

$$\sinh u = \frac{1}{2}(e^u - e^{-u}) \quad \text{and} \quad \sin\theta = \frac{1}{2j}(e^{j\theta} - e^{-j\theta}).$$

Many other similarities follow from this. For example, starting with the definitions and differentiating,

$$\frac{d}{du}(\cosh u) = \frac{1}{2}(e^u - e^{-u}) = \sinh u \quad \text{and} \quad \frac{d}{du}(\sinh u) = \frac{1}{2}(e^u + e^{-u}) = \cosh u.$$

Also, since

$$\cosh^2 u = \frac{1}{4}(e^u + e^{-u})^2 = \frac{1}{4}(e^{2u} + 2 + e^{-2u})$$

and

$$\sinh^2 u = \frac{1}{4}(e^u - e^{-u})^2 = \frac{1}{4}(e^{2u} - 2 + e^{-2u})$$

by subtracting

$$\cosh^2 u - \sinh^2 u = 1$$

An important result, but not surprising since it gets us back to $x^2 - y^2 = 1$.

and by adding

$$\cosh^2 u + \sinh^2 u = \frac{1}{2}(e^{2u} + e^{-2u}) = \cosh 2u.$$

ACTIVITY 6.2 Using $\cosh^2 u - \sinh^2 u = 1$ and $\cosh 2u = \cosh^2 u + \sinh^2 u$, write down two further versions of $\cosh 2u$. Compare all three formulae for $\cosh 2u$ with the corresponding formulae for $\cos 2\theta$.

ACTIVITY 6.3 Use the definitions of $\sinh u$ and $\cosh u$ to prove that

(i) $\sinh 2u = 2 \sinh u \cosh u$
(ii) $\sinh(u + v) = \sinh u \cosh v + \cosh u \sinh v$
(iii) $\cosh(u + v) = \cosh u \cosh v + \sinh u \sinh v$.

[**Hint:** Start with the right-hand sides.]

The only difference between these identities and the corresponding ones for the circular functions is that the sign is reversed whenever a product of two sines is replaced by the product of two sinhs. This is called Osborn's rule: it arises because of the factor j in the denominator of $\sin\theta$ as defined above.

EXAMPLE 6.1

Solve the equation $\cosh u = 2 \sinh u - 1$.

SOLUTION

It is simplest to work from the definitions.

$$\cosh u = 2 \sinh u - 1 \quad \Leftrightarrow \quad \tfrac{1}{2}(e^u + e^{-u}) = e^u - e^{-u} - 1$$
$$\Leftrightarrow \quad e^u - 3e^{-u} - 2 = 0$$
$$\Leftrightarrow \quad (e^u)^2 - 2e^u - 3 = 0$$
$$\Leftrightarrow \quad (e^u - 3)(e^u + 1) = 0$$
$$\Leftrightarrow \quad e^u = 3 \quad (\text{since } e^u \text{ cannot be negative})$$
$$\Leftrightarrow \quad u = \ln 3.$$

EXERCISE 6A

1 Prove that
$$\cosh A + \cosh B = 2 \cosh \frac{A+B}{2} \cosh \frac{A-B}{2}.$$

Write down the corresponding results for $\cosh A - \cosh B$ and for $\sinh A \pm \sinh B$, and prove one of these.

2 Given that $\sin 3\theta = 3 \sin \theta - 4 \sin^3 \theta$ and $\cos 3\theta = 4 \cos^3 \theta - 3 \cos \theta$, write down expressions for $\sinh 3u$ in terms of $\sinh u$, and $\cosh 3u$ in terms of $\cosh u$.

3 **(i)** Find all the real solutions of these equations.
   (a) $\cosh x + 2 \sinh x = -1$
   (b) $10 \cosh x - 2 \sinh x = 11$
   (c) $7 \cosh x + 4 \sinh x = 3$
   (ii) Find conditions on a, b, c which are necessary and sufficient to ensure that the equation $a \cosh x + b \sinh x = c$ has two distinct real roots.

4 Given that $\sinh x + \sinh y = \frac{25}{12}$
   and $\cosh x - \cosh y = \frac{5}{12}$,

   show that $2e^x = 5 + 2e^{-y}$ and $3e^{-x} = -5 + 3e^y$.

   Hence find the real values of x and y.

5 The diagram below represents a cable hanging between two points A and B, where AB is horizontal. The lowest point of the cable, O, is taken as the origin of co-ordinates as shown.

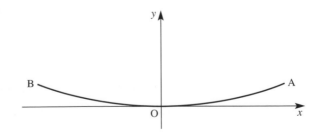

If the cable is flexible and has uniform density then the curve in which it hangs is called a *catenary*. In 1691 John Bernoulli (responding to a challenge set by his brother James) proved that the equation of the catenary is

$$y = c\left(\cosh\frac{x}{c} - 1\right), \text{ where } c \text{ is a constant.}$$

If for a particular cable $c = 20\,\text{m}$ and $AB = 16\,\text{m}$, find the sag of the cable, i.e. the distance of O below AB, and the angle that the tangent at A makes with the horizontal.

6 P is any point on the curve $y = c\cosh\dfrac{x}{c}$, M is the foot of the perpendicular from P to the x axis, and Q is the foot of the perpendicular from M to the tangent of the curve at P. Prove that

(i) $MQ = c$

(ii) the product of the y co-ordinates of P and Q is c^2.

7 Differentiate each of the following with respect to x.

(i) $\sinh 4x$ **(ii)** $\cosh(x^2)$

(iii) $\cosh^2 x$ **(iv)** $\cos x \sinh x$

(v) $\sinh(\ln x)$ **(vi)** $e^{5x}\sinh 5x$

(vii) $(1+x)^3 \cosh^3 3x$ **(viii)** $\ln(\cosh x + \sinh x)$

8 Express $\cosh^2 x$ and $\sinh^2 x$ in terms of $\cosh 2x$.
Hence find $\int \cosh^2 x\,dx$ and $\int \sinh^2 x\,dx$.

9 Integrate each of the following with respect to x.

(i) $\sinh 3x$ **(ii)** $x\cosh(1+x^2)$

(iii) $x\sinh x$ **(iv)** $\cosh^3 x$

(v) $x\sinh^2 x$ **(vi)** $e^{4x}\cosh 5x$

(vii) $\cosh^2 x \sinh^3 x$ **(viii)** $\cosh 6x \sinh 8x$

10 Prove that $\cosh x > x$ for all x. Prove that the point on the curve $y = \cosh x$ which is closest to the line $y = x$ has co-ordinates $(\ln(1+\sqrt{2}), \sqrt{2})$.

11 Prove that $(\cosh x + \sinh x)^n = \cosh nx + \sinh nx$ for all integers n. State and prove the corresponding result for $(\cosh x - \sinh x)^n$. Deduce expressions for $\cosh 5x$ in terms of $\cosh x$ and for $\sinh 5x$ in terms of $\sinh x$.

12 In this question, the function $f(x)$ is defined to be

$$f(x) = 13\cosh x + 5\sinh x.$$

(i) For the curve with equation $y = f(x)$, show that the area under the curve between $x = -a$ and $x = a$ (where $a > 0$) is $\frac{13}{5}\{f(a) - f(-a)\}$.

(ii) By first expressing $f(x)$ in terms of e^x and e^{-x}, or otherwise, find the minimum value of $f(x)$.

(iii) Solve the equation $f(x) = 20$, giving the answers as natural logarithms.

(iv) Differentiate $\arctan\left(\frac{3}{2}e^x\right)$ with respect to x. Hence find $\displaystyle\int \frac{1}{f(x)}\,dx$.

[MEI]

Other hyperbolic functions

The four remaining hyperbolic functions are defined in a similar way to the corresponding circular functions:

$$\tanh x = \frac{\sinh x}{\cosh x}, \coth x = \frac{1}{\tanh x}, \operatorname{sech} x = \frac{1}{\cosh x}, \operatorname{cosech} x = \frac{1}{\sinh x}.$$

ACTIVITY 6.4

For each of these functions state any necessary restriction on the domain, give the range, and say whether the function is even or odd.

The most important of these is the tanh function (pronounced 'than' or 'tan–ch').

Let $y = \tanh x$. Then $\quad y = \dfrac{e^x - e^{-x}}{e^x + e^{-x}} = \dfrac{1 - e^{-2x}}{1 + e^{-2x}}$ ⤷ dividing top and bottom by e^x

so that $\qquad\qquad\qquad y \to 1$ as $x \to \infty$.
By a similar method, $\quad y \to -1$ as $x \to -\infty$.

Using the quotient rule to differentiate $\dfrac{\sinh x}{\cosh x}$ gives

$$\frac{dy}{dx} = \frac{\cosh x \cosh x - \sinh x \sinh x}{\cosh^2 x} = \operatorname{sech}^2 x,$$

since $\cosh^2 x - \sinh^2 x = 1$.

So the graph of $y = \tanh x$ (see figure 6.3) has

- a positive gradient everywhere, never more than 1 (since $0 < \operatorname{sech} x \leqslant 1$)
- half-turn symmetry about the origin
- asymptotes $y = \pm 1$.

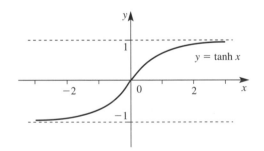

Figure 6.3

EXERCISE 6B

1 Sketch the graph of each of the following, giving the equations of any asymptotes.
  (i) $y = \operatorname{sech} x$ (ii) $y = \operatorname{cosech} x$ (iii) $y = \coth x$

2 Prove that
  (i) $1 - \tanh^2 x = \operatorname{sech}^2 x$
  (ii) $\coth^2 x - 1 = \operatorname{cosech}^2 x$
  (iii) $\tanh 2x = \dfrac{2 \tanh x}{1 + \tanh^2 x}$.

3 Find all the real solutions of these equations.

    (i) $4 \tanh x = \coth x$

    (ii) $3 \tanh x = 4(1 - \operatorname{sech} x)$

    (iii) $3 \operatorname{sech}^2 x + \tanh x = 3$

4 **(i)**   Find exact expressions for p and q, where $\sinh p = \operatorname{sech} p$ and $\cosh q = \coth q$.

    (ii) Arrange $\cosh x$, $\sinh x$, $\tanh x$, $\operatorname{sech} x$, $\operatorname{cosech} x$, $\coth x$ in ascending order of magnitude

       (a) when $0 < x < p$

       (b) when $p < x < q$.

5 If $-\dfrac{\pi}{2} < x < \dfrac{\pi}{2}$ and k is any real constant, show that the equation

$\sin x = \tanh k$ has just one solution, and prove that $\tan x = \sinh k$ and $\sec x = \cosh k$ for this value of x.

6 Prove that:

    (i) $\alpha = \ln(\tan \beta) \Leftrightarrow \tanh \alpha = -\cos 2\beta$

    (ii) $\alpha = \ln\left(\tan\left(\dfrac{\pi}{4} + \dfrac{\beta}{2} \right) \right) \Leftrightarrow \tanh \alpha = \sin \beta.$

7 Differentiate each of the following with respect to x.

    (i) $\operatorname{sech} x$ **(ii)** $\operatorname{cosech} x$ **(iii)** $\coth x$ **(iv)** $\ln(\tanh x)$

8 Integrate each of the following with respect to x.

    (i) $\tanh x$ **(ii)** $\coth x$ **(iii)** $\operatorname{sech} x$ **(iv)** $\operatorname{cosech} x$

    [**Hint:** For **(iii)** and **(iv)** use the substitution $u = e^x$.]

9 Find the Maclaurin series for $\cosh x$, including the general term,

    (i)   by finding the values of successive derivatives at $x = 0$

    (ii) by using the definition $\cosh x = \frac{1}{2}(e^x + e^{-x})$.

    (The Maclaurin series for $\cosh x$ and $\sinh x$ are valid for all values of x.)

10 **(i)** **(a)** Show, by successive differentiation of $\sinh x$, that its Maclaurin series is

$$x + \frac{x^3}{3!} + \frac{x^5}{5!} + \cdots.$$

       (b) Write down the series for $\sinh(x^2)$ in ascending powers of x, giving the first three non-zero terms and the general term.

       (c) Given that $f(x) = \sinh(x^2)$, use the series in part **(i)(b)** to find the values of $f^{(5)}(0)$ and $f^{(6)}(0)$. [$f^{(n)}(x)$ denotes the nth derivative of $f(x)$.]

    (ii) Use the series in part **(i)(b)** to find the value of

$$\int_0^{0.6} x^2 \sinh(x^2)\, dx$$

    correct to 4 decimal places

[MEI, part]

11 (i) Show that $\cosh^4 x = \frac{1}{8}\cosh 4x + \frac{1}{2}\cosh 2x + \frac{3}{8}$.

(ii) Find the series expansion for $\cosh^4 x$, as far as the term in x^4.

[MEI, part]

12 (i) Show that the only stationary point on the curve $y = \cosh 2x - 3\sinh x$ is $(\ln 2, -\frac{1}{8})$.

(ii) Find $\displaystyle\int_0^{\ln 2} (\cosh 2x - 3\sinh x)\,dx$

[MEI part]

The inverse hyperbolic functions

The cosh function is a many-to-one function, since more than one value of x can yield the same value of y (e.g. $\cosh x_1 = \cosh(-x_1) = y_1$ in figure 6.4).

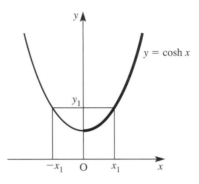

Figure 6.4

But if the domain is restricted to the non-negative real numbers, i.e. to $x \geqslant 0$, then the function is one-to-one, with the graph shown by the heavy line in figure 6.4. This restricted cosh function has an inverse function, which is denoted by *arcosh* (or sometimes $\cosh^{-1}$), so that

$$v = \text{arcosh}\, u \quad \Leftrightarrow \quad u = \cosh v \text{ and } v \geqslant 0.$$

The usual process of reflecting the graph of a function in the line $y = x$ to give the graph of its inverse function produces the graph of $y = \text{arcosh}\, x$ shown in figure 6.5.

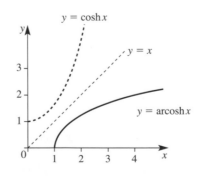

Figure 6.5

Since the sinh and tanh functions are already one-to-one there is no need for any similar restrictions in defining their inverse functions *arsinh* and *artanh* (or $\sinh^{-1}$ and $\tanh^{-1}$).

Thus $v = \text{arsinh}\, u \quad \Leftrightarrow \quad u = \sinh v$
$\qquad v = \text{artanh}\, u \quad \Leftrightarrow \quad u = \tanh v.$

The graphs are shown in figure 6.6.

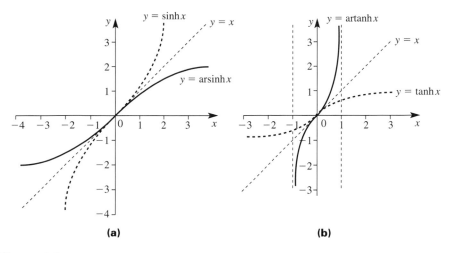

(a)   (b)

Figure 6.6

ACTIVITY 6.5 State the domain and range of each of these three inverse hyperbolic functions.

Just as the hyperbolic functions are defined using the exponential function, so their inverses can be put in terms of the natural logarithm function. The most straightforward to deal with is artanh x:

$$y = \text{artanh}\, x \quad \Leftrightarrow \quad x = \tanh y$$
$$= \frac{e^y - e^{-y}}{e^y + e^{-y}}$$
$$= \frac{e^{2y} - 1}{e^{2y} + 1}$$

> multiplying top and botttom by e^y

$$\Leftrightarrow \quad x(e^{2y} + 1) = e^{2y} - 1$$
$$\Leftrightarrow \quad e^{2y} = \frac{1 + x}{1 - x}$$
$$\Leftrightarrow \quad 2y = \ln\left(\frac{1 + x}{1 - x}\right).$$

Therefore artanh $x = \dfrac{1}{2}\ln\left(\dfrac{1 + x}{1 - x}\right).$

As you might expect, arcosh x is a bit more complicated:

$$y = \text{arcosh } x \quad \Leftrightarrow \quad x = \cosh y$$
$$\Rightarrow \quad 2x = e^y + e^{-y}$$
$$\Rightarrow \quad (e^y)^2 - 2xe^y + 1 = 0$$
$$\Rightarrow \quad e^y = \frac{2x \pm \sqrt{4x^2 - 4}}{2} \qquad \text{using the quadratic equation formula}$$
$$= x \pm \sqrt{x^2 - 1}$$
$$\Rightarrow \quad y = \ln(x + \sqrt{x^2 - 1}) \text{ or } \ln(x - \sqrt{x^2 - 1}).$$

The sum of these two roots is

$$\ln[(x + \sqrt{x^2 - 1})(x - \sqrt{x^2 - 1})] = \ln[x^2 - (x^2 - 1)] = \ln 1 = 0,$$

so the second root is the negative of the first (as shown in figure 6.4). Since arcosh $x > 0$ by definition, the required root is the positive one. Therefore arcosh $x = \ln(x + \sqrt{x^2 - 1})$.

ACTIVITY 6.6   Use a similar method to prove that arsinh $x = \ln(x + \sqrt{x^2 + 1})$.

Explain why the root $\ln(x - \sqrt{x^2 + 1})$ is rejected.

The derivatives of arcosh x and arsinh x can be found by differentiating these logarithmic versions, but it is easier to work as follows.

$$y = \text{arcosh } x \quad \Leftrightarrow \quad \cosh y = x$$
$$\Rightarrow \quad \sinh y \frac{dy}{dx} = 1 \qquad \text{differentiating both sides with respect to } x$$
$$\Rightarrow \quad \frac{dy}{dx} = \frac{1}{\sinh y}$$
$$= \frac{1}{\pm\sqrt{\cosh^2 y - 1}} \qquad \text{using } \cosh^2 y - \sinh^2 y = 1$$
$$= \frac{1}{\pm\sqrt{x^2 - 1}}.$$

Since the gradient of $y = \text{arcosh } x$ is always positive you must take the positive square root, and therefore $\dfrac{d}{dx}(\text{arcosh } x) = \dfrac{1}{\sqrt{x^2 - 1}}$.

This result is equivalent to the integral $\displaystyle\int \frac{1}{\sqrt{x^2 - 1}} \, dx = \text{arcosh } x + c$, from which it is easy to integrate related functions. For example, to find $\displaystyle\int \frac{1}{\sqrt{x^2 - a^2}} \, dx$, use the substitution $x = au$. Then $dx = a\,du$ and

$$\int \frac{1}{\sqrt{x^2 - a^2}} \, dx = \int \frac{1}{\sqrt{a^2 u^2 - a^2}} \, a \, du$$

$$= \int \frac{1}{a\sqrt{u^2 - 1}} \, a \, du$$

$$= \int \frac{1}{\sqrt{u^2 - 1}} \, du$$

$$= \text{arcosh } u + c$$

$$= \text{arcosh } \frac{x}{a} + c.$$

ACTIVITY 6.7

Prove by similar methods that

(i) $\dfrac{d}{dx}(\text{arsinh } x) = \dfrac{1}{\sqrt{x^2 + 1}}$

(ii) $\displaystyle\int \frac{1}{\sqrt{x^2 + a^2}} \, dx = \text{arsinh } \frac{x}{a} + c.$

Inverse hyperbolic functions are used in integration in much the same way as inverse trigonometric functions. More complicated examples use techniques such as taking out constant factors or completing the square, just as on pages 15–17.

EXAMPLE 6.2

Find

(i) $\displaystyle\int \frac{1}{\sqrt{9x^2 - 25}} \, dx$ **(ii)** $\displaystyle\int \sqrt{x^2 - 1} \, dx$ **(iii)** $\displaystyle\int_1^5 \frac{1}{\sqrt{x^2 + 6x + 13}} \, dx.$

SOLUTION

(i) $\displaystyle\int \frac{1}{\sqrt{9x^2 - 25}} \, dx = \frac{1}{3} \int \frac{1}{\sqrt{x^2 - \frac{25}{9}}} \, dx$

$$= \frac{1}{3} \text{arcosh } \frac{3x}{5} + c.$$

(ii) Let $x = \cosh u$ so that $dx = \sinh u \, du$. Then

$$\int \sqrt{x^2 - 1} \, dx = \int \sqrt{\cosh^2 u - 1} \sinh u \, du$$

$$= \int \sinh^2 u \, du$$

$$= \int \tfrac{1}{2}(\cosh 2u - 1) \, du$$

$$= \tfrac{1}{4} \sinh 2u - \tfrac{1}{2} u + c$$

$$= \tfrac{1}{2} \sinh u \cosh u - \tfrac{1}{2} u + c$$

$$= \tfrac{1}{2} x\sqrt{x^2 - 1} - \tfrac{1}{2} \text{arcosh } x + c.$$

(iii) $x^2 + 6x + 13 = x^2 + 6x + 9 + 4 = (x + 3)^2 + 4.$

Therefore $\displaystyle\int_1^5 \frac{1}{\sqrt{x^2 + 6x + 13}}\, dx = \int_1^5 \frac{1}{\sqrt{(x + 3)^2 + 4}}\, dx$

$$= \left[\operatorname{arsinh} \frac{x + 3}{2} \right]_1^5$$

$$= \operatorname{arsinh} 4 - \operatorname{arsinh} 2$$

$$= \ln(4 + \sqrt{17}) - \ln(2 + \sqrt{5})$$

$$\approx 0.651.$$

EXERCISE 6C

1 Differentiate $\ln(x + \sqrt{x^2 - 1})$ with respect to x, and show that your answer simplifies to $\dfrac{1}{\sqrt{x^2 - 1}}$.

2 Prove that $\dfrac{d}{dx}(\operatorname{artanh} x) = \dfrac{1}{1 - x^2}$. By using partial fractions and integrating, deduce from this the logarithmic form of $\operatorname{artanh} x$.

3 Sketch the graphs of the inverse functions $y = \operatorname{arsech} x$, $y = \operatorname{arcosech} x$, $y = \operatorname{arcoth} x$, giving the domain and range of each.

4 Differentiate each of the following with respect to x.

(i) $\operatorname{arsinh} 3x$

(ii) $\operatorname{arcosh}(x^2)$

(iii) $\arctan(\sinh x)$

(iv) $\operatorname{artanh}(\sin x)$

(v) $\operatorname{arsech} x$

5 Integrate the following with respect to x.

(i) $\operatorname{arcosh} x$

(ii) $\operatorname{arsinh} x$

(iii) $\operatorname{artanh} x.$

[**Hint:** Write $\operatorname{arcosh} x = 1 \times \operatorname{arcosh} x$ and integrate by parts.]

6 Integrate the following with respect to x.

(i) $\dfrac{1}{\sqrt{4 + x^2}}$

(ii) $\dfrac{1}{\sqrt{x^2 - 9}}$

(iii) $\dfrac{1}{\sqrt{9 - x^2}}$

(iv) $\dfrac{1}{\sqrt{36x^2 + 16}}$

(v) $\dfrac{1}{\sqrt{x^2 - 4x + 8}}$

(vi) $\dfrac{1}{\sqrt{x^2 + x}}$

(vii) $\dfrac{1}{\sqrt{9x^2 + 6x - 8}}$

(viii) $\dfrac{x^2}{\sqrt{x^6 - 1}}$

7 Evaluate each of the following, correct to 3 significant figures.

(i) $\displaystyle\int_1^3 \frac{1}{\sqrt{x^2 + 4x + 5}}\,dx$ **(ii)** $\displaystyle\int_{10}^{20} \frac{1}{\sqrt{4x^2 + 12x - 40}}\,dx.$

8 The points $P_1(a\cos\theta,\, a\sin\theta)$ and $P_2(a\cosh\phi,\, a\sinh\phi)$ lie on the circle $x^2 + y^2 = a^2$ and the rectangular hyperbola $x^2 - y^2 = a^2$ respectively (see diagram below).

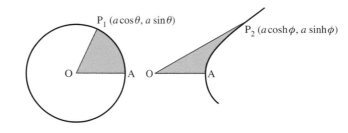

Prove that area OAP_1 is proportional to θ and that area OAP_2 is proportional to ϕ, with the same constant of proportionality.

9 By substituting suitable circular or hyperbolic functions, find

(i) $\displaystyle\int \sqrt{a^2 - x^2}\,dx$

(ii) $\displaystyle\int \sqrt{a^2 + x^2}\,dx$

(iii) $\displaystyle\int \sqrt{x^2 - a^2}\,dx.$

10 Show that $\displaystyle\int_5^6 \frac{1}{\sqrt{25x^2 - 576}}\,dx = \frac{1}{5}\ln\left(\frac{3}{2}\right).$

[MEI, part]

11 Show that $\displaystyle\int_0^4 \frac{4x + 1}{\sqrt{x^2 + 9}}\,dx = 8 + \ln 3.$

[MEI, part]

12 (i) Find $\displaystyle\int x\sinh(x^2)\,dx.$

(ii) By writing $x^3\sinh(x^2)$ as $x^2(x\sinh(x^2))$, or otherwise, find $\displaystyle\int x^3\sinh(x^2)\,dx.$

[MEI, part]

13 (i) By differentiating the equation $\tanh y = x$, show that

$$\frac{d}{dx}(\operatorname{artanh} x) = \frac{1}{1 - x^2}.$$

(ii) Using integration by parts, find $\displaystyle\int \operatorname{artanh} x\,dx.$

(iii) Prove that $\operatorname{artanh} x = \dfrac{1}{2}\ln\left(\dfrac{1 + x}{1 - x}\right).$

(iv) Show that $\displaystyle\int_0^{\frac{1}{2}} \operatorname{artanh} x\,dx = \tfrac{1}{4}\ln\left(\tfrac{27}{16}\right).$

(v) Show that the expansion of $\operatorname{artanh} x$ in ascending powers of x begins
$$x + \tfrac{1}{3}x^3 + \cdots.$$

[MEI]

14 (i) Find the exact value of $\displaystyle\int_{-0.4}^{0.4} \dfrac{1}{25x^2 + 4}\,\mathrm{d}x$.

   (ii) (a) Differentiate the following with respect to x (where $0 < x < 2$), simplifying your answers as much as possible.

   (A) $\operatorname{arcsin}\dfrac{x}{2}$ (B) $\operatorname{arcosh}\dfrac{2}{x}$

   (b) Using integration by parts, show that

   $$\int_0^{\sqrt{3}} \operatorname{arcsin}\frac{x}{2}\,\mathrm{d}x = \frac{\pi}{\sqrt{3}} - 1.$$

   (c) Find $\displaystyle\int \dfrac{2 + 3x}{x\sqrt{4 - x^2}}\,\mathrm{d}x.$

   [MEI]

15 (i) Obtain the formula

   $$\sinh 2x - \sinh 2y = 2\cosh(x + y)\sinh(x - y)$$

   and prove that

   $$\cosh\theta + \cosh 2\theta + \cdots + \cosh n\theta = \cosh\tfrac{1}{2}(n + 1)\theta \sinh\tfrac{1}{2}n\theta \operatorname{cosech}\tfrac{1}{2}\theta.$$

   (ii) Evaluate the integral

   $$\int_{\frac{3}{2}}^{\frac{7}{2}} \frac{\mathrm{d}x}{\sqrt{4x^2 - 4x - 3}}.$$

   [MEI]

16 Prove that the curves $y = \operatorname{arsinh} x$ and $y = \operatorname{arcosh} 2x$ intersect where

   $$x = \frac{1}{\sqrt{3}}.$$

   Find the area bounded by the x axis and these curves.

KEY POINTS

1 $\cosh x = \dfrac{e^x + e^{-x}}{2}$, $\quad \sinh x = \dfrac{e^x - e^{-x}}{2}$, $\quad \tanh x = \dfrac{\sinh x}{\cosh x} = \dfrac{e^{2x} - 1}{e^{2x} + 1}$,

$\coth x = \dfrac{1}{\tanh x}$, $\quad \operatorname{sech} x = \dfrac{1}{\cosh x}$, $\quad \operatorname{cosech} x = \dfrac{1}{\sinh x}$.

2 $\cosh^2 x - \sinh^2 x = 1$,

$1 - \tanh^2 x = \operatorname{sech}^2 x$,

$\coth^2 x - 1 = \operatorname{cosech}^2 x$.

3 $\cosh(x \pm y) = \cosh x \cosh y \pm \sinh x \sinh y$,

$\sinh(x \pm y) = \sinh x \cosh y \pm \cosh x \sinh y$,

$\tanh(x \pm y) = \dfrac{\tanh x \pm \tanh y}{1 \pm \tanh x \tanh y}$.

4 $\dfrac{d}{dx}(\cosh x) = \sinh x$, $\qquad \displaystyle\int \cosh x \, dx = \sinh x + c$,

$\dfrac{d}{dx}(\sinh x) = \cosh x$, $\qquad \displaystyle\int \sinh x \, dx = \cosh x + c$,

$\dfrac{d}{dx}(\tanh x) = \operatorname{sech}^2 x$, $\qquad \displaystyle\int \tanh x \, dx = \ln(\cosh x) + c$.

5 $\operatorname{arcosh} x = \ln(x + \sqrt{x^2 - 1})$,

$\operatorname{arsinh} x = \ln(x + \sqrt{x^2 + 1})$,

$\operatorname{artanh} x = \dfrac{1}{2} \ln\left(\dfrac{1 + x}{1 - x}\right)$.

6 $\displaystyle\int \dfrac{1}{\sqrt{x^2 - a^2}} \, dx = \operatorname{arcosh} \dfrac{x}{a} + c$, $\displaystyle\int \dfrac{1}{\sqrt{x^2 + a^2}} \, dx = \operatorname{arsinh} \dfrac{x}{a} + c$.

7 Maclaurin series (See also page 83.)

Valid for all x: $\quad \cosh x = 1 + \dfrac{x^2}{2!} + \dfrac{x^4}{4!} + \dfrac{x^6}{6!} + \cdots + \dfrac{x^{2r}}{(2r)!} + \cdots$

$\sinh x = x + \dfrac{x^3}{3!} + \dfrac{x^5}{5!} + \cdots + \dfrac{x^{2r-1}}{(2r-1)!} + \cdots$

Valid for $|x| < 1$: $\quad \operatorname{artanh} x = x + \dfrac{x^3}{3} + \dfrac{x^5}{5} + \dfrac{x^7}{7} + \cdots + \dfrac{x^{2r-1}}{2r-1} + \cdots$

7 Investigation of curves

> ...he seemed to approach the grave as an hyperbolic curve approaches a
> line, less directly as he got nearer, till it was doubtful if he would ever
> reach it at all.
>
> *Thomas Hardy, Far from the Madding Crowd*

 This chapter is based on the assumption that you have a graphic calculator.

Defining a curve

As a train moves, a point on the edge of the wheel follows the path shown in
figure 7.1.

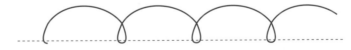

Figure 7.1

❓ How would you describe this path? What are its important features?

Locus

Many curves were first studied as a result of locus problems. They are the
paths of moving points, like the point on the wheel of a train. Three locus
problems are described on the next page. For each one think about the path
traced out by the point P.

- A and B are two fixed points in a plane. P moves in such a way that its distance from A is always double its distance from B.

P
•

A •   • B

Figure 7.2

- P is a point on the rim of a circular coin as it rolls around another coin of the same size.

Figure 7.3

A circle, S, has diameter 2*a*. A is a fixed point on S and Q moves around S in a clockwise direction from A. P lies on the chord AQ produced, at a fixed distance *a* from Q.

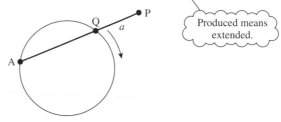

Produced means extended.

Figure 7.4

According to the nature of the locus problem, a particular form of approach (cartesian, parametric or polar) may be more appropriate than the others. The three examples above will be used to illustrate this point.

Cartesian equations

A and B are two fixed points in a plane. P moves in such a way that its distance from A is always double its distance from B.

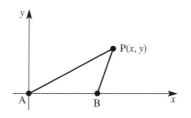

Figure 7.5

Let the two fixed points A and B have co-ordinates $(0, 0)$ and $(a, 0)$.

The point P satisfies the equation $|PA| = 2|PB|$ and so the path it traces out has equation

$$\sqrt{x^2 + y^2} = 2\sqrt{(x - a)^2 + y^2}.$$

So $\qquad\qquad x^2 + y^2 = 4((x - a)^2 + y^2)$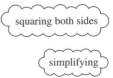

$\Rightarrow \qquad 3x^2 - 8ax + 3y^2 + 4a^2 = 0$

$\Rightarrow \qquad x^2 - \frac{8}{3}ax + y^2 + \frac{4}{3}a^2 = 0$

$\Rightarrow \qquad \left(x - \frac{4}{3}a\right)^2 + y^2 = \left(\frac{2}{3}a\right)^2.$

Therefore the locus of P is a circle, centre $\left(\frac{4}{3}a, 0\right)$ and radius $\frac{2}{3}a$.

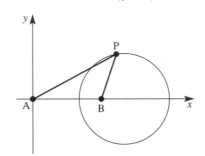

Figure 7.6

In this case the curve is well described by the cartesian equation.

| ACTIVITY 7.1   Show that the requirement $|PA| = k|PB|$ leads to a circle for any value of $k > 1$.

Parametric equations

P is a point on the rim of a circular coin as it rolls around another coin of the same size.

Initially let the coins, with radius r, be lined up in the position shown in figure 7.7, with their centres on the x axis and P at A.

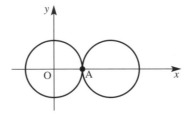

Figure 7.7

Since the coin rolls without slipping, the arc lengths BA and BP in figure 7.8 must be equal and so $T = \phi$.

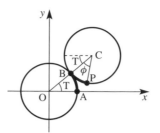

Figure 7.8

Then $\overrightarrow{OP} = \overrightarrow{OC} + \overrightarrow{CP} = 2r\begin{pmatrix} \cos T \\ \sin T \end{pmatrix} - r\begin{pmatrix} \cos 2T \\ \sin 2T \end{pmatrix}$, giving the parametric equations

$$x = 2r\cos T - r\cos 2T, \quad y = 2r\sin T - r\sin 2T.$$

Figure 7.9 shows the fixed coin and the path of P.

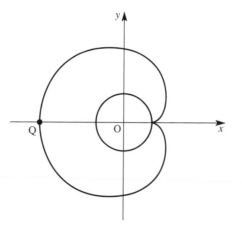

Figure 7.9

In this case the parametric approach has allowed us to describe the locus efficiently.

 What are the cartesian co-ordinates of the point Q?

Polar equations

A circle, S, has diameter $2a$. A is a fixed point on S and Q moves around S in a clockwise direction from A. P lies on the chord AQ produced, at a fixed distance a from Q.

One possible position of P is shown in figure 7.10.

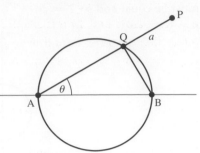

Figure 7.10

It is easy to find the equation of this curve using polar coordinates.

Start by taking A as the pole. Then AB is a diameter, the angle AQB is a right angle and so $|AQ| = 2a \cos \theta$.

Therefore $|AP| = 2a \cos \theta + a$ and so the polar equation of the curve traced out by P is $r = 2a \cos \theta + a$. Since Q starts at A and moves in a clockwise direction back to A, θ goes from $\dfrac{\pi}{2}$ to $-\dfrac{\pi}{2}$. The path of P, along with the circle S, is shown in figure 7.11.

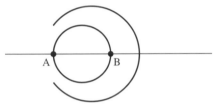

Figure 7.11

You might like to model the path of P using dynamic geometry software.

❓ If you used values of θ across the whole range $-\pi \leqslant \theta \leqslant \pi$, what would the graph of $r = 2a \cos \theta + a$ look like?

Converting between forms

In the final example above you saw that the polar equation of the curve was $r = 2a \cos \theta + a$. The complete curve, taking the full range $-\pi \leqslant \theta \leqslant \pi$, is a curve called a *limaçon* and is shown in figure 7.12.

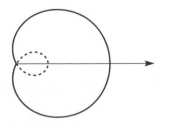

Figure 7.12

⚠ In Chapter 2 of this book you met the convention of using dotted lines for negative values of r. In this chapter you are looking at the curves as a whole rather than the process of drawing polar curves. For this reason you are not required to use the dotted line convention but may choose to do so if you wish.

You can derive the *cartesian* equation of this limaçon from the polar equation in the following way.

Rearrange the polar equation to give

$$a = r - 2a\cos\theta$$

Then
$$ar = r^2 - 2ar\cos\theta$$

$$\Rightarrow \quad a\sqrt{x^2 + y^2} = x^2 + y^2 - 2ax$$

$$\Rightarrow \quad a^2(x^2 + y^2) = (x^2 + y^2)^2 - 4ax(x^2 + y^2) + 4a^2x^2$$

$$\Rightarrow \quad (a^2 + 4ax)(x^2 + y^2) = (x^2 + y^2)^2 + 4a^2x^2.$$

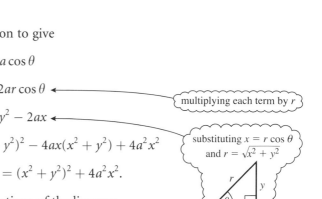

multiplying each term by r

substituting $x = r\cos\theta$ and $r = \sqrt{x^2 + y^2}$

To find the *parametric* equations of the limaçon, substitute $r = 2a\cos\theta + a$ into both $x = r\cos\theta$ and $y = r\sin\theta$.

? Show that this leads to the parametric equations

$$x = a(\cos T + \cos 2T + 1), \quad y = a(\sin T + \sin 2T).$$

? Why is a parameter other than θ often used in parametric equations?

In this case the polar form gives the most elegant equation.

Being able to convert from one form to another is a useful skill and will be used throughout this chapter.

Parametric ↔ cartesian

You can convert certain parametric equations into cartesian equations by eliminating the parameter, for example

$$x = 2t + 1, \quad y = t^2 \quad \Rightarrow \quad y = \left(\frac{x-1}{2}\right)^2.$$

You can also convert a cartesian equation into an equivalent parametric form if

- either the cartesian equation is in a relatively straightforward form, for example

$$y^2 = 16x \quad \Rightarrow \quad x = t^2, \quad y = 4t$$

Try drawing both of these on your calculator.

- or the cartesian equation is in a form which can be compared with a known identity. For example, comparing the circle $x^2 + y^2 = a^2$ with the identity $\cos^2 t + \sin^2 t \equiv 1$ gives the parametric equations of the circle

$$x = a \cos t, \quad y = a \sin t.$$

Cartesian ↔ polar

In Chapter 2 of this book you saw how to convert cartesian equations to polar equations, and vice versa, using the substitution $x = r \cos \theta$ and $y = r \sin \theta$. For example

$$x + 2y = 10 \quad \Rightarrow \quad r \cos \theta + 2r \sin \theta = 10 \quad \Rightarrow \quad r = \frac{10}{\cos \theta + 2 \sin \theta}$$

and $\qquad r = 3 \cos \theta \quad \Rightarrow \quad r^2 = 3r \cos \theta \quad \Rightarrow \quad x^2 + y^2 = 3x.$

Parametric ↔ polar

In this case you could use a combination of the techniques above (using the cartesian form as an intermediate step) or, when converting from polar to parametric form, you could substitute $r = f(\theta)$ in $x = r \cos \theta$, $y = r \sin \theta$. For example

$$r = \tan \theta \quad \Rightarrow \quad x = r \cos \theta = \tan \theta \cos \theta = \sin \theta, \quad y = r \sin \theta = \tan \theta \sin \theta.$$

 Many equations, such as the parametric equations $x = e^{-t}(1 + t)$, $y = t + \cos t$ cannot be converted into other forms.

Figure 7.13 summarises these techniques.

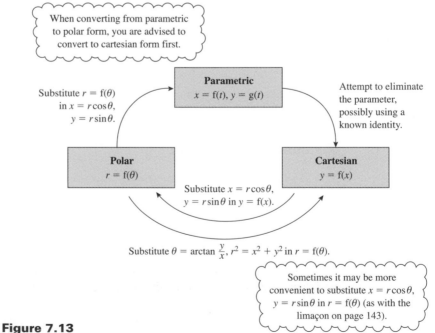

When converting from parametric to polar form, you are advised to convert to cartesian form first.

Parametric
$x = f(t), y = g(t)$

Substitute $r = f(\theta)$ in $x = r \cos \theta$, $y = r \sin \theta$.

Attempt to eliminate the parameter, possibly using a known identity.

Polar
$r = f(\theta)$

Cartesian
$y = f(x)$

Substitute $x = r \cos \theta$, $y = r \sin \theta$ in $y = f(x)$.

Substitute $\theta = \arctan \frac{y}{x}$, $r^2 = x^2 + y^2$ in $r = f(\theta)$.

Sometimes it may be more convenient to substitute $x = r \cos \theta$, $y = r \sin \theta$ in $r = f(\theta)$ (as with the limaçon on page 143).

Figure 7.13

⚠ Notice that, in general, the parameter used in the parametric equations should not be confused with the angle θ in the polar equation. To see why, think about the curve with parametric equations $x = 3\cos T$, $y = 2\sin T$.

For a point P($3\cos\alpha$, $2\sin\alpha$) on the curve in figure 7.14, α has no direct relationship with the angle θ that the line OP makes with the positive x axis.

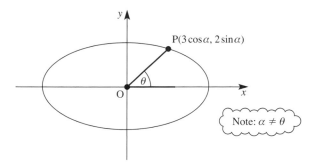

Figure 7.14

Had the parametric equations been given as

$$x = 3\cos\theta, \quad y = 2\sin\theta$$

then it would be *incorrect* to say that the polar equation was

$$
\begin{aligned}
r^2 &= x^2 + y^2 \\
&= 9\cos^2\theta + 4\sin^2\theta \\
&= 4 + 5\cos^2\theta
\end{aligned}
$$

The polar curve $r^2 = 4 + 5\cos^2\theta$ and the curve defined by the parametric equations $x = 3\cos T$, $y = 2\sin T$ are not the same, as shown in figure 7.15.

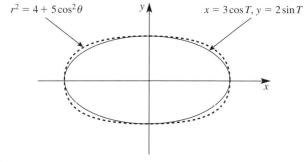

Figure 7.15

Each form, cartesian, parametric or polar, can give new insights into the nature of the curve. You will find this useful when analysing curves later in the chapter. In the following exercise you will practise converting between the three forms.

All the graphs you will be asked to draw in this chapter can be drawn using a graphic calculator. However, for your convenience, if you have access to a computer you are encouraged to use graph-plotting software.

After completing each question, draw the graphs on your calculator or computer (by allocating particular numerical values to the constants a, c, l, etc. where appropriate) to check that the two forms give the same graph.

1 Convert the parametric equations given into cartesian form.

   (i) $x = at^2$, $y = 2at$ **(ii)** $x = a\cos t$, $y = b\sin t$

   (iii) $x = a\sec t$, $y = b\tan t$ **(iv)** $x = ct$, $y = \dfrac{c}{t}$

2 Convert the polar equation $r = \dfrac{l}{1 + e\cos\theta}$ into cartesian form.

3 Convert the polar equation $r = 3\sin 2\theta$ into
   (i) parametric form
   (ii) cartesian form.

4 Convert the polar equation $r = 2a\tan\theta\sin\theta$ (known as the *cissoid of Diocles*) into cartesian form.

5 Convert the parametric equations $x = \dfrac{2at^2}{1 + t^2}$, $y = \dfrac{2at^3}{1 + t^2}$ into cartesian form.

6 Convert the polar equation $r = 2a\tan\theta\sin\theta$ into parametric form
   (i) giving x and y in terms of the parameter θ
   (ii) giving x and y in terms of the parameter t, where $t = \tan\theta$.

7 Explain the connection between your answers to Questions 4, 5 and 6.

8 The *witch of Agnesi* has parametric equations $x = at$, $y = \dfrac{a}{1 + t^2}$.

   Find the cartesian equation of this curve.

9 The *right strophoid* has parametric equations $x = \dfrac{t^2 - 1}{t^2 + 1}$, $y = \dfrac{t(t^2 - 1)}{t^2 + 1}$.

   Convert these into
   (i) cartesian form
   (ii) polar form.

10 The *folium of Descartes* has parametric equations $x = \dfrac{3at}{1 + t^3}$, $y = \dfrac{3at^2}{1 + t^3}$.

   Find the cartesian equation of this curve.

11 The *trisectrix of Maclaurin* has polar equation $r = 2a \dfrac{\sin 3\theta}{\sin 2\theta}$.

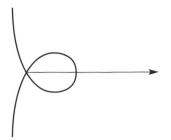

Explain why the following equations all give the trisectrix of Maclaurin.

(i) $r = a(4\cos\theta - \sec\theta)$

(ii) $x = a(2\cos 2T + 1),\ y = a(2\sin 2T - \tan T)$

(iii) $x = a\left(\dfrac{3 - t^2}{1 + t^2}\right),\ y = at\left(\dfrac{3 - t^2}{1 + t^2}\right)$

(iv) $y^2 = x^2\left(\dfrac{3a - x}{a + x}\right)$

12 (i) Write down the cartesian equations of the straight lines A, B, C and D shown below.

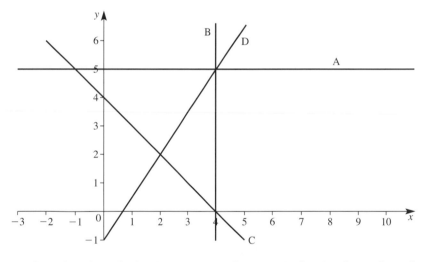

(ii) By using the substitution $x = r\cos\theta,\ y = r\sin\theta$ write down the polar equations of lines A, B, C and D in the form $r = f(\theta)$.

(iii) Comment on the relative simplicity of the cartesian and polar equations of straight lines.

13 The *Maltese cross*, shown in the diagram, has cartesian equation
$$xy(x^2 - y^2) = x^2 + y^2.$$

Notice that the Maltese cross includes the (isolated) point $(0, 0)$.

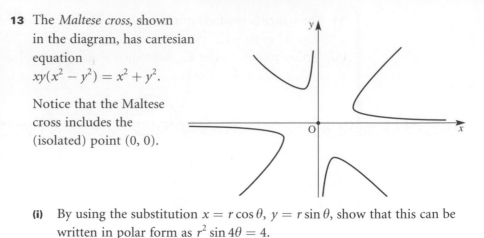

(i) By using the substitution $x = r\cos\theta$, $y = r\sin\theta$, show that this can be written in polar form as $r^2\sin 4\theta = 4$.

(ii) On your calculator draw the polar curves $r = \sqrt{\dfrac{4}{\sin 4\theta}}$ and $r = 2$.

(iii) Using your answer to part **(i)** explain how you know that the curve $xy(x^2 - y^2) = x^2 + y^2$ and the circle $x^2 + y^2 = 4$ touch but do not cross.

14 The *eight curve* has polar equation $r^2 = \cos 2\theta \sec^4\theta$.

(i) Draw the polar curve $r = \sec^2\theta\sqrt{\cos 2\theta}$ on your graphic calculator.

(ii) Sketch this polar curve, clearly showing the points where it crosses the initial line.

(iii) Using $x = r\cos\theta$, $y = r\sin\theta$ and $r^2 = x^2 + y^2$, show that the cartesian equation of the eight curve is $x^4 = x^2 - y^2$.

(iv) Show that the curve with parametric equations $x = \sqrt{1 - t^2}$, $y = t\sqrt{1 - t^2}$, where $0 \leqslant t \leqslant 1$, gives that part of the eight curve which lies in the first quadrant.

A point P lies on this curve. The cartesian co-ordinates of P are $(\sqrt{1 - p^2}, p\sqrt{1 - p^2})$. The polar co-ordinates of P are (R, α).

(v) Find, in their simplest forms, equations connecting
    (a) p and R **(b)** p and α.

Features of curves

This section explores the links between the *shape* of a curve and the *equation* or equations describing it. You have already met even, odd and periodic functions. In this chapter you will meet many other important properties of curves, including symmetry, nodes, cusps, dimples, loops and asymptotes.

 Sketch the curves of the functions $f(x) = \cos 3x$ and $g(x) = \sin 2x$. Using $f(x)$ and $g(x)$ as examples, explain the terms even function, odd function and periodic function, describing the symmetry properties of the curves.

To start you will investigate two curves, one parametric, the other polar. In each case you are required to think about the accompanying questions. By the end of this section you will know the techniques required to analyse these curves. Begin by exploring them for yourself.

Parametric curves

The parametric equations for a simplified fairground ride are

$$x = 4\cos T + 2\cos 3T, \quad y = 4\sin T + 2\sin 3T.$$

These equations give the curve shown in figure 7.16.

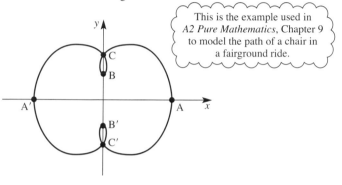

This is the example used in *A2 Pure Mathematics*, Chapter 9 to model the path of a chair in a fairground ride.

Figure 7.16

Think about the relationship between the shape of the curve and the equations describing it.

(i) What are the co-ordinates of the points A, A′, B and B′?

(ii) The curve is symmetrical about both axes. How do you account for this?

(iii) Substituting $T = \dfrac{\pi}{3}$ and $T = \dfrac{2\pi}{3}$ in $x = 4\cos T + 2\cos 3T$,

$y = 4\sin T + 2\sin 3T$ gives the node (or 'crossover point') labelled C. What are the values of the parameter T at the node C′?

Now use your calculator to draw the curve.

 This investigation, like many other questions in this chapter, involves circles. It is good practice to use the 'equal aspect' or 'square' facility on your calculator so that circles do indeed appear circular.

(iv) As T increases from 0 to 2π how does the curve unfold? Is the range 0 to 2π necessary, or do values of T from 0 to π give the entire curve?

Look at figure 7.17, which shows the graph and two circles, centre the origin, with radii 2 and 6.

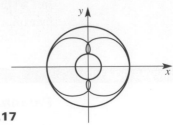

Figure 7.17

(v) The curve *touches* the two circles but does not cross them. Explain how you can predict this from the equations.

Polar curves

The curve $r = 1 + 2\cos\theta$ is shown in figure 7.18.

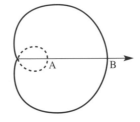

Figure 7.18

(i) What are the polar co-ordinates (r, θ) of the points A and B?
(ii) As the curve unfolds it passes through the pole twice. What are the two values of θ corresponding to this point?
(iii) Think about the curves $r = 1 + \cos\theta$ and $r = 1 + 3\cos\theta$. Do you expect them to be significantly different from the curve $r = 1 + 2\cos\theta$?

On your calculator plot the curves for $r = 1 + b\cos\theta$ for $b = 1, 2, 3$.

(iv) What insight has this given you into the role of b in the shape of the curve $r = 1 + b\cos\theta$?

The questions above all relate to members of a family of curves called *limaçons*; that is, curves of the form $r = a + b\cos\theta$. The special case $a = b$ gives the curve in figure 7.19.

You met the limaçon with $b = 2a$ on page 142.

Figure 7.19

(v) Think about a point P moving along the limaçon. What happens to the tangent to the curve at P as P passes through the pole?

Parallel curves

The *cartesian* curves $y = 1 + f(x)$ and $y = f(x)$ could be said to be, in one sense, 'parallel': for every value of x the curves are separated by a vertical distance of one unit (see figure 7.20).

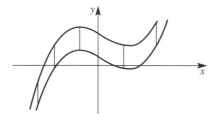

Figure 7.20

Is there a similar relationship between the polar curves $r = 1 + 2\cos\theta$ and $r = 2\cos\theta$ shown in figure 7.21?

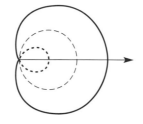

Figure 7.21

The concept of parallel curves is not required in this module. Strictly speaking, two curves are *parallel* if every normal to one of them is a normal to the other and the distance between the points where the normals cut the two curves is a constant.

Loops, cusps and dimples

Figure 7.22 shows the curve $r = k + \cos\theta$ for three values of k.

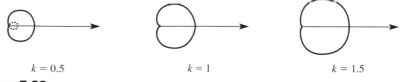

$k = 0.5$ $k = 1$ $k = 1.5$

Figure 7.22

The curve with $k = 0.5$ contains a loop, that with $k = 1$ a cusp, and that with $k = 1.5$ a dimple. Many other curves, and families of curves, whether polar, parametric or cartesian, display these features.

Note

At a cusp, two arcs of a curve meet. Tangents at points on the two arcs become progressively closer to each other as the points approach the cusp. You do not need to know how to analyse cusps using calculus, but you will need to recognise them.

The following example concerns *epicycloids*: curves generated when one circle rolls around the outside of another. (You met an epicycloid on page 140.) The example derives the parametric equations governing the path of a point on the rotating circle and then uses these to find the co-ordinates of the cusps.

EXAMPLE 7.1

A circle of radius *r* rolls, without slipping, around the outside of a circle of radius *R* in an anticlockwise direction. Initially the point P on the smaller circle coincides with A on the larger circle as shown in figure 7.23.

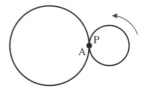

Figure 7.23

(i) State the maximum and minimum distances of P from the origin.

(ii) Show that the parametric equations describing the path traced out by P are

$$x = (R + r)\cos T - r\cos\left(\frac{r + R}{r}\right)T, \ y = (R + r)\sin T - r\sin\left(\frac{r + R}{r}\right)T.$$

(iii) Using your calculator draw the curve with these parametric equations using the values $r = 1$ and $R = 3$. On the same diagram draw the circle, centre the origin, radius 3.

(iv) Using your answer to (i), or otherwise, work out the co-ordinates of the cusps on this curve.

(v) With $r = 1$, a different value of R results in the curve shown in figure 7.24. State the value of R used here and find the co-ordinates of the points where this curve crosses the *x* axis.

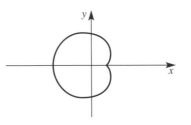

Figure 7.24

SOLUTION

(i) The minimum distance is R, as in the initial position, and the maximum distance is $R + 2r$ when the line OP passes through B, the point of contact of the two circles (see figure 7.25).

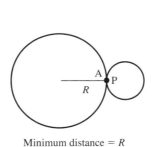

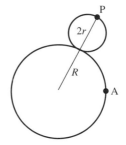

Minimum distance = R Maximum distance = $R + 2r$

Figure 7.25

(ii)

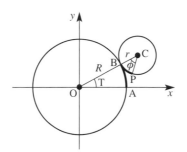

Figure 7.26

Since the circle rolls without sliding, the arc lengths BA and BP must be equal. Therefore, with T and ϕ measured in radians, we have $RT = r\phi$.

Then $\overrightarrow{OP} = \overrightarrow{OC} + \overrightarrow{CP} = (R + r)\begin{pmatrix} \cos T \\ \sin T \end{pmatrix} - r\begin{pmatrix} \cos (T + \phi) \\ \sin (T + \phi) \end{pmatrix}.$

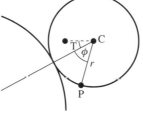

Figure 7.27

Substituting $\phi = \dfrac{R}{r} T$ leads to the parametric equations

$$x = (R + r)\cos T - r\cos\left(\frac{r + R}{r}\right)T, \quad y = (R + r)\sin T - r\sin\left(\frac{r + R}{r}\right)T.$$

(iii) With $r = 1$ and $R = 3$ the curve is as shown in figure 7.28.

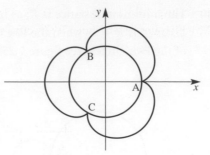

Figure 7.28

(iv) There are three cusps. In this example they occur at the points where the curve is at its minimum distance of 3 units from the pole.

The cusp marked A is at the point (3, 0) and the co-ordinates of the other cusps can be found using trigonometry and the symmetrical nature of their positions:

$$B(-3\cos 60°, 3\sin 60°) = \left(-\frac{3}{2}, \frac{3\sqrt{3}}{2}\right)$$

$$C(-3\cos 60°, -3\sin 60°) = \left(-\frac{3}{2}, -\frac{3\sqrt{3}}{2}\right)$$

(v) $R = 1$. In other words, the circle rolls exactly once around the fixed circle (see figure 7.29).

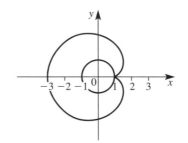

Figure 7.29

The x axis intercepts are at (1, 0) and (−3, 0). (These are the points where the point of contact of the circles lies on the line OP.)

In Example 7.1 you found the locus of P. Now think about the locus of a point M which lies on the line CP (produced if necessary) at a fixed distance from C.

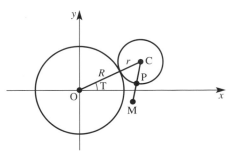

Figure 7.30

Find the parametric equations describing the path of M and use your graphic calculator to investigate the following statement.

'If $|CM| < |CP|$, the path traced out by M features 'dimples' (as in figure 7.31a) whereas if $|CM| > |CP|$ the path features 'loops' (as in figure 7.31b).'

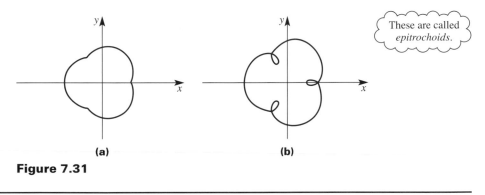

These are called *epitrochoids*.

(a)　　　　　　**(b)**

Figure 7.31

Symmetry and nodes

It is often the case that as a curve is traced out, it crosses over itself. These points are called *nodes* (or *crossover points*).

For parametric curves, if two values of the parameter correspond to the same pair of co-ordinates then this is a node. Example 7.2 illustrates a method for finding the co-ordinates of such points using the symmetrical nature of the curve in question.

EXAMPLE 7.2

Figure 7.32 shows the curve with parametric equations $x = \sin 2t$, $y = \sin 3t$.

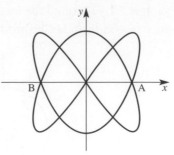

Figure 7.32

Draw this curve on your calculator, noticing the symmetry in both the x and y axes.

(i) What range of values for t is necessary in order to plot the entire curve?

The substitution $t \to \pi - t$ corresponds to a reflection in the y axis:

$$x = \sin 2(\pi - t) = \sin (2\pi - 2t) = -\sin 2t,$$
$$y = \sin 3(\pi - t) = \sin (3\pi - 3t) = \sin 3t$$

(ii) Find the substitution that corresponds to a reflection in the x axis.

(iii) Find the co-ordinates of the points where the curve crosses the x axis and the corresponding values of t.

(iv) Using your answer to part **(iii)** and the graph, write down the two pairs of values of t corresponding to the nodes A and B.

From the graph the other nodes appear to lie on the lines $x = \pm\frac{1}{2}$.

(v) Working with this assumption, find the co-ordinates of the node in the first quadrant and verify that two values of t in the range $0 \leqslant t < \pi$ do indeed give this point.

SOLUTION

(i) $0 \leqslant t < 2\pi$.

(ii) As the curve is plotted on the calculator it can be seen that the relevant substitution is $t \to t + \pi$:

$$x = \sin 2(t + \pi) = \sin (2t + 2\pi) = \sin 2t,$$
$$y = \sin 3(t + \pi) = \sin (3t + 3\pi) = -\sin 3t$$

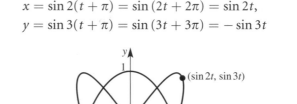

Figure 7.33

(iii) $y = 0 \quad \Rightarrow \quad t = 0, \dfrac{\pi}{3}, \dfrac{2\pi}{3}, \pi, \dfrac{4\pi}{3}, \dfrac{5\pi}{3}$

$\Rightarrow \quad (x, y) = (\sin 2t, 0) = (0, 0), \left(\dfrac{\sqrt{3}}{2}, 0\right), \left(-\dfrac{\sqrt{3}}{2}, 0\right)$

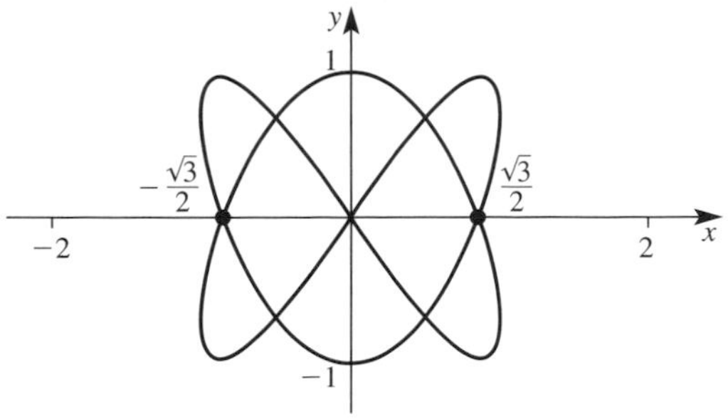

Figure 7.34

(iv) At A $\left(\dfrac{\sqrt{3}}{2}, 0\right), \quad t = \dfrac{\pi}{3}, \dfrac{4\pi}{3}.$

At B $\left(-\dfrac{\sqrt{3}}{2}, 0\right), \quad t = \dfrac{2\pi}{3}, \dfrac{5\pi}{3}.$

(v) $x = \dfrac{1}{2} \quad \Rightarrow \quad 2t = \sin^{-1}\dfrac{1}{2} = \dfrac{\pi}{6}, \dfrac{5\pi}{6}, \dfrac{13\pi}{6}, \dfrac{17\pi}{6}.$

Tracing out the curve as t increases from $t = 0$ at the origin we require the first and fourth times the curve passes through the line $x = \frac{1}{2}$.

$$t = \dfrac{\pi}{12} \quad \Rightarrow \quad \sin 3t = \sin\dfrac{3\pi}{12} = \dfrac{\sqrt{2}}{2}$$

$$t = \dfrac{17\pi}{12} \quad \Rightarrow \quad \sin 3t = \sin\dfrac{51\pi}{12} = \dfrac{\sqrt{2}}{2}$$

Therefore the node is $\left(\dfrac{1}{2}, \dfrac{\sqrt{2}}{2}\right)$ and this corresponds to the values of the parameter $t = \dfrac{\pi}{12}$ and $t = \dfrac{17\pi}{12}$.

ACTIVITY 7.2

Use your calculator to plot the curve $x = \sin 2t$, $y = \cos 3t$. Explain the similarities and differences between this curve and the curve with parametric equations $x = \sin 2t$, $y = \sin 3t$.

Asymptotes

In *AS Further Pure Mathematics* (*FP1*), Chapter 3 you looked at horizontal and vertical asymptotes of cartesian graphs. For example, you should be able to explain why the graph $y = 4 + \dfrac{2}{x-3}$ in figure 7.35 has a horizontal asymptote of $y = 4$ and a vertical asymptote of $x = 3$.

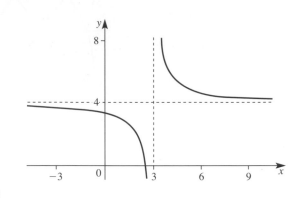

Figure 7.35

Being able to find horizontal and vertical asymptotes is important. If you feel unsure about this you should refer to your *FP1* textbook.

The next example introduces oblique asymptotes.

EXAMPLE 7.3

The graph with parametric equations $x = \dfrac{1}{1+t}$, $y = \dfrac{4}{(1+t)(1-t)}$ is shown in figure 7.36.

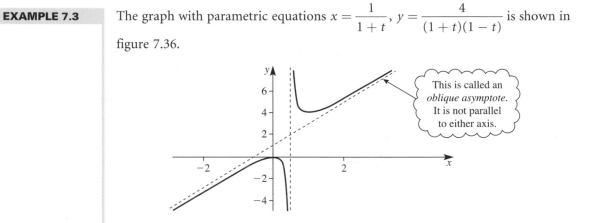

Figure 7.36

Draw this graph on your calculator, paying attention to the way in which it unfolds as the value of the parameter t increases from -5 to 5.

(i) State the equation of the vertical asymptote.

(ii) By eliminating t, show that the cartesian equation of the curve is

$y = \dfrac{4x^2}{2x-1}$. Write this in the form $y = Ax + B + \dfrac{C}{2x-1}$, where A, B and C are constants, and explain how this gives the equation of the oblique asymptote.

SOLUTION

(i) It can be seen from the calculator that the vertical asymptote is $x = \frac{1}{2}$.

Note

A more analytical approach involves thinking about $y = \dfrac{4}{(1+t)(1-t)}$

as t approaches 1.

As $t \to 1$ from above, $y = \dfrac{4}{(1+t)(1-t)}$ becomes increasingly large and negative.

As $t \to 1$ from below, $y = \dfrac{4}{(1+t)(1-t)}$ becomes increasingly large and positive.

When $t = 1$, $x = \dfrac{1}{1+t} = \dfrac{1}{2}$. Therefore the vertical asymptote is $x = \dfrac{1}{2}$.

(ii) $x = \dfrac{1}{1+t} \Rightarrow t = \dfrac{1-x}{x}$ and $\dfrac{1}{1-t} = \dfrac{x}{2x-1}$.

Notice that, as $x \to \frac{1}{2}$,
$y = \dfrac{4x^2}{2x-1} \to \infty$,
showing that the vertical asymptote is $x = \frac{1}{2}$, as in part **(i)**.

Therefore

$$y = 4 \times \dfrac{1}{1+t} \times \dfrac{1}{1-t} = \dfrac{4x^2}{2x-1}.$$

Since $4x^2 = (2x-1)(2x+1)+1$ then

$$y = \dfrac{4x^2}{2x-1} = 2x+1+\dfrac{1}{2x-1}.$$

As $x \to \infty$, $\dfrac{1}{2x-1} \to 0$ and so $y \to 2x+1$.

Thus the equation of the oblique asymptote is $y = 2x+1$. Figure 7.37 shows the graph and the oblique asymptote $y = 2x+1$.

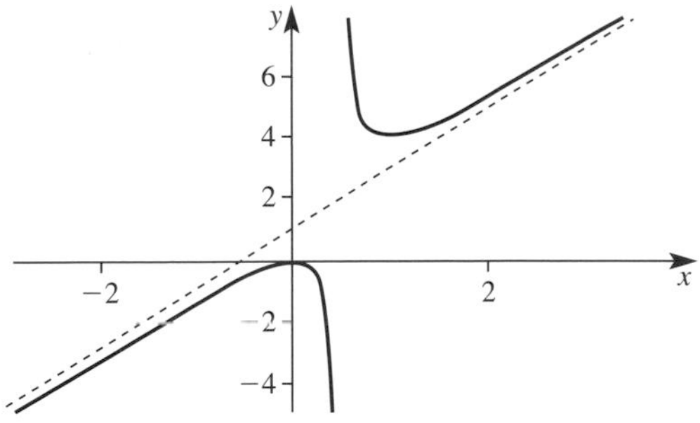

Figure 7.37

? Use the quotient rule on $y = \dfrac{4x^2}{2x-1}$ to find $\dfrac{dy}{dx}$.

What is the significance of the limiting value of $\dfrac{dy}{dx}$ as $x \to \infty$?

Families of curves

All the parallel lines of the form $y = 3x + c$ can be thought of as belonging to a 'family' of lines, the common property being that they all have a gradient of 3.

? What is the common property of the family of quadratics shown in figure 7.38?

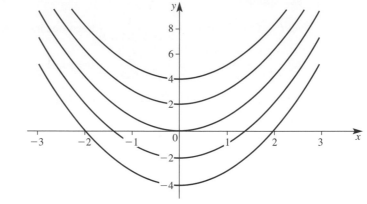

Figure 7.38

In the investigation on page 149, you looked at the curve with parametric equations

$$x = 4 \cos T + 2 \cos 3T, \quad y = 4 \sin T + 2 \sin 3T.$$

This curve can be thought of as one of the family of curves described by the equations

$$x = 4 \cos T + 2 \cos nT, \quad y = 4 \sin T + 2 \sin nT.$$

When $n = 3$ these give the 'fairground ride' curve in figure 7.39.

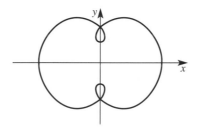

Figure 7.39

Other values of n give very different graphs, as shown in figure 7.40.

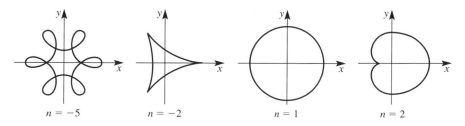

| $n = -5$ | $n = -2$ | $n = 1$ | $n = 2$ |

Figure 7.40

The important question to ask yourself is

- How does the value of n influence the general shape of the curve?

For this particular family of curves it is helpful to consider $x^2 + y^2$. As with all cartesian and parametric curves, this expression gives the square of the distance of a point on the curve from the origin.

With
$$x = 4 \cos T + 2 \cos nT, \quad y = 4 \sin T + 2 \sin nT$$

we have
$$\begin{aligned} x^2 + y^2 &= (4 \cos T + 2 \cos nT)^2 + (4 \sin T + 2 \sin nT)^2 \\ &= 16(\cos^2 T + \sin^2 T) + 4(\cos^2 nT + \sin^2 nT) \\ &\quad + 16(\cos T \cos nT + \sin T \sin nT) \\ &= 20 + 16 \cos (n - 1) T \end{aligned}$$

From this we can see that

- the maximum distance from the origin is $\sqrt{20 + 16} = 6$ units and
- the minimum distance from the origin is $\sqrt{20 - 16} = 2$ units.

Therefore each graph will be bounded by the circles of radii 2 and 6, centre the origin.

 How does $x^2 + y^2 = 20 + 16 \cos (n - 1) T$ help to explain the number of cusps or loops each graph possesses?

ACTIVITY 7.3 The parametric equations on the previous page can be modified to give other families of curves.

- *Family A:* $x = 4\cos T + k\cos nT,\quad y = 4\sin T + k\sin nT$
- *Family B:* $x = 4\cos T - k\cos nT,\quad y = 4\sin T - k\sin nT$
- *Family C:* $x = 4\cos T + k\cos nT,\quad y = 4\sin T - k\sin nT$

Using various values for k and n, explore these families using a graph-plotting package.

How do the values of k and n affect the shape of the graph?

Finally, a word of warning.

Suppose you were asked to decide which graph in figure 7.41 shows the curve $y = \dfrac{x^3 - 2}{x}$, known as the *trident*, without using your calculator.

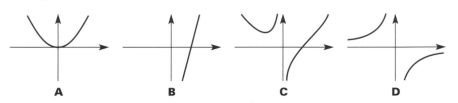

A   **B**   **C**   **D**

Figure 7.41

Although these four graphs look very different they are all a result of entering $y = \dfrac{x^3 - 2}{x}$ on a graphic calculator and choosing different ranges for the axes.

The correct one is graph C, shown here with the axes limits set at

$$-3 \leqslant x \leqslant 3,\quad -7 \leqslant y \leqslant 7.$$

 The other ranges used are

(i) $-0.1 \leqslant x \leqslant 0.1,\quad -100 \leqslant y \leqslant 100$
(ii) $-3 \leqslant x \leqslant 3,\quad -2 \leqslant y \leqslant 2$
(iii) $-50 \leqslant x \leqslant 50,\quad -1000 \leqslant y \leqslant 1000.$

Without using your calculator, match these with graphs A, B and D.

⚠ When using your calculator to investigate curves it is important that you are aware of the limitations of the calculator (as seen in graph A) and the importance of ensuring that the range you choose (for x, y, θ, etc.) does give the whole picture.

1 Look at the graphs of $y = 4 + 2\cos 3x$ and $r = 4 + 2\cos 3\theta$ and the table showing their related properties.

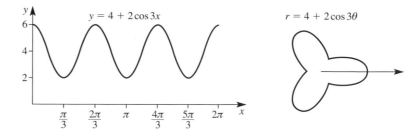

Cartesian: $y = 4 + 2\cos 3x$	Polar: $r = 4 + 2\cos 3\theta$
$y_{max} = 4 + (2 \times 1) = 6$	$r = 4 + 2\cos 3\theta$ touches circle $r = 6$
$y_{min} = 4 + (2 \times -1) = 2$	$r = 4 + 2\cos 3\theta$ touches circle $r = 2$
$y = 4 + 2\cos 3x$ is periodic, with period $\frac{1}{3} \times 2\pi$	$r = 4 + 2\cos 3\theta$ has rotational symmetry of order 3

(i) Use the cartesian graphs below to think about the properties of the corresponding polar curves, including cusps, loops and rotational symmetry. Copy and complete the tables (without using your calculator to draw the polar curves).

(a) $y = 3(1 + \cos 2x)$

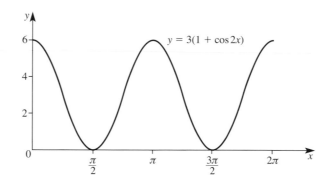

$y = 3(1 + \cos 2x)$	$r = 3(1 + \cos 2\theta)$
$y_{max} = 6$	
$y_{min} = 0$	
y has period $\frac{1}{2} \times 2\pi$	
y is an even function	

(b) $y = 1 + 2\cos x$

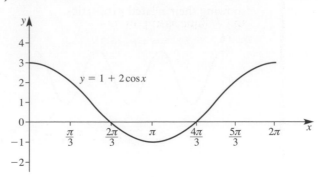

$y = 1 + 2\cos x$

$y = 1 + 2\cos x$	$r = 1 + 2\cos\theta$
$y_{\text{max}} = 3$	
$y < 0$ for $\dfrac{2\pi}{3} < x < \dfrac{4\pi}{3}$	
$y_{\text{min}} = -1$	
y has period 2π	

(ii) Check your answers by plotting the polar curves $r = 3(1 + \cos 2\theta)$ and $r = 1 + 2\cos\theta$ on your calculator.

2 The curves with parametric equations $x = \cos t(1 + \cos^{2n} t)$, $y = \sin t(1 + \sin^{2n} t)$ are shown below for different values of n.

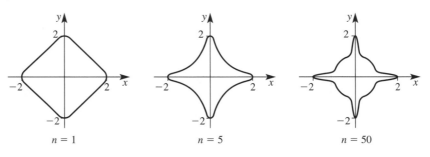

$n = 1$ $n = 5$ $n = 50$

(i) Find the closest distance from the origin to the curve in terms of n.
(ii) Describe the curve as $n \to \infty$.

3 The diagram below shows the graph of $y = \dfrac{2x^2 + 5x - 2}{2x - 1}$ and its vertical and oblique asymptotes.

(i) Express $\dfrac{2x^2 + 5x - 2}{2x - 1}$ in the form $Ax + B + \dfrac{C}{2x - 1}$.

(ii) Write down the equations of the vertical and oblique asymptotes of the graph $y = \dfrac{2x^2 + 5x - 2}{2x - 1}$. Check your answer by drawing them on your calculator.

(iii) Find all the asymptotes (horizontal, vertical and oblique) of the following graphs.

(a) $y = \dfrac{5 - 2x}{2x - 3}$

(b) $y = \dfrac{x(2x - 1)}{x - 1}$

(c) $y = \dfrac{x^3 + 2x^2 - 8x - 18}{x^2 - 9}$

(d) $x = \dfrac{1}{t + 1}, \quad y = \dfrac{t}{t - 2}$

(e) $x = \dfrac{1}{t - 3}, \quad y = \dfrac{12}{t^2 - 9}$

4 (i) Show that $x = \cos^3 T$, $y = \sin^3 T$ are parametric equations for the curve

$$x^{\frac{2}{3}} + y^{\frac{2}{3}} = 1.$$

(ii) Draw a sketch of this curve for $0 \leqslant T \leqslant 2\pi$. The curve is an *astroid*.

Now investigate the family of curves of the form $x = \pm \cos^n T$, $y = \pm \sin^n T$, starting with cases for which $n \geqslant 0$.

(iii) Explain why the parametric equations include the $\pm$ signs.

(iv) Find the values of n for which the curve is

(a) a circle   **(b)** a point

(c) a square at an angle of $\dfrac{\pi}{4}$ to the co-ordinate axes.

(v) Describe what happens to the curve in the cases when

(a) $n \to +\infty$ **(b)** $n \to 0$,   for positive values of n.

(vi) Complete your investigation by drawing some typical members of the family of curves for negative values of n.

5 A circle of radius r rolls around the inside of a circle of radius $4r$.

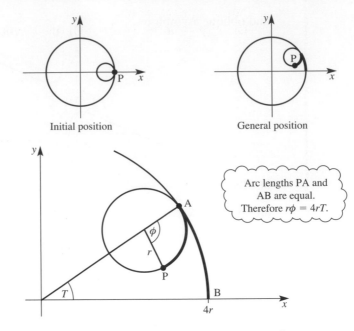

Initial position   General position

Arc lengths PA and
AB are equal.
Therefore $r\phi = 4rT$.

(i) Using the diagram, show that the co-ordinates of P are

$$(3r\cos T + r\cos(\phi - T), \; 3r\sin T - r\sin(\phi - T)).$$

(ii) Eliminate ϕ (by using $r\phi = 4rT$) to show that the parametric equations for the locus of P are

$$x = 4r\cos^3 T, \quad y = 4r\sin^3 T.$$

(iii) Draw this curve on your calculator using the value $r = 1$.

If the radius of the smaller circle is increased to $3r$, the parametric equations become

$$x = 4r\cos^3\left(\frac{T}{3}\right), \quad y = -4r\sin^3\left(\frac{T}{3}\right).$$

(iv) Draw this curve on your calculator and explain, with reasons, the similarities and differences between this and the curve in part (iii).

6 (i) State the type(s) of symmetry which each curve below possesses, and prove this algebraically.

(a) $y^2(y^2 - 96) = x^2(x^2 - 100)$ (the *electric motor*)

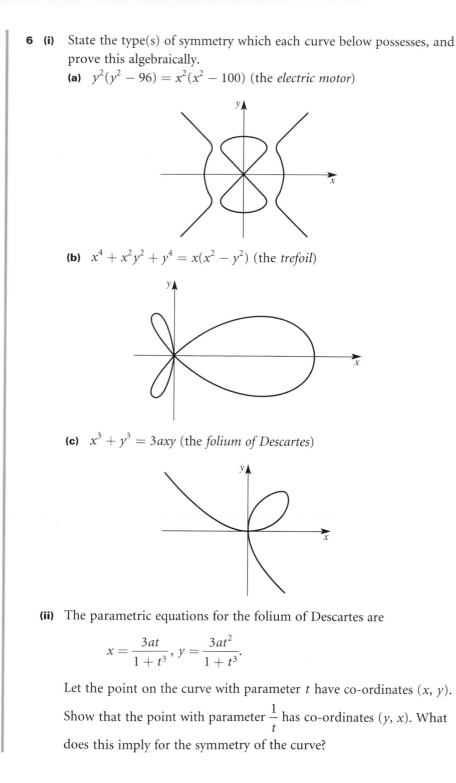

(b) $x^4 + x^2y^2 + y^4 = x(x^2 - y^2)$ (the *trefoil*)

(c) $x^3 + y^3 = 3axy$ (the *folium of Descartes*)

(ii) The parametric equations for the folium of Descartes are

$$x = \frac{3at}{1 + t^3}, \ y = \frac{3at^2}{1 + t^3}.$$

Let the point on the curve with parameter t have co-ordinates (x, y).

Show that the point with parameter $\dfrac{1}{t}$ has co-ordinates (y, x). What does this imply for the symmetry of the curve?

7 (i) Explain the effect that the matrix $\mathbf{M} = \begin{pmatrix} 0 & 1 \\ -1 & 0 \end{pmatrix}$ has on points in the plane.

The *Maltese cross*, shown below, has cartesian equation $xy(x^2 - y^2) = x^2 + y^2$.

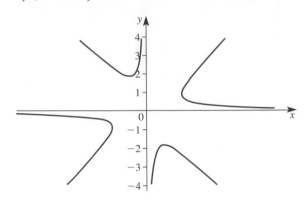

(ii) Prove that if the point P(a, b) lies on the curve then the point Q(c, d) where $\begin{pmatrix} c \\ d \end{pmatrix} = \begin{pmatrix} 0 & 1 \\ -1 & 0 \end{pmatrix} \begin{pmatrix} a \\ b \end{pmatrix}$ also lies on the curve.

(iii) Explain the geometrical significance of your answer to part **(ii)**.

8 A curve, C, has parametric equations $x = \sin T$, $y = \cos T$.

(i) Describe C.

C is transformed into a family of curves by the matrix $\begin{pmatrix} 1 & k \\ -k & 1 \end{pmatrix}$, for different values of k (positive and negative).

(ii) Enter several members of the family onto your calculator and then describe the family.

(iii) Justify your answer to part **(ii)** using algebra and trigonometry.

(iv) Prove that C is the smallest member of the family.

9 (i) Enter the parametric equations $x = 2\sin t + \sin 3t$, $y = \sin 2t + \sin 4t$ into your graphic calculator. Plot the curve and notice how the curve unfolds as t increases from 0 to 2π.

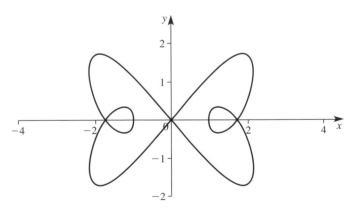

(ii) Explain carefully how substituting $\pi + t$ and $\pi - t$ for t shows that the curve is symmetrical in both the x and y axes.

In addition to $t = 0$, $t = \pi$ and $t = 2\pi$, which give the node, or crossing point, at the origin, there are six other values of t in the range $0 < t < 2\pi$ that correspond to points where the curve cuts the x axis.

(iii) Find the six values of t corresponding to points on the x axis, and find the co-ordinates of these points. State clearly which pair of values of t correspond to each of the nodes.

10 (i) On your calculator draw the circles centre the origin, with radius 1 and radius 3. You may wish to set the axes so that these do indeed look like circles.

(ii) By considering $x^2 + y^2$, or otherwise, prove that the curve with parametric equations

$$x = 2\cos T + \sin kT, \quad y = 2\sin T + \cos kT$$

will touch but not cross these circles for any positive integer value of k.

(iii) On your calculator draw the curve

$$x = 2\cos T + \sin 2T, \quad y = 2\sin T + \cos 2T,$$

along with the two circles.

(iv) Using part **(ii)** and the symmetrical properties of the curve, calculate the co-ordinates of the cusps. You may assume that the curve possesses rotational symmetry.

The diagram below shows the two circles and the curve with parametric equations

$$x = 2\cos T + \sin 4T, \quad y = 2\sin T + \cos 4T.$$

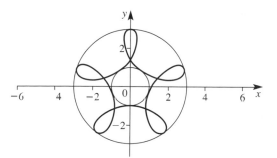

(v) Let the node on the y axis have co-ordinates $(0, a)$. Express in terms of a the co-ordinates of the node in the first quadrant.

The diagram below shows the graphs of

$$x = 2\cos T + \sin kT, \quad y = 2\sin T + \cos kT \quad \text{for } k = 3 \text{ and } k = -5,$$

both of which possess rotational symmetry of order 4.

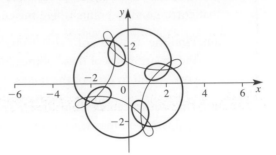

(vi) Experiment with curves of this form on your calculator. Write down the two values of k which would give graphs with rotational symmetry of order m.

11 A family of curves has parametric equations

$$x = \sin\theta + a\cos b\theta, \quad y = \cos\theta + a\sin b\theta$$

where a and b are integers with $a \geqslant 2$ and $b \geqslant 1$. One member of this family of curves is shown below.

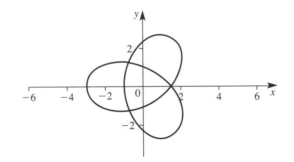

(i) Given that, for this particular curve, $a = b$, find the values of a and b and plot this curve on your calculator.

(ii) The curve crosses the x axis at three points: $(-3, 0)$, $(-1, 0)$ and one other point. Calculate the exact co-ordinates of this third point.

You may assume that this curve has rotational symmetry of order 3.

(iii) Using your answer to part (ii), write down the exact co-ordinates of the three nodes on the curve.

Think about the general curve with parametric equations

$$x = \sin\theta + a\cos b\theta, \quad y = \cos\theta + a\sin b\theta.$$

(iv) Find expressions in terms of a for the greatest and least distances from the origin to this curve. Hence give the equations of the two circles which the curve touches but does not cross.

(v) Explain briefly in words the effect that
    (a) changing a has on the curve   **(b)** changing b has on the curve.

INVESTIGATION

The superellipse

On your calculator or using a graph-plotting package, experiment with curves of the form $|x|^n + |y|^n = 1$. Using a calculator, you will probably need to enter the two curves $y = (1 - |x|^n)^{\frac{1}{n}}$ and $y = -(1 - |x|^n)^{\frac{1}{n}}$ (with your own choice of n) and set the limits $-1 \leqslant x \leqslant 1$ and $-1 \leqslant y \leqslant 1$. (Your calculator may use the terminology 'abs(x)' for $|x|$.)

When $n = 1$ the curve is a square and $n = 2$ gives a circle (see figure 7.42).

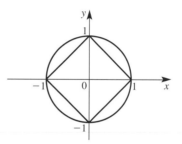

Figure 7.42

What happens for large values of n?
Which value of n do you think gives the most aesthetically pleasing curve?

When $n = 2.5$ the curve is a *superellipse*, shown in figure 7.43.

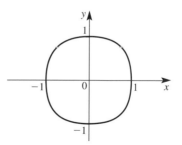

Figure 7.43

If you extend your search to curves of the form $\left|\dfrac{x}{a}\right|^n + \left|\dfrac{y}{b}\right|^n = 1$, what ratio $\dfrac{a}{b}$ gives the most pleasing shape now?

Historical note

The term 'superellipse' was coined by the Danish mathematician, philosopher and poet Piet Hein. He believed that the superellipse was the most aesthetically pleasing shape to the human eye, being a compromise between the circle and the square. Many architects and designers agree and have used the superellipse in their work.

Using calculus

So far you have looked at features of curves which can be found by algebraic techniques. In this section you will see the role that calculus plays in analysing curves.

For curves described by cartesian equations you know that stationary points are found by solving the equation $\frac{dy}{dx} = 0$. In this section calculus techniques are also used to find

- the maximum and minimum distances of the curve from the origin (or pole)
- points on curves where the tangent is parallel or perpendicular to the x axis (or initial line)
- the equations of the tangent and normal to a curve at a given point.

? **(i)** For *polar* curves, what is the geometrical significance of points where

  (a) $\frac{dr}{d\theta} = 0$ **(b)** $\frac{d}{d\theta}(r\cos\theta) = 0$ **(c)** $\frac{d}{d\theta}(r\sin\theta) = 0$?

(ii) For *parametric* curves, what is the geometrical significance of points where

  (a) $\frac{dx}{dt} = 0$ **(b)** $\frac{dy}{dt} = 0$?

Distance from the origin or pole

For cartesian and parametric curves the maximum and minimum distances of the curve from the origin can be found by considering extreme values of $x^2 + y^2$ as on page 161.

For polar curves $\frac{dr}{d\theta}$ is the rate of change of r with respect to θ. At those points where the value of r reaches a maximum or a minimum value then $\frac{dr}{d\theta} = 0$.

As an example think about the curve with polar equation $r = a + b\cos\theta$ where $a > b$, shown in figure 7.44.

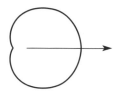

Figure 7.44

Differentiating $r = a + b\cos\theta$ with respect to θ gives $\dfrac{dr}{d\theta} = -b\sin\theta$. To find the maximum and minimum values of r, solve the equation $\dfrac{dr}{d\theta} = 0$. This gives $\sin\theta = 0$ and so $\cos\theta = \sqrt{1 - \sin^2\theta} = \pm 1$. Finally, substituting these values of $\cos\theta$ into $r = a + b\cos\theta$ gives $r_{max} = a + b$ when $\cos\theta = 1$ and $r_{min} = a - b$ when $\cos\theta = -1$.

> *Note*
>
> For this particular example it is possible to find the maximum and minimum distances from the curve to the pole without using calculus. Since the range of values taken by $\cos\theta$ is $-1 \leqslant \cos\theta \leqslant 1$, then the maximum distance from the pole to the curve is $r_{max} = a + b(1) = a + b$ and the minimum distance is $r_{min} = a + b(-1) = a - b$. These, not surprisingly, agree with the maximum and minimum distances of the curve from the pole found using calculus.

 The curve $r = 3 + \cos\theta + \sin\theta$ is shown in figure 7.45. What are the maximum and minimum distances of the curve from the pole?

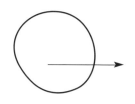

Figure 7.45

Maxima and minima

Returning to the fairground ride curve on page 149, the parametric equations

$$x = 4\cos T + 2\cos 3T, \quad y = 4\sin T + 2\sin 3T$$

give the curve in figure 7.46.

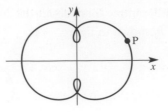

Figure 7.46

As the point P moves around this curve the tangent to the curve at P is parallel to the x axis at six points. At each of these points the rate of change of y with respect to T is zero, i.e. $\dfrac{dy}{dT} = 0$.

$$y = 4 \sin T + 2 \sin 3T \quad \Rightarrow \quad \frac{dy}{dT} = 4 \cos T + 6 \cos 3T.$$

In order to solve the equation $\dfrac{dy}{dT} = 0$ you first need to find $\dfrac{dy}{dT}$ in a useful form.

$$\frac{dy}{dT} = 4 \cos T + 6 \cos 3T$$

$$= 4 \cos T + 6(4 \cos^3 T - 3 \cos T)$$

$$\cos 3T \equiv 4 \cos^3 T - 3 \cos T$$

$$= 24 \cos^3 T - 14 \cos T$$

$$= 2 \cos T(12 \cos^2 T - 7).$$

Therefore, when $\dfrac{dy}{dT} = 0$, $\cos T = 0$, $\sqrt{\dfrac{7}{12}}$ or $-\sqrt{\dfrac{7}{12}}$.

- Using the trace function on your calculator, verify that the points on the curve corresponding to these values of T are indeed the points where the tangent to the curve is horizontal.

 What are the advantages of solving $\dfrac{dy}{dT} = 0$ rather than $\dfrac{dy}{dx} = 0$?

Similarly, at the points where the tangent is vertical, the rate of change of x with respect to T is zero.

ACTIVITY 7.4 Solve $\dfrac{dx}{dT} = 0$ and so find the co-ordinates of the points on the curve at which the tangent to the curve is parallel to the y axis.

Gradients: tangents and normals

You already know how to find the equations of the tangent and normal at a point on a cartesian curve. For example, on the curve $y = 2x^3$, $\dfrac{dy}{dx} = 6x^2$ and so the gradient of the curve at the point $P\left(\frac{1}{2}, \frac{1}{4}\right)$ is $6 \times \left(\frac{1}{2}\right)^2 = \frac{3}{2}$. Therefore the tangent is $y - \frac{1}{4} = \frac{3}{2}\left(x - \frac{1}{2}\right)$ and the normal is $y - \frac{1}{4} = -\frac{2}{3}\left(x - \frac{1}{2}\right)$.

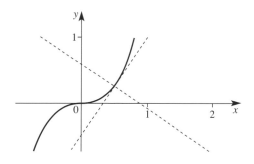

Figure 7.47

As with cartesian curves, you can find the equations of the tangent and normal at a point on a curve defined parametrically.

EXAMPLE 7.4

A circle of radius a rolls along a straight line.

(i) Draw a rough sketch of the path followed by a point on the circumference of the circle highlighting any important characteristics.

Figure 7.48 shows the general position of the circle where the *centre* of the circle, C, has moved from its initial point with co-ordinates $(0, a)$ to the point with co-ordinates (d, a). The point marked P was initially at the origin O.

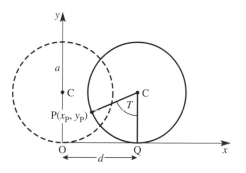

Figure 7.48

Let $\angle PCQ = T$.

(ii) By using the fact that the arc length PQ is equal to the length of the line OQ, show that the parametric equations of the curve traced out by P are

$$x = a(T - \sin T), \quad y = a(1 - \cos T).$$

This curve is called a *cycloid*. The tangent to the cycloid gives the direction in which the point P is moving.

(iii) Find the equations of the tangent and normal to the cycloid at the point with co-ordinates $(a(T - \sin T), a(1 - \cos T))$. Show that the normal passes through the point with co-ordinates $(aT, 0)$ and explain the geometrical significance of this point.

SOLUTION

(i) The curve is symmetrical about the line $x = \pi a$ and the highest point has co-ordinates $(\pi a, 2a)$, as in figure 7.49.

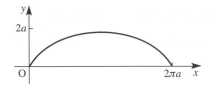

Figure 7.49

(ii) $\angle PCQ = T$ radians and $|OQ| = d$.

Since the arc length PQ is equal to the distance OQ, then $aT = d$. Referring back to figure 7.48,

$$x_P = d - a \sin T = aT - a \sin T \quad \text{and} \quad y_P = a - a \cos T.$$

Therefore, the parametric equations of the cycloid are

$$x = a(T - \sin T) \quad \text{and} \quad y = a(1 - \cos T).$$

(iii) $\dfrac{dx}{dt} = a(1 - \cos T)$ and $\dfrac{dy}{dt} = a \sin T$. Therefore

$$\frac{dy}{dx} = \frac{a \sin T}{a(1 - \cos T)} = \frac{\sin T}{(1 - \cos T)}.$$

The equation of the tangent is

$$y - a(1 - \cos T) = \frac{\sin T}{(1 - \cos T)}(x - a(T - \sin T))$$

and the equation of the normal is

$$y - a(1 - \cos T) = -\frac{(1 - \cos T)}{\sin T}(x - a(T - \sin T)).$$

Substituting $y = 0$ shows that the point $(aT, 0)$ lies on the normal.

When the circle is in the position shown in figure 7.50, $(aT, 0)$ is the point where the circle touches the line.

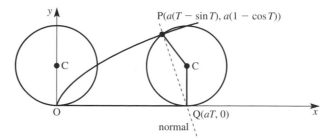

Figure 7.50

ACTIVITY 7.5

Given that the area under the cycloid in figure 7.51 is $\displaystyle\int_0^{2\pi a} y \, dx = \int_0^{2\pi} y \frac{dx}{dT} \, dT$, show that this area is three-quarters of the area of the containing rectangle.

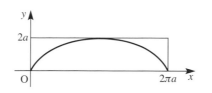

Figure 7.51

⚠ Finding the equations of the tangent and normal to a polar curve is beyond the scope of this book. As seen in Question 12 of Exercise 7A, straight lines (including tangents and normals) do not lend themselves to being expressed in polar form. The following activity shows how you can use your calculator to find the equation of a tangent to a polar curve.

ACTIVITY 7.6

Figure 7.52 shows the curve $r = \sin^2 \theta$ for $0 < \theta < \dfrac{\pi}{2}$. P is a point on the curve and L is the tangent to the curve at P.

On your calculator draw the curve $r = \sin^2 \theta$ for $0 < \theta < \dfrac{\pi}{2}$.

Given that the line L makes an angle of $\dfrac{3\pi}{4}$ with the initial line, show that the polar equation of L is of the form $r = \dfrac{c}{\cos \theta + \sin \theta}$.

Figure 7.52

Using your calculator, find the value of c to an accuracy of 2 decimal places.

EXERCISE 7C

1 On your calculator experiment with polar curves of the form $r = k + \cos\theta$, where $k > 0$.

When $k = 1$, the curve generated has a cusp.

(i) Write down the range of values of k for which the curve
   (a) contains a loop   (b) contains a dimple   (c) is convex.

(ii) Using $x = r\cos\theta$ and $y = r\sin\theta$ find parametric equations for this curve with parameter θ.

(iii) For those values of k where the curve contains a dimple, explain why there must be four values of θ between 0 and 2π satisfying the equation
$$\frac{\mathrm{d}x}{\mathrm{d}\theta} = 0.$$

(iv) By considering the number of values of θ satisfying $\dfrac{\mathrm{d}x}{\mathrm{d}\theta} = 0$, explain how this shows that the curve makes the transition from having a dimple to becoming convex when $k = 2$.

2 The diagram below shows the curve with parametric equations
$$x = \sin 2T, \quad y = \sin 3T.$$

Enter these on your calculator, noticing the symmetry in both the x axis and the y axis.

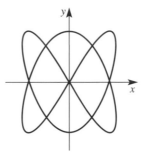

(i) The curve passes through the origin. Find the two values of T corresponding to this, and the gradient of the curve for each of these values.

(ii) Find the values of the parameter T between 0 and $\dfrac{\pi}{2}$ corresponding to the points on the curve where the tangent to the curve is
   (a) vertical   (b) horizontal,
   and use these to write down the co-ordinates at these points.

3 The diagram shows the graph
of $r = \cos\theta + \sin\theta$.

(i) Prove that the maximum distance
from the pole to the curve is $\sqrt{2}$.

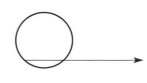

The graph of $r = \cos^n\theta + \sin^n\theta$ is shown below for various positive integer
values of n.

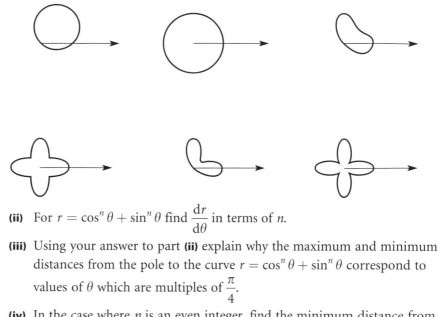

(ii) For $r = \cos^n\theta + \sin^n\theta$ find $\dfrac{dr}{d\theta}$ in terms of n.

(iii) Using your answer to part (ii) explain why the maximum and minimum
distances from the pole to the curve $r = \cos^n\theta + \sin^n\theta$ correspond to
values of θ which are multiples of $\dfrac{\pi}{4}$.

(iv) In the case where n is an even integer, find the minimum distance from
the pole to the curve in terms of n.

4 On your calculator draw the curve with parametric equations
$$x = \sin t, \quad y = \sin 4t.$$
This is called a *Lissajous curve*.

(i) By using the trigonometric double angle formulae show that
$$\sin^2 4t = 16\sin^2 t(1 - \sin^2 t)(1 - 2\sin^2 t)^2$$
and hence write down the cartesian equation of this Lissajous curve,
expressing y^2 in terms of x.

(ii) Using your answer to part (i) or otherwise prove that the curve is
symmetrical in both the x axis and the y axis.

(iii) There are three nodes (or crossover points) on the x axis. Find their
co-ordinates and the corresponding values of the parameter t.

(iv) The horizontal tangents to the curve occur at points where $\dfrac{dy}{dt} = 0$. Use this fact to explain why the y co-ordinates of all points where the tangent is horizontal are either 1 or -1.

5 The graph with cartesian equation $y = \dfrac{x^2}{2x - 1}$ is shown below. The point S has coordinates $\left(\frac{1}{2}, \frac{1}{2}\right)$.

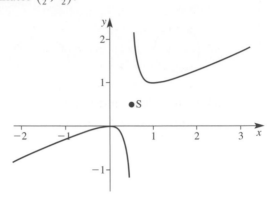

(i) Draw this graph on your calculator.

The line passing through the point S with gradient m where $m > \frac{1}{2}$ meets the curve at P and Q.

(ii) Show that S is the mid-point of PQ and that the gradients of the tangents at P and Q are both equal to $1 - m$.

6 (i) Enter the parametric equations

$$x = 2 \sin t + \sin 3t, \quad y = \sin 2t + \sin 4t$$

into your graphic calculator. Plot this curve, called a *harmonograph*, and notice how the curve unfolds as t increases from 0 to 2π.

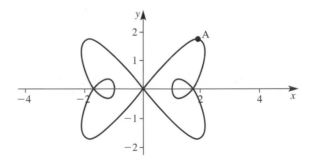

(ii) The curve passes through the origin twice. Find the gradient of the two branches of the curve at this point.

(iii) The tangent to the curve has gradient 0 at eight points. Show that at these points the parameter t satisfies the equation $4 \cos^2 2t + \cos 2t - 2 = 0$ and use this to find the co-ordinates of the point marked A.

7 (i) Draw the graph of $y^2 = \dfrac{x^3 - 2}{x}$ on your graphic calculator (entering

$y = \sqrt{\dfrac{x^3 - 2}{x}}$ and $y = -\sqrt{\dfrac{x^3 - 2}{x}}$ if necessary).

The curve has one vertical asymptote of $x = 0$ and two oblique asymptotes.

(ii) By considering the behaviour of y^2 as $x \to \infty$ write down the equations of these two oblique asymptotes. Check your answer by drawing these oblique asymptotes along with the curve on your graphic calculator.

(iii) Calculate the co-ordinates of the two points on the curve where the tangent to the curve is horizontal. Check your answer by using the trace function on your calculator.

(iv) By using the substitution $x = r \cos \theta$, $y = r \sin \theta$, show that a polar form of the curve is $2 = r^3 \cos \theta \cos 2\theta$.

(v) Use this form to show that

$$3 \frac{dr}{d\theta} \cos \theta \cos 2\theta = r \sin \theta (5 - 6 \sin^2 \theta).$$

Hence find the minimum distance from the origin to the curve. Check your answer by drawing the circle with this radius, centre the origin, on your graphic calculator.

8 The *cardioid* has polar equation
$r = 2a(1 + \cos \theta)$. A chord passes through
the pole and meets the cardioid at P and Q.

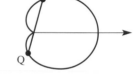

(i) Prove that, for any such chord, $|PQ| = 4a$.

(ii) Show that the parametric equations of the cardioid are

$$x = a(2 \cos \theta + \cos 2\theta + 1), \quad y = a(2 \sin \theta + \sin 2\theta).$$

(iii) Find $\dfrac{dx}{d\theta}$ and $\dfrac{dy}{d\theta}$ and hence show that $\dfrac{dy}{dx} = -\cot \dfrac{3\theta}{2}$.

(iv) Prove that the tangents to the curve at P and Q are perpendicular to each other.

(v) Using your answer to part **(iii)**, prove that there are exactly three parallel tangents to the cardioid with any given gradient.

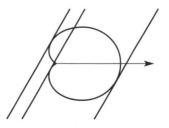

9 The graphs of $x = \dfrac{3at}{1 + t^3}$ and $y = \dfrac{3at^2}{1 + t^3}$ are shown below (for $a > 0$).

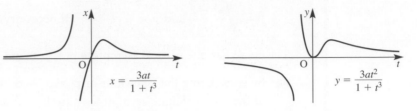

(i) Write down the equation of the vertical asymptote in each case.

The *folium of Descartes* has parametric equations

$$x = \frac{3at}{1 + t^3}, \quad y = \frac{3at^2}{1 + t^3}.$$

(ii) Draw the folium of Descartes on your calculator and, using the graphs above or otherwise, describe the way in which the curve unfolds as t varies from $t = -10$ to $t = 10$.

(iii) Find $\dfrac{dy}{dx}$ in terms of t and use this to show that as $t \to -1$ the gradient of the curve approaches -1.

(iv) Show that $x + y = \dfrac{3at}{t^2 - t + 1}$.

By considering the value of this expression as $t \to -1$, deduce that $x + y + a = 0$ is an oblique asymptote to the curve. (You can check this result by drawing the line $x + y + a = 0$ and the curve on your calculator for several values of a.)

10 The graph of $r = \dfrac{\sin \theta}{\theta}$ is shown below for $0 < \theta < 2\pi$. The tangents to the curve are parallel and perpendicular to the initial line at B and C respectively.

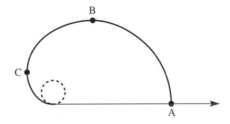

(i) Using Maclaurin's expansion for $\sin x$ show that, for small x,

$$\frac{\sin x}{x} \approx 1 - \frac{x^2}{6}$$ and use this to write down the polar co-ordinates of point A.

At point B, $\dfrac{d}{d\theta}(r \sin \theta) = 0$.

(ii) Show that $\dfrac{d}{d\theta}(r \sin \theta) = \dfrac{\sin \theta(2\theta \cos \theta - \sin \theta)}{\theta^2}$.

(iii) Using the Newton–Raphson method to solve

$$f(\theta) = 2\theta \cos\theta - \sin\theta = 0,$$

find the value of θ at B to an accuracy of 5 decimal places and write down the corresponding value of $r\sin\theta$.

(iv) Find the values of θ and $r\cos\theta$ at point C.

11 The graphs of $x^n + y^n = 1$ for some values of n are shown below.

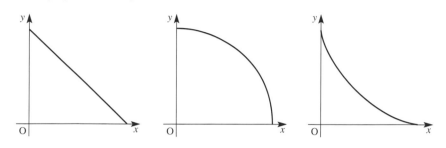

(i) Using your calculator, familiarise yourself with this family of curves for values of n in the range $0 < n \leqslant 3$.

A point $P(p, q)$ lies on the curve $x^n + y^n = 1$.

(ii) Show that the tangent to the curve at P has equation $p^{n-1}x + q^{n-1}y = 1$.

This tangent crosses the axes at points $A(X, 0)$ and $B(0, Y)$.

(iii) Show that $X^{\frac{n}{1-n}} + Y^{\frac{n}{1-n}} = 1$.

(iv) Deduce that AB has constant length for all positions of P if and only if $n = \frac{2}{3}$. (This is the *astroid*, $x^{\frac{2}{3}} + y^{\frac{2}{3}} = 1$.)

12 The line L makes an angle of $\dfrac{3\pi}{4}$ with the initial line.

(i) Show that the polar equation of L is of the form $r = \dfrac{c}{\cos\theta + \sin\theta}$.

The diagram below shows the curve $r = \sin\theta$ for $0 < \theta < \dfrac{\pi}{2}$ and the straight line, L, with equation $r = \dfrac{c}{\cos\theta + \sin\theta}$. In the diagram, c takes the value 1.

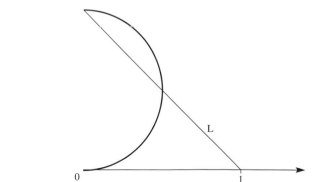

☆ **(ii)** Using your calculator find, by trial and improvement, the value of c, to
☆ an accuracy of 1 decimal place, which results in L being a tangent to the
☆ curve $r = \sin\theta$.
☆ **(iii)** Express the curve $r = \sin\theta$ and the straight line $r = \dfrac{c}{\cos\theta + \sin\theta}$ in
☆ cartesian form, and hence find the exact values of c for which the line is
☆ a tangent to the curve.

Conics

The family of curves called *conics* takes a central place in mathematics, having a
long history, a rich geometry, and many important applications. You have
already met some members of the family: parabolas, ellipses and hyperbolas.
This section shows that these curves truly are a family, and explores their
similarities and differences.

Historical note

The Greek mathematician Apollonius of Perga (c.262–190 BC) wrote an eight-volume study of conics,
building on earlier work. The astronomer Johannes Kepler gave conics new importance when he
announced in 1609 that the orbits of the planets are ellipses, and in *The Two New Sciences* (1638)
Galileo Galilei showed that the path of a projectile is a parabola.

Focus–directrix property

ACTIVITY 7.7   On squared paper draw a set of parallel vertical lines 1 cm apart, and label one of
these d. Mark a grid point S 3 cm from d. Draw circles with centre S and radii
2, 3, ... cm. Mark the points of intersection of the circle with radius r cm and
the line r cm from d for several values of r. Connect these points of intersection
with a smooth curve.

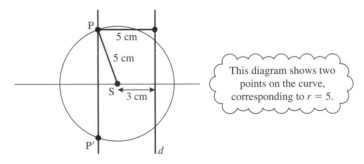

Figure 7.53

The curve you have drawn is a *parabola*. The parabola can be thought of as one
of a family of curves characterised by a similar property. This property is
described in the following locus problem.

ACTIVITY 7.8   Figure 7.54 shows a fixed point S and a fixed line d. The point P moves in such a way that, at all times $\dfrac{|PS|}{|PM|} = e$, where e is a constant called the *eccentricity*; that is, $|PS| = e|PM|$.

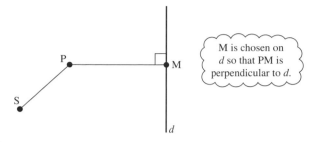

M is chosen on d so that PM is perpendicular to d.

Figure 7.54

When $e = 1$ the procedure to find the locus is the same as the one you used in Activity 7.7. Therefore the curve is a parabola.

Adapt the method used in Activity 7.7 to draw the curves for $e = \frac{1}{2}$ and $e = 2$, and explore the curves generated by other values of e.

A natural way to attempt an analysis of this family of curves is to use polar co-ordinates, taking the point S as the pole and the line through S which is perpendicular to d as the initial line. In the terminology of conics, the point S is called the *focus* of the conic and the line d is called the *directrix*.

Figure 7.55 shows the focus S, the directrix d, and the point P, satisfying the condition $|PS| = e|PM|$. The polar co-ordinates of P are (r, θ) and the perpendicular distance from S to d is k.

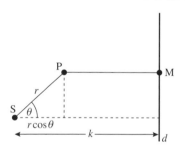

Figure 7.55

The polar equation of the curve follows directly from the property $|PS| = e|PM|$:

$$|PS| = r, \quad |PM| = k - r\cos\theta \quad \Rightarrow \quad r = e(k - r\cos\theta)$$

$$ek = r + er\cos\theta$$

$$r = \frac{ek}{1 + e\cos\theta}.$$

Since both e and k are constants, their product, ek, can be replaced by another constant l, giving the polar equation $r = \dfrac{l}{1 + e\cos\theta}$.

ACTIVITY 7.9 On your graphic calculator plot $r = \dfrac{l}{1 + e\cos\theta}$ for $l = 4$ and

(i) $e = 0$ **(ii)** $e = 1$ **(iii)** $e = \frac{1}{2}$ **(iv)** $e = 2$.

What do you notice?

Now repeat this for $l = 2$. How does changing l affect the shape of the graph?

In general, what can you say about the curve $r = \dfrac{l}{1 + e\cos\theta}$ for

(i) $e = 1$ **(ii)** $0 < e < 1$ **(iii)** $e > 1$?

You can see from Activities 7.7, 7.8 and 7.9 above that the parabola, ellipse and hyperbola are truly a *family* of curves. These curves are called the *conic sections* and the family is defined in the following way.

- A conic is the locus of a point in a plane such that its distance from a fixed point S is a constant multiple of its distance from a fixed line d, both S and d being in the plane.

They are called conics because they were originally studied as plane sections of a right circular cone.

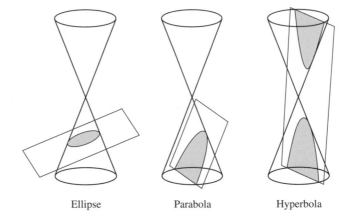

Ellipse Parabola Hyperbola

Figure 7.56

Figure 7.56 shows a double cone standing with its axis vertical. A horizontal plane not through the vertex cuts the cone in a circle. When the plane is tilted slightly the section is an ellipse. As the angle of tilt increases the section becomes more elongated until, when the plane is parallel to a generator of the cone (i.e. a straight line through the vertex in the surface of the cone), the section is a parabola. With further tilting, the plane cuts the other half of the cone too, and the section is a hyperbola. So the parabola is the borderline case, separating ellipses from hyperbolas.

Cartesian equations of the conics

The method used in Activity 7.8 can be adapted to find the cartesian equations of the conics. In order to ensure that the resulting equations are relatively simple it is helpful to choose specific positions for the directrix and the focus as described below. (You could choose to work with the same focus and directrix (as in Activity 7.12), but the equations turn out to be more cumbersome.)

The parabola, *e* = 1

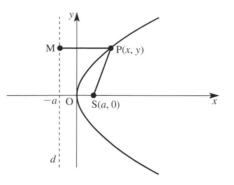

Figure 7.57

Let the line $x = -a$ be the directrix and let the point $(a, 0)$ be the focus. Then

$$\text{P}(x, y) \text{ is on the parabola} \quad \Leftrightarrow \quad \text{SP} = \text{PM} \quad \text{(by definition)}$$
$$\Leftrightarrow \quad \text{SP}^2 = \text{PM}^2$$
$$\Leftrightarrow \quad (x - a)^2 + y^2 = (x + a)^2$$
$$\Leftrightarrow \quad y^2 = (x + a)^2 - (x - a)^2$$
$$\Leftrightarrow \quad y^2 = 4ax.$$

This is the cartesian equation of the parabola in its standard form.

The ellipse, 0 < *e* < 1

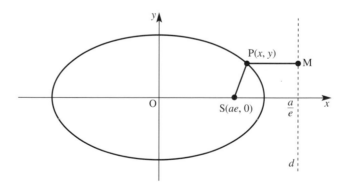

Figure 7.58

Let the line $x = \dfrac{a}{e}$ be the directrix and let the point $(ae, 0)$ be the focus. Then

$$\text{P}(x, y) \text{ is on the ellipse} \quad \Leftrightarrow \quad \text{SP} = e\text{PM} \quad \text{(by definition)}$$
$$\Leftrightarrow \quad \text{SP}^2 = e^2\text{PM}^2$$
$$\Leftrightarrow \quad (x - ae)^2 + y^2 = e^2\left(\frac{a}{e} - x\right)^2$$

$$\Leftrightarrow \quad x^2 - 2aex + a^2e^2 + y^2 = a^2 - 2aex + e^2x^2$$

The same ellipse results if you use directix $x = -\dfrac{a}{e}$ and focus $(-ae, 0)$.

$$\Leftrightarrow \quad x^2(1 - e^2) + y^2 = a^2(1 - e^2)$$

$$\Leftrightarrow \quad \frac{x^2}{a^2} + \frac{y^2}{a^2(1 - e^2)} = 1.$$

The point $(a, 0)$ lies on the ellipse.

Since $0 < e < 1$ it follows that $a^2(1 - e^2) > 0$ and so you can replace this expression by b^2, giving

$$\frac{x^2}{a^2} + \frac{y^2}{b^2} = 1.$$

This is the standard cartesian equation of the ellipse.

? Given the equation for an ellipse $\dfrac{x^2}{16} + \dfrac{y^2}{9} = 1$, how would you find the eccentricity, the focus and the directrix?

ACTIVITY 7.10 An equivalent definition of the ellipse is the locus of a point P in a plane such that the sum of the distances of P from two fixed points S and S′ in the plane is fixed.

PS + PS′ = a constant.

Figure 7.59

An ellipse can be drawn by passing a loop of thread around fixed pins at S and S′, and pulling this taut with a pencil pressed against the paper. As the pencil moves, keeping the string taut, it draws an ellipse.

Draw some ellipses by this method. Describe the effect of changing the separation SS′ without changing the length of the loop.

The hyperbola, $e > 1$

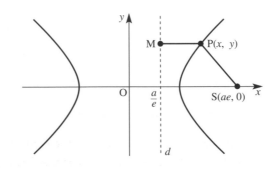

Figure 7.60

As with the ellipse, let the line $x = \dfrac{a}{e}$ be the directrix and let the point $(ae, 0)$ be the focus. However, since $e > 1$, the directrix is now positioned between the origin and the focus (see figure 7.60).

 Proceeding as with the ellipse, show that the cartesian equation for the hyperbola is

$$\frac{x^2}{a^2} + \frac{y^2}{a^2(1 - e^2)} = 1.$$

Since $e > 1$, it follows that $a^2(1 - e^2) < 0$ and so you can replace this expression with $-b^2$, giving

$$\frac{x^2}{a^2} - \frac{y^2}{b^2} = 1.$$

This is the standard cartesian equation of the hyperbola.

By factorising, $\dfrac{x^2}{a^2} - \dfrac{y^2}{b^2} = 1$ can be written as

$$\left(\frac{x}{a} - \frac{y}{b}\right)\left(\frac{x}{a} + \frac{y}{b}\right) = 1.$$

It follows that the hyperbola has oblique asymptotes with equations $\dfrac{x}{a} - \dfrac{y}{b} = 0$ and $\dfrac{x}{a} + \dfrac{y}{b} = 0$ (see figure 7.61).

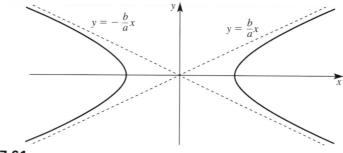

Figure 7.61

ACTIVITY 7.11 On your graphic calculator plot the hyperbola $\dfrac{x^2}{a^2} - \dfrac{y^2}{b^2} = 1$ and the two straight lines $\dfrac{x}{a} - \dfrac{y}{b} = 0$ and $\dfrac{x}{a} + \dfrac{y}{b} = 0$ for various values of a and b. You will notice that the two lines are asymptotes to the hyperbola.

The rectangular hyperbola

In the special case where $a = b$, the equation of the hyperbola is $x^2 - y^2 = a^2$. The two asymptotes are the perpendicular lines $y = x$ and $y = -x$. For this reason this hyperbola is called the *rectangular hyperbola*.

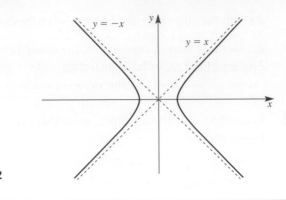

Figure 7.62

❓ Show that for the rectangular hyperbola the eccentricity is $\sqrt{2}$.

So far you have worked with specific foci and directrices, which have resulted in the standard cartesian forms for the conics. In Activity 7.12 you will see the effect of using the same focus and directrix for each of the conics.

ACTIVITY 7.12   Using the y axis for the directrix and the point $(a, 0)$ for the focus, show that $|PS| = e|PM|$ leads to the cartesian equation

$$(x - a)^2 + y^2 = e^2 x^2.$$

Draw this on your graphic calculator (entering both $y = \sqrt{e^2 x^2 - (x - a)^2}$ and $y = -\sqrt{e^2 x^2 - (x - a)^2}$ with a fixed value for a). Investigate these curves for various values of $e > 0$.

Parametric equations of the conics

The point P with co-ordinates $(at^2, 2at)$ lies on $y^2 = 4ax$ for all values of t:

$$y^2 = 4ax = 4a(at^2) = 4a^2 t^2 = (2at)^2.$$

In addition, every point of the curve corresponds to a unique value of t. Therefore the equations $x = at^2$, $y = 2at$ can be used as parametric equations for the parabola $y^2 = 4ax$.

The standard cartesian and parametric equations of the conics are given in the table below.

	Parabola $e = 1$	Ellipse $0 < e < 1$	Hyperbola $e > 1$	Rectangular hyperbola $e = \sqrt{2}$
Cartesian form	$y^2 = 4ax$	$\dfrac{x^2}{a^2} + \dfrac{y^2}{b^2} = 1$	$\dfrac{x^2}{a^2} - \dfrac{y^2}{b^2} = 1$	$xy = c^2$
Parametric form	$x = at^2$ $y = 2at$	$x = a\cos t$ $y = b\sin t$	$x = a\sec t$ $y = b\tan t$	$x = ct$ $y = \dfrac{c}{t}$

In Question 1 of Exercise 7A you demonstrated an equivalence between these parametric and cartesian forms.

For the ellipse, in order to maintain a one-to-one correspondence between the points on the curve and the values of the parameter t, you need to restrict values of t to the range $0 \leqslant t < 2\pi$.

 What are the corresponding restrictions, if any, for the hyperbola and rectangular hyperbola?

 Since $\cosh^2 t - \sinh^2 t = 1$, it would appear that we could use the hyperbolic parametric equations $x = a\cosh t$, $y = b\sinh t$ for the hyperbola. Enter these parametric equations on your calculator and use this to explain why the parametric equations $x = a\sec t$, $y = b\tan t$ are used for the hyperbola in preference to $x = a\cosh t$, $y = b\sinh t$.

Examples

EXAMPLE 7.5

The points T and U of the parabola $y^2 = 4ax$ have co-ordinates $(at^2, 2at)$ and $(au^2, 2au)$ respectively. Find the equation of

(i) the chord TU

(ii) the tangent to the parabola at T

(iii) the normal to the parabola at T.

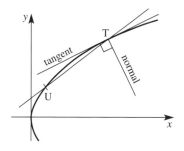

Figure 7.63

A *focal chord* is a chord which passes through the focus.

(iv) Prove that TU is a focal chord if and only if $tu = -1$.

(v) Prove that the tangents at the ends of a focal chord meet at right angles on the directrix (see figure 7.64).

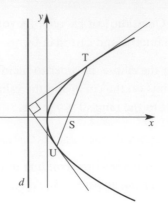

Figure 7.64

SOLUTION

(i) The gradient of TU is

$$\frac{2at - 2au}{at^2 - au^2} = \frac{2(t - u)}{t^2 - u^2} = \frac{2}{t + u}.$$

The line through T with this gradient has the equation

$$y - 2at = \frac{2}{t + u}(x - at^2)$$

$$\Leftrightarrow \quad (t + u)y - 2at(t + u) = 2x - 2at^2$$

$$\Leftrightarrow \quad 2x - (t + u)y + 2atu = 0.$$

(Note that this is symmetrical in t and u, as the geometry demands.)

(ii) The tangent at T is the limiting position of the chord TU as U $\to$ T along the curve, i.e. as $u \to t$. Letting $u \to t$ in the equation of the chord (and cancelling the common factor 2) gives the equation of the tangent:

$$x - ty + at^2 = 0.$$

Alternatively, using calculus,

$$y^2 = 4ax \quad \Rightarrow \quad 2y\frac{dy}{dx} = 4a \quad \Rightarrow \quad \frac{dy}{dx} = \frac{2a}{y}.$$

Therefore the tangent at T has equation

$$y - 2at = \frac{2a}{2at}(x - at^2)$$

$$\Leftrightarrow \quad ty - 2at^2 = x - at^2$$

$$\Leftrightarrow \quad x - ty + at^2 = 0.$$

(iii) From part (ii) the gradient of the tangent at T is $\frac{1}{t}$, so the gradient of the normal is $-t$. The equation of the normal is

$$y - 2at = -t(x - at^2)$$

$$\Leftrightarrow tx + y - 2at - at^3 = 0.$$

(iv) The chord $2x - (t + u)y + 2atu = 0$ passes through the focus $(a, 0)$ if and only if

$$2a - (t + u) \times 0 + 2atu = 0$$
$$\Leftrightarrow \qquad\qquad tu = -1.$$

(v) The gradients of the tangents at T and U are $\dfrac{1}{t}$ and $\dfrac{1}{u}$, and $tu = -1$.

Therefore the product of the gradients is -1, and so the tangents are perpendicular.

The equations of the tangents are

$$x - ty + at^2 = 0, \qquad\qquad\qquad ①$$
$$x - uy + au^2 = 0. \qquad\qquad\qquad ②$$

Taking $① \times u - ② \times t$ to eliminate y gives

$$(u - t)x + at^2u - au^2t = 0$$
$$\Leftrightarrow \qquad (u - t)x = atu(u - t)$$
$$\Leftrightarrow \qquad\qquad\qquad x = atu$$
$$= -a \text{ since } tu = -1.$$

> rearranging and factorising

> Cancelling $(u - t)$, which is not zero since T and U are distinct.

Therefore the tangents meet on the directrix.

EXAMPLE 7.6

Find the equation of **(i)** the tangent **(ii)** the normal to the standard ellipse at $P(a \cos \theta, \, b \sin \theta)$.

SOLUTION

(i) $x = a \cos \theta \Rightarrow \dfrac{dx}{d\theta} = -a \sin \theta \quad$ and $\quad y = b \sin \theta \Rightarrow \dfrac{dy}{d\theta} = b \cos \theta.$

Therefore $\dfrac{dy}{dx} = -\dfrac{b \cos \theta}{a \sin \theta}$ and the equation of the tangent at P is

$$y - b \sin \theta = -\frac{b \cos \theta}{a \sin \theta}(x - a \cos \theta)$$
$$\Leftrightarrow \quad ay \sin \theta - ab \sin^2 \theta = -bx \cos \theta + ab \cos^2 \theta$$
$$\Leftrightarrow \quad bx \cos \theta + ay \sin \theta = ab(\cos^2 \theta + \sin^2 \theta)$$
$$\Leftrightarrow \quad \frac{x \cos \theta}{a} + \frac{y \sin \theta}{b} - 1.$$

(ii) Using $mm' = -1$ for perpendicular lines, the gradient of the normal is $\dfrac{a \sin \theta}{b \cos \theta}.$

The equation of the normal at P is

$$y - b \sin \theta = \frac{a \sin \theta}{b \cos \theta}(x - a \cos \theta)$$
$$\Leftrightarrow \quad by \cos \theta - b^2 \cos \theta \sin \theta = ax \sin \theta - a^2 \cos \theta \sin \theta$$
$$\Leftrightarrow \quad ax \sin \theta - by \cos \theta = (a^2 - b^2) \cos \theta \sin \theta.$$

EXAMPLE 7.7

Prove that the equation of the tangent to the hyperbola $\dfrac{x^2}{a^2} - \dfrac{y^2}{b^2} = 1$ at

$P(a \sec \theta, b \tan \theta)$ may be written as $\dfrac{x \sec \theta}{a} - \dfrac{y \tan \theta}{b} = 1$ or as

$\dfrac{x}{a} - \dfrac{y}{b} \sin \theta = \cos \theta.$

SOLUTION

$x = a \sec \theta \Rightarrow \dfrac{dx}{d\theta} = a \sec \theta \tan \theta$ and $y = b \tan \theta \Rightarrow \dfrac{dy}{d\theta} = b \sec^2 \theta.$

Therefore $\dfrac{dy}{dx} = \dfrac{b \sec^2 \theta}{a \sec \theta \tan \theta} = \dfrac{b \sec \theta}{a \tan \theta}$ and the equation of the tangent at P is

$$y - b \tan \theta = \dfrac{b \sec \theta}{a \tan \theta}(x - a \sec \theta)$$

$$\Leftrightarrow \quad ay \tan \theta - ab \tan^2 \theta = bx \sec \theta - ab \sec^2 \theta$$

$$\Leftrightarrow \quad bx \sec \theta - ay \tan \theta = ab(\sec^2 \theta - \tan^2 \theta)$$

$$\Leftrightarrow \quad \dfrac{x \sec \theta}{a} - \dfrac{y \tan \theta}{b} = 1, \text{ since } \sec^2 \theta - \tan^2 \theta = 1.$$

Multiplying throughout by $\cos \theta$ and using $\tan \theta = \dfrac{\sin \theta}{\cos \theta}$ gives the alternative

form $\dfrac{x}{a} - \dfrac{y}{b} \sin \theta = \cos \theta.$

EXAMPLE 7.8

Lines are drawn parallel to the asymptotes through any point P of the hyperbola
$\dfrac{x^2}{a^2} - \dfrac{y^2}{b^2} = 1$, meeting the asymptotes at H and K.
Prove that $PH \times PK = \frac{1}{4}(a^2 + b^2).$

SOLUTION

By symmetry there is no loss of generality in taking P to be $(a \sec \theta, b \tan \theta)$ in
the first quadrant as in figure 7.65. Let $PH = h$, $PK = k$, and let the angle
between the asymptote and the x axis be ϕ.

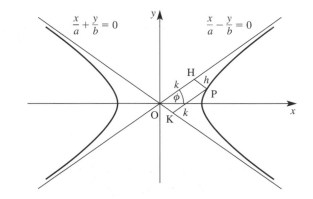

Figure 7.65

Then $\quad a\sec\theta = k\cos\phi + h\cos\phi \Rightarrow k+h = a\sec\theta\sec\phi$

and $\quad b\tan\theta = k\sin\phi - h\sin\phi \Rightarrow k-h = b\tan\theta\operatorname{cosec}\phi.$

So $\qquad 4hk = (k+h)^2 - (k-h)^2$
$$= a^2\sec^2\theta\sec^2\phi - b^2\tan^2\theta\operatorname{cosec}^2\phi$$
$$= (a\sec\phi)^2\sec^2\theta - (b\operatorname{cosec}\phi)^2\tan^2\theta.$$

But since $\tan\phi = \dfrac{b}{a}$, $a\sec\phi = b\operatorname{cosec}\phi = \sqrt{a^2+b^2}$

(see figure 7.66).

Therefore $\quad 4hk = (a^2+b^2)(\sec^2\theta - \tan^2\theta) = (a^2+b^2)$

and so $\qquad \text{PH} \times \text{PK} = \tfrac{1}{4}(a^2+b^2).$

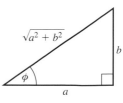

Figure 7.66

1 The graph of $y^2 + |x^2 - 9| = 16$ is shown below.

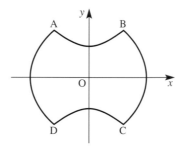

(i) Find the co-ordinates of the x and y intercepts and the points A, B, C and D.

(ii) Prove that arcs AB and CD lie on a rectangular hyperbola and write down its equation.

The graph of $y^2 + a|x^2 - 9| = 16$ is shown below for several values of a.

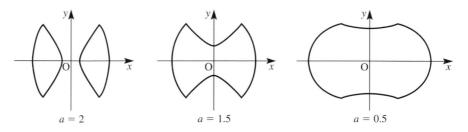

$a = 2 \qquad\qquad a = 1.5 \qquad\qquad a = 0.5$

(iii) Show that in general for $a > 0$ $(a \neq 1)$ two arcs lie on a hyperbola and two arcs lie on an ellipse. Write down the equations of these conics in terms of a.

(iv) Show that, when $a = \tfrac{4}{3}$, these conics meet at right angles to each other at all four points.

(v) Find the exact value of a which results in the graph shown below.

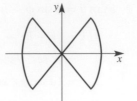

2 A parabola has parametric equations $x = at^2$, $y = 2at$.

(i) Find the equation of the tangent to the parabola at the point $P(ap^2, 2ap)$.

The tangents to the parabola at the points $P(ap^2, 2ap)$ and $Q(aq^2, 2aq)$, where $p \neq q$, meet at the point T.

(ii) Show that the co-ordinates of T are $(apq, a(p + q))$.

The mid-point of PQ is M, and the mid-point of TM is R.

(iii) Show that TM is parallel to the x axis.
(iv) Show that R lies on the parabola.
(v) Show that the tangent to the parabola at R is parallel to PQ.

[MEI]

3 The parametric equations of a parabola are $x = at^2$, $y = 2at$. P and Q are two points on this parabola with parameters t_1 and t_2 respectively.

(i) **(a)** Derive the equation of the chord PQ.
    (b) P and Q now vary in such a way that line PQ has a fixed gradient. Show that $t_1 + t_2$ is constant.
    (c) Write down the co-ordinates of the mid-point of PQ.
    Show that the mid-points of chords of a parabola which are in a fixed direction, lie on a line parallel to the x axis.
(ii) **(a)** Find the equation of the tangent to the parabola at $R(aT^2, 2aT)$.
    (b) Show that this tangent will also be a tangent to the circle
$$x^2 + y^2 = \tfrac{1}{2}a^2$$
    if $2T^4 - T^2 - 1 = 0$.
    (c) Find the equations of the two real common tangents to the circle and the parabola.

[MEI]

4 The focus of the parabola $y^2 = 4ax$ is the point with co-ordinates $(a, 0)$. Any chord of the parabola which passes through the focus is called a *focal chord*. The directrix of the parabola is the line $x = -a$.

For the parabola $y^2 = 4ax$, prove that a circle which has a focal chord as diameter touches the directrix.

5 The *elliptic trammel* is a mechanical device for drawing ellipses.

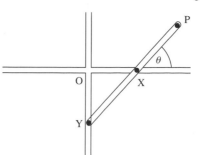

It consists of a straight rod with a pencil at P and pegs at X, Y which run in perpendicular grooves OX, OY. Prove that if OX, OY are taken as x and y axes with $PX = b$, $PY = a$, then the locus of P is the ellipse $\dfrac{x^2}{a^2} + \dfrac{y^2}{b^2} = 1$.

[**Hint:** Use the angle θ shown in the diagram.]

6 (i) Show that the x co-ordinates of the points of intersection of the line $y = mx + c$ and the ellipse $\dfrac{x^2}{a^2} + \dfrac{y^2}{b^2} = 1$ (where $a > b > 0$) satisfy the quadratic equation $(a^2m^2 + b^2)x^2 + (2a^2mc)x + a^2(c^2 - b^2) = 0$.

(ii) Deduce that if $y = mx + c$ is a tangent to the ellipse, then $c^2 = a^2m^2 + b^2$, and show that the point of contact is $\left(-\dfrac{a^2m}{c}, \dfrac{b^2}{c} \right)$.

(iii) Use the result in part **(ii)** to prove that the gradients of the two tangents from the point (X, Y) to the ellipse are the roots of the quadratic equation
$$m^2(a^2 - X^2) + 2mXY + b^2 - Y^2 = 0.$$

(iv) Find the condition for this equation to have complex roots, and interpret this geometrically.

(v) Find the condition for the product of the roots to equal -1. Deduce that the tangents from the point (X, Y) to the ellipse are perpendicular if and only if (X, Y) lies on the circle $x^2 + y^2 = a^2 + b^2$. (This is called the *director circle* of the ellipse.)

(vi) An elliptical disc slides between two fixed perpendicular lines. Prove that the locus of its centre is an arc of a circle.

7 The line $y = mx + c$ meets the hyperbola $\dfrac{x^2}{a^2} - \dfrac{y^2}{b^2} = 1$ at P_1, P_2 and meets the asymptotes at Q_1, Q_2.

(i) Write down the quadratic equation whose roots are the x co-ordinates of P_1, P_2, and find the sum of these roots.

(ii) Write down the quadratic equation whose roots are the x co-ordinates of Q_1, Q_2, and find the sum of these roots.

(iii) Hence show that P_1, P_2 and Q_1, Q_2 have the same mid-point.

(iv) Deduce that $P_1Q_1 = P_2Q_2$.

8 The tangent at a point P of the hyperbola $\dfrac{x^2}{a^2} - \dfrac{y^2}{b^2} = 1$ meets the asymptotes at Q_1, Q_2.

(i) Prove that P is the mid-point of $Q_1 Q_2$. [**Hint:** Use Question 7 part **(iv)**.]

(ii) Prove that as P varies the area of triangle $OQ_1 Q_2$ remains constant.

9 Prove that the equation of the normal to the hyperbola $\dfrac{x^2}{a^2} - \dfrac{y^2}{b^2} = 1$ at $P(a \sec \theta, b \tan \theta)$ is $ax \sin \theta + by = (a^2 + b^2) \tan \theta$.

This normal meets the x axis at G, and the mid-point of PG is Q. Prove that the locus of Q is a hyperbola.

10 Find the co-ordinates of the two points where the hyperbolas $x^2 - y^2 = 5$ and $xy = 6$ intersect. Prove that the tangents to the hyperbolas at these points form a rectangle.

11 Sketch on a single diagram three members of each of the following families of rectangular hyperbolas:

(A) those with equations $x^2 - y^2 = a^2$ for various a
(B) those with equations $xy = c^2$ for various c.

Prove that every member of family (A) meets every member of family (B) at right angles, unless $a = c = 0$.

12 Find the equation of the normal to the rectangular hyperbola $xy = c^2$ at the point $P\left(ct, \dfrac{c}{t} \right)$. Prove that this normal meets the hyperbola again at $Q\left(-\dfrac{c}{t^3}, -ct^3 \right)$.

The circle with PQ as diameter meets the rectangular hyperbola $xy = c^2$ again at N. Prove that PN passes through the origin, and that the normal at N is parallel to PQ.

13 The mid-point of the chord joining the points $\left(ct, \dfrac{c}{t} \right)$, and $\left(cT, \dfrac{c}{T} \right)$ on the rectangular hyperbola $xy = c^2$ has co-ordinates (X, Y).

Prove that $t + T = \dfrac{2X}{c}$ and $tT = \dfrac{X}{Y}$.

A variable chord of the rectangular hyperbola $xy = c^2$ passes through the fixed point (h, k). Prove that the locus of the mid-point of the chord is another rectangular hyperbola, and give the equations of its asymptotes.

14 A curve, C, has parametric equations $x = \sin T$, $y = \cos T$.

(i) Describe C.

C is transformed into a family of curves by the matrix $\begin{pmatrix} 1 & k \\ k & 1 \end{pmatrix}$, for

different values of k. The general member of this family is denoted by K.

(ii) Enter several members of the family onto your calculator using various values of k (but not 1, −1 or 0).
Name the conic they look like and state the equations of the lines that appear to be their axes.

The matrix **M** is $\begin{pmatrix} \frac{1}{\sqrt{2}} & \frac{1}{\sqrt{2}} \\ -\frac{1}{\sqrt{2}} & \frac{1}{\sqrt{2}} \end{pmatrix}$.

(iii) State the transformation represented by **M**.

(iv) Apply the matrix **M** to the general curve K to obtain the curve E.
Find the cartesian equation of E and hence confirm your observations in part **(ii)**.

(v) Explain why values of 1, −1 and 0 for k are special cases. Use your calculator to investigate what happens in each of these cases and explain your findings.

15 The diagram below shows the circle S, $x^2 + y^2 = a^2$, and the ellipse S′,
$\dfrac{x^2}{a^2} + \dfrac{y^2}{b^2} = 1$. The point $P(a\cos\theta,\ a\sin\theta)$ lies on S.

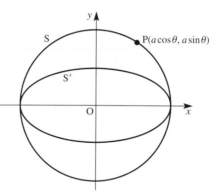

P′ is the image of P under the transformation given by the matrix

$$\mathbf{M} = \begin{pmatrix} 1 & 0 \\ 0 & \dfrac{b}{a} \end{pmatrix}.$$

(i) Prove that P′ lies on S′ and, on a copy of the diagram, show the position of P′.

A second point on the ellipse has co-ordinates $(a\cos T,\ b\sin T)$

(ii) Explain the geometrical significance of T.

(iii) Write down det**M** and explain how this shows that the area of the ellipse is πab.

16 The diagram below shows the *lemniscate* $r^2 = \cos 2\theta$ and the circle $r = 1$.

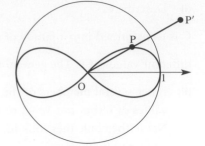

A half-line, L, is drawn from the pole, O, as shown. L meets the lemniscate at the point P. The point P′ on L is chosen so that $|OP'| = \dfrac{1}{|OP|}$.

(i) On an accurate copy of the diagram, draw the lemniscate and six such pairs of points P and P′ in the first quadrant.

(ii) Prove that as P moves along the lemniscate, P′ traces out a rectangular hyperbola.

State the cartesian equation of the hyperbola (where the origin is at the pole and the *x* axis is the initial line).

Applying the same process to points on the curve $r^2 = \sin 2\theta$ also results in a rectangular hyperbola.

(iii) Draw the curve $r^2 = \sin 2\theta$ and the resulting hyperbola on your calculator.

State the cartesian equation of the hyperbola in this case.

INVESTIGATION

Sinusoidal spirals are curves with polar equation $r^p = \cos p\theta$. Figure 7.67 shows some pairs of sinusoidal spirals for different values of *p*.

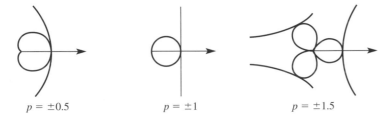

$p = \pm 0.5$ $p = \pm 1$ $p = \pm 1.5$

Figure 7.67

Investigate other pairs of sinusoidal spirals.

Do they always touch rather than cross?

1 A rectangle ABCD slides down a wall so that A remains in contact with the wall and D remains in contact with the ground. M is the centre of the rectangle ABCD and D is initially at O. BC is of length p and AB is of length q. The angle that AD makes with the ground at any time is given by T.

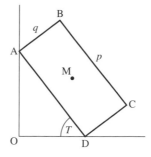

(i) Taking OD as the x axis and OA as the y axis, find the parametric equations of the locus of M.

For the remainder of this question, let $p = 8$ and $q = 6$.

(ii) Using your graphic calculator, plot the path of M. Sketch this path, stating the range of values of the parameter T.

(iii) By symmetry considerations, or otherwise, state the value of T when the distance $|OM|$ is a maximum and find this maximum distance.

Now assume that, rather than sliding down a wall, the rectangle moves in such a way that A remains in contact with the y axis, as shown, and D remains in contact with the x axis.

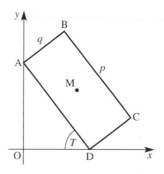

(iv) Explain how the locus of M differs from part **(ii)** above.

(v) Sketch the locus of M in this case. What type of curve might this be?

(vi) Express $\sin T$ and $\cos T$ in terms of x and y and hence show that the cartesian equation for the locus of M is $25(x^2 + y^2) - 48xy = 49$.

(vii) By using the substitutions $x = \dfrac{X - Y}{\sqrt{2}}$ and $y = \dfrac{X + Y}{\sqrt{2}}$ show that this reduces to the ellipse $\dfrac{X^2}{49} + Y^2 = 1$.

Explain carefully what this tells you about the locus of M.

2 The ancient Greek mathematicians attempted to solve any geometrical construction problem using just straight edge and compasses. However, there were three problems that they found they could not solve by these means: how to construct a circle with the same area as a given square, how to double the volume of a given cube, and how to trisect a given angle. In the nineteenth century, it was finally shown that these constructions are impossible using just straight edge and compasses. However, the Greeks did devise other ways of solving them, using unusual curves like the one described below.

OABC is a square of side 1 unit.
When $t = 0$ the line L lies along OA and the line M lies along AB.
The line L rotates clockwise about O at 1 radian per second and, simultaneously, the line M drops towards OC at a constant rate, so that L and M reach OC at exactly the same time.

Point D, the intersection point of L and M, traces out a curve called the *trisectrix.*

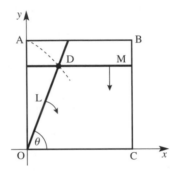

(i) If t is the time that has elapsed, in seconds, find the cartesian co-ordinates of D
  (a) in terms of t **(b)** in terms of θ.
(ii) Taking the x axis as the initial line and O as the pole, what is the polar equation of the trisectrix?
(iii) Plot the trisectrix on your calculator and sketch your result.
(iv) Using the trace function, find the co-ordinates of D when it meets the x axis.
  Why do your answers to **(i)** and **(ii)** not give you this information?

Suppose now that a vertical line is dropped from D, cutting OC at E. Then the point F is constructed so that $EF = \frac{1}{3}ED$. Finally the horizontal line FG is constructed with G on the trisectrix.

(v) Show that $\angle GOC$ is exactly a third of $\angle DOC$.

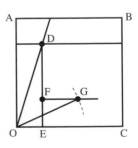

3 (i) The point P with co-ordinates $\left(t, \dfrac{1}{t} \right)$ is on the rectangular hyperbola $xy = 1$. Prove that the equation of the tangent at P is $x + yt^2 = 2t$

(ii) The point Q is the intersection of this tangent with the line through the origin O perpendicular to this tangent. Show that the x co-ordinate of Q is $\dfrac{2t}{1 + t^4}$, and find the y co-ordinate of Q in terms of t. The locus of Q as t varies through all non-zero values is called a *lemniscate*.

(iii) (a) With the aid of your calculator draw a diagram showing the rectangular hyperbola and the lemniscate.

(b) By replacing t by $\dfrac{1}{t}$ in the parametric equations, prove that the line $y = x$ is an axis of symmetry of the lemniscate.

(c) Prove that the line $y = -x$ is also an axis of symmetry of the lemniscate.

(iv) The line OQ is extended beyond Q to meet the hyperbola at R. Prove that OQ $\times$ OR $= 2$.

4 You are given that the foci of the conic with equation $\dfrac{x^2}{p} + \dfrac{y^2}{q} = 1$, where $p > 0$ and $p > q$, are the two points $(\pm \sqrt{p - q}, 0)$.

(i) Prove that all the conics with equations

$$\frac{x^2}{7 + \lambda} + \frac{y^2}{3 + \lambda} = 1,$$

where λ is a parameter, $\lambda > -7$, $\lambda \neq -3$, have the same foci, and state the co-ordinates of these foci.

(ii) State the ranges of values of λ for which this conic is
(a) an ellipse **(b)** a hyperbola.
With the aid of your calculator sketch on a single diagram the conics obtained when λ takes the values 1, -2, -4. Label each conic with its value of λ. Show also the common foci of these conics.

(iii) Find the two values of λ for which the conic $\dfrac{x^2}{7 + \lambda} + \dfrac{y^2}{3 + \lambda} = 1$ passes through the point $P\left(\frac{5}{2}, \frac{3}{2}\right)$.

(iv) Prove that the tangents at P to the two conics found in part **(iii)** are perpendicular.

5 The diagram shows a circle of radius 1 with centre C, a diameter OCA, the tangent at A and the radius CB which is perpendicular to OCA.

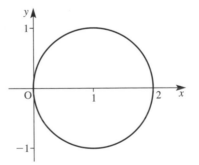

(i) Taking O as the pole and OA as the initial line of polar co-ordinates, write down the polar equations of this circle and this tangent. Enter this circle and tangent into your calculator, setting the scales so that the shape of the circle is displayed correctly.

A straight line through O meets the circle again at Q and meets the tangent at R. The point P on this line is such that |OP| = |QR|. The locus of P as the line varies is a curve called the *cissoid of Diocles*.

(ii) Taking angle AOP = θ, prove that the polar equation of this cissoid can be written in the form $r = \dfrac{2\sin^2\theta}{\cos\theta}$.

(iii) Prove that B lies on the cissoid.

(iv) Enter the cissoid into your calculator.
On a copy of the diagram shown, draw the cissoid.
Describe briefly the main features of the cissoid.

(v) **(a)** The straight line AP produced meets CB produced at the point U, and the straight line OP meets CB produced at V. Add AP, U and V to your diagram.

  (b) Let $\angle AOV = \theta$. By using cartesian co-ordinates, or otherwise, prove that the length of CV is the cube root of the length of CU.

6 The diagram shows a circle, C, of unit radius, passing through O.

(i) Taking O as the pole and the horizontal axis to be the initial line, show that the curve C has polar equation $r = 2\cos\theta$ and enter this curve onto your calculator.

The line through O making angle θ with the initial line cuts C again at Q. P and P$'$ are the points on OQ (extended, with P beyond Q) which are k units from Q, where $k > 0$. As θ varies, the set of points P and P$'$ form a curve called a *limaçon*.

(ii) Prove that the polar equation of this limaçon is $r = 2\cos\theta + k$, explaining how this gives *both* the points P and P'.

(iii) With the aid of your calculator draw on separate diagrams
   (a) the circle C and the limaçon for which $k = 1$
   (b) the circle C and the limaçon for which $k = 3$.
   What is the key difference between these two limaçons?

(iv) Describe in general terms the shape and position of the limaçon when
   (a) k is very close to zero
   (b) k is very large.

(v) In the case $k = 2$, prove that
   (a) the circle C' with diameter PP' touches the circle C at the point Q', where QQ' is a diameter of C
   (b) the arc length P'Q' on C' equals the arc length OQ' on C.

7 (i) A curve, C, has parametric equations

$$x = 6\cos T, \quad y = 6\sin T.$$

Prove that this curve is a circle.

Before proceeding with the rest of this question, you are advised to enter this curve onto your calculator and to set the scales so that it appears as a circle.

(ii) Another curve, H, has parametric equations

$$x = 5\cos T + \cos 5T, \quad y = 5\sin T - \sin 5T.$$

Enter this curve, also, onto your calculator.
Describe its main features and state its greatest and least distances from the origin.

The curve H is a particular member of a family of curves. The general member is defined by the parametric equations

$$x = k\cos T + \cos kT, \quad y = k\sin T - \sin kT$$

for positive integer values of k.

(iii) Predict, in terms of k, the features of the general member of the family of curves.

(iv) Show that the distance, r, of the point (x, y) from the origin is given by

$$r^2 = k^2 + 2k\cos(k + 1)T + 1.$$

Use this result to justify the predictions you made in part **(iii)**.

The curves in this family are called *hypocycloids*. A hypocycloid is the locus of a point on the circumference of a circle as it rolls round the inside of a circle of larger radius.

(v) In this case, the radius of the smaller circle is 1 unit. Write down the radius of the larger circle.

8 (i) Copy and complete this table of values for $y = \sqrt{1 + \cos^2 2x}$.

x	0	$\dfrac{\pi}{6}$	$\dfrac{\pi}{4}$	$\dfrac{\pi}{3}$	$\dfrac{\pi}{2}$	$\dfrac{3\pi}{4}$	π	$\dfrac{5\pi}{4}$	$\dfrac{3\pi}{2}$	$\dfrac{7\pi}{4}$	2π
$y = \sqrt{1 + \cos^2 2x}$											

(ii) Sketch the curve $y = \sqrt{1 + \cos^2 2x}$ for $0 \leqslant x \leqslant 2\pi$.

(iii) Without using your calculator, use your answer to part **(ii)** to draw a sketch of what you think the curve $r = \sqrt{1 + \cos^2 2\theta}$ will look like.

(iv) Now use your calculator to check your answer to part **(iii)**.

A family of curves has the form $r = \sqrt{a + (2 - a)\cos^2 2\theta}$ for different values of a.

(v) Draw diagrams to illustrate typical members of the family, including any special cases, stating the appropriate value or range of values for a.

(vi) Is it possible to find values of a for which the curve has

    (a) cusps   **(b)** nodes?

9 The diagram below shows a circle with radius a and centre C. O is the pole and C is on the initial line at a distance $a\sqrt{2}$ from O.

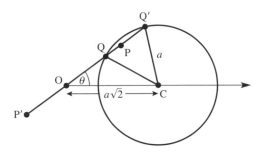

A straight line through O meets the circle at points Q and Q′. P and P′ are chosen so that $|OP| = |OP'| = |QQ'|$. Repeating this for other points Q and connecting all the points P and all the points P′ gives a curve called the *lemniscate of Bernoulli*.

Let $|OQ| = r$ and $|OQ'| = r'$.

(i) Use the cosine rule in triangle OQC to find an equation linking a and r.

(ii) Show that $|QQ'| = r' - r = 2a\sqrt{\cos 2\theta}$ and hence write down the polar equation of the lemniscate.

Draw this curve on your graphic calculator, setting $a = 1$.

(iii) Show that the cartesian equation of the lemniscate is

$$(x^2 + y^2)^2 = 4a^2(x^2 - y^2).$$

(iv) Show that the area of the smallest rectangle containing the lemniscate, with sides parallel and perpendicular to the initial line, is $4\sqrt{2}a^2$.

10 The diagram shows a point T on the initial line at a distance d from the pole S. The point P moves in such a way that $|PS| = k|PT|$.

(i) Describe the path traced out by P when $k = 1$.

(ii) For the case $k = \frac{1}{2}$ use the cosine rule to show that the polar equation of the path traced out by P is given by

$$r = \frac{d}{3}\left(\pm\sqrt{3 + \cos^2\theta} - \cos\theta\right).$$

(iii) Explain why, in the context of the locus problem described, P will cross the initial line at the point D, a distance $\frac{d}{3}$ from S. Substitute $\theta = 0$ and $\theta = \pi$ in the expression given for r in part (ii) and comment on the values of r.

On your graphic calculator plot $r = \frac{d}{3}\left(\sqrt{3 + \cos^2\theta} - \cos\theta\right)$ for various values of d. You should find that the path is a circle.

In the general case $|PS| = k|PT|$, the locus of P has polar equation

$$r = \frac{-dk}{1 - k^2}\left(k\cos\theta \pm \sqrt{1 - k^2\sin^2\theta}\right).$$

(iv) Show that, for $k = \frac{1}{2}$, this agrees with the formula in part (ii).

(v) Describe the similarity between the case $k = 2$ and the original problem with $k = \frac{1}{2}$.

(vi) What potential problems are there for substituting values of $k > 1$ in

$$r = \frac{-dk}{1 - k^2}\left(k\cos\theta \pm \sqrt{1 - k^2\sin^2\theta}\right)?$$

11 A curve S is given parametrically by

$$x = \cos T + 2\sin T, \quad y = \cos T - 2\sin T.$$

(i) Using your graphic calculator, sketch the curve and state which conic it looks like.

The distance of a point (x, y) on the curve from the origin is denoted by r.

(ii) Show that $r^2 = 2 + 6\sin^2 T$.

(iii) Differentiate this expression for r^2 with respect to T.

(iv) Hence find the co-ordinates of the two points on S nearest to the origin and those of the two points furthest from the origin.

(v) Show that your answers to part (iv) are compatible with the curve S being an ellipse.

Each point on the curve S is rotated by the matrix $\mathbf{R} = \begin{pmatrix} \frac{1}{\sqrt{2}} & -\frac{1}{\sqrt{2}} \\ \frac{1}{\sqrt{2}} & \frac{1}{\sqrt{2}} \end{pmatrix}$ to

give the curve S'.

(vi) Write down the angle of rotation represented by $\mathbf{R}$, and the direction of the rotation.

(vii) Find the image on S' of the point $(\cos T + 2 \sin T, \ \cos T - 2 \sin T)$ on S under this rotation.

Hence find the cartesian equation for S' and verify that it is an ellipse. What does this tell you about the curve S? Justify your answer.

12 The *limaçon of Pascal* is the locus of P in the following construction.

The circle S has polar equation $r = 2a \cos \theta$ and Q is a variable point on S. The line L passes through the pole, A, and Q. Points P and P' on L satisfy $|QP| = |QP'| = k$, where k is a constant.

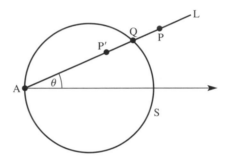

(i) Show that the polar equation of the limaçon is $r = 2a \cos \theta + k$. State which values of θ give the locus of P and explain why the remaining values of θ give the locus of P'.

(ii) On your calculator draw the limaçon with equation $r = 4 \cos \theta + 2$. On a copy of this diagram draw the circle which gave rise to this limaçon and, on the limaçon, mark the points generated when Q is at the pole.

The limaçon below has a cusp at the pole.

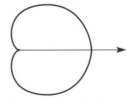

(iii) What is the relationship between a and k for this limaçon?

(iv) Find the values of θ satisfying $\dfrac{\mathrm{d}}{\mathrm{d}\theta}(r \sin \theta) = 0$ in this case.

Explain carefully the geometrical significance of each of these values.

13 The point C has co-ordinates $(0, a)$. D moves along the line $y = a$ and L is the variable line through O and D. The point P lies on L such that $|OP| = |CD|$. The locus of P is a curve known as the *Kappa curve*.

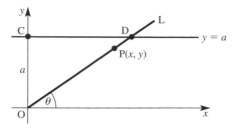

(i) Make a rough sketch of the curve, identifying any symmetry and asymptotes.

(ii) Show that the polar equation of the Kappa curve is $r = a \cot \theta$ and find the equivalent cartesian equation.

(iii) Plot the Kappa curve on your calculator and explain any differences from your sketch in part **(i)**.

14 In the diagram below, O is the origin, R is the point with co-ordinates $(0, 2a)$ and S is the circle with OR as diameter.

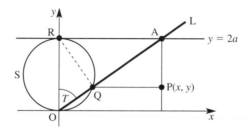

The point A moves along the line $y = 2a$ and L is the variable line through O and A. The line L meets the circle S at the point Q. QP is parallel to the x axis and PA is parallel to the y axis. The curve traced out by P is known as the *witch of Agnesi*.

(i) Show that $|OQ| = 2a \cos T$ and use this to find the co-ordinates of Q in terms of T.

(ii) Show that $|RA| = 2a \tan T$ and use this, and your answer to part **(i)**, to show that the co-ordinates of P are $(2a \tan T, 2a \cos^2 T)$.

(iii) Sketch the curve using the parametric equations $x = 2a \tan T$, $y = 2a \cos^2 T$, setting $a = 1$.

(iv) By eliminating T from the parametric equations, find the cartesian equation of the curve.

(v) Show that $\dfrac{d^2 y}{dx^2} = 0$ when $x = \pm \dfrac{2a\sqrt{3}}{3}$ and explain the significance of this result.

15 In the diagram below, A is the pole and D is a line perpendicular to the initial line at a distance b from A. Q is a variable point on D.

The line L passes through A and Q. Points P and P' are drawn on L so that $|QP| = |QP'| = a$, where a is a constant. The locus of P, as Q moves along D, is a curve called the *conchoid of Nicomedes*.

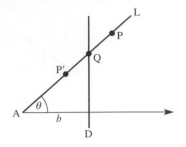

(i) Make a rough sketch of the locus of P and P' for the case $a < b$. Show the line D and state the intercepts with the initial line.

(ii) Write down the polar co-ordinates of Q.

(iii) Using your answer to part (ii) show that the polar equation of the curve is $r = b \sec \theta + a$. State which values of θ give the locus of P and explain why the remaining values of θ give the locus of P'.

Investigate the shapes of the conchoids for various values of a and b, including the case $a > b$.

The diagram below shows one such conchoid which has a cusp.

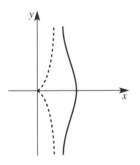

(iv) Write down the relationship between a and b for the conchoid to have a cusp.

(v) By considering $(ar \cos \theta)^2$, or otherwise, find the cartesian equation of the conchoid.

Use this to find the values of x corresponding to $y = 0$ and explain the significance of this in terms of loops and cusps.

(vi) In the special case $a = 2b\sqrt{2}$ work out the cartesian co-ordinates of the points where $\dfrac{dy}{d\theta} = 0$, i.e. where the tangent to the curve is horizontal.

16 The diagram below shows a fixed circle S with centre C and radius a. L_1 is the fixed line $x = ka$ and F_1 is the point where this line meets the x axis. P_1 is a variable point on L_1. P_2 lies on S and P_1P_2 is parallel to the x axis.

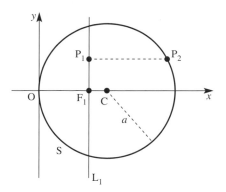

L_2 is the line parallel to L_1 passing through P_2. F_2 is the point where L_2 meets the x axis. The point P is where the line OP_1 produced meets L_2.

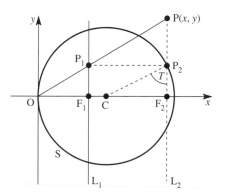

The locus of P is a curve called the *piriform* (or pear-shaped quartic).

(i) Let $T = \angle CP_2F_2$. Show that
  (a) P_1 has co-ordinates $(ka,\ a\cos T)$
  (b) P_2 has co-ordinates $(a + a\sin T,\ a\cos T)$.

(ii) Using the expressions in **(i)**, and the gradient of line OP_1, or otherwise, show that the parametric equations of the piriform are

$$x = a(1 + \sin T), \quad y = \frac{a}{k}\cos T(1 + \sin T).$$

(iii) Draw this curve on your calculator with $a = 1$ and $k = 0.5$, along with the circle and the line L_1. On a copy of this graph indicate clearly how the piriform unfolds as T varies.

(iv) Find the range of values of $x = a(1 + \sin T)$ and $y = \dfrac{a}{k}\cos T(1 + \sin T)$ in terms of a and k. How does the position of the line L_1 affect the value of T which corresponds to the maximum value of y?

1 The equations of many curves can be expressed in cartesian, parametric and polar form.

2 The substitutions $x = r\cos\theta$, $y = r\sin\theta$ are useful when converting between these forms.

3 The important features of curves to recognise are
- symmetry and periodicity
- vertical, horizontal and oblique asymptotes
- cusps, loops and dimples
- nodes (or crossover points).

4 For curves given in cartesian and parametric form, calculus techniques are used to find
- the equations of tangents and normals
- the maximum and minimum values of x and y
- the maximum and minimum distances of a curve from the origin.

5 For curves given in polar form, calculus techniques are used to find
- the maximum and minimum distances of the curve from the pole
- the points on the curve where the tangent is parallel, or perpendicular, to the initial line.

6 The standard cartesian and parametric equations of the conics are given in the table below.

	Cartesian	Parametric
Parabola	$y^2 = 4ax$	$x = at^2, \quad y = 2at$
Ellipse	$\dfrac{x^2}{a^2} + \dfrac{y^2}{b^2} = 1$	$x = a\cos t, \quad y = b\sin t$
Hyperbola	$\dfrac{x^2}{a^2} - \dfrac{y^2}{b^2} = 1$	$x = a\sec t, \quad y = b\tan t$
Rectangular hyperbola	$xy = c^2$	$x = ct, \quad y = \dfrac{c}{t}$

Glossary of curves

Details and properties of many other curves can be found at
http://www-groups.dcs.st-and.ac.uk/history/Curves/Curves.html.

Circle

$x = a\cos t, \quad y = a\sin t$

$x^2 + y^2 = a^2$

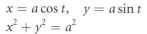

Parabola

$x = at^2, \quad y = 2at$

$y^2 = 4ax$

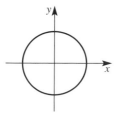

Ellipse

$x = a\cos t, \quad y = b\sin t$

$\dfrac{x^2}{a^2} + \dfrac{y^2}{b^2} = 1$

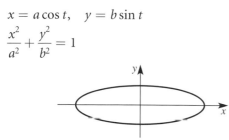

Hyperbola

$x = a\sec t, \quad y = b\tan t$

$\dfrac{x^2}{a^2} - \dfrac{y^2}{b^2} = 1$

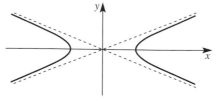

Rectangular Hyperbola

$x = ct, \quad y = \dfrac{c}{t}$

$xy = c^2$

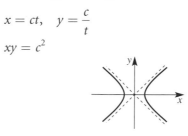

Cycloid

$x = a(t - \sin t), \quad y = a(1 - \cos t)$

Curtate cycloid

$x = at - b\sin t, \; y = a - b\cos t$ where $b < a$.

Prolate cycloid

$x = at - b\sin t, \; y = a - b\cos t$ where $b > a$.

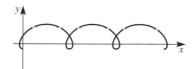

Epicycloid

$x = ka\cos t - a\cos kt, \quad y = ka\sin t - a\sin kt$

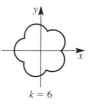

$k = 6$

Hypocycloid

$$x = ka \cos t + a \cos kt, \quad y = ka \sin t - a \sin kt$$

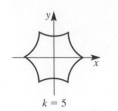

$k = 5$

Cardioid

$$r = 2a(1 + \cos \theta)$$

Nephroid

$$x = 3a \cos t - a \cos 3t, \quad y = 3a \sin t - a \sin 3t$$

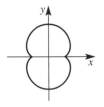

Conchoid of Nicomedes

$$r = a \sec \theta + k$$

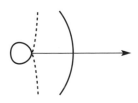

Astroid

$$x^{\frac{2}{3}} + y^{\frac{2}{3}} = a^{\frac{2}{3}}$$

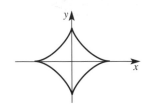

Right strophoid

$$x = \frac{a(t^2 - 1)}{t^2 + 1}, \quad y = \frac{at(t^2 - 1)}{t^2 + 1}$$

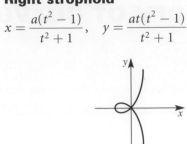

Cissoid of Diocles

$$r = 2a(\sec \theta - \cos \theta)$$

Limaçon

$$r = 2a \cos \theta + k$$

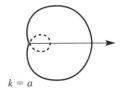

$k = a$

Trisectrix of Maclaurin

$$r = 2a \frac{\sin 3\theta}{\sin 2\theta}$$

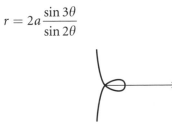

Lissajous curves

$$x = a \sin (ct + d), \quad y = b \sin t$$

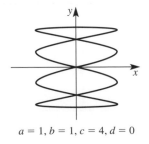

$a = 1, b = 1, c = 4, d = 0$

Spiral

$r = k\theta$

Lemniscate

$r^2 = a^2 \cos 2\theta$

The folium of Descartes

$x^3 + y^3 = 3axy$

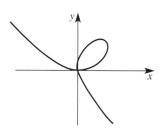

Eight curve

$r^2 = \cos 2\theta \sec^4 \theta$

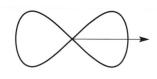

Witch of Agnesi

$x = 2a \tan t, \quad y = 2a \cos^2 t$

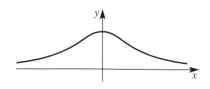

Trident

$xy = x^3 - a^3$

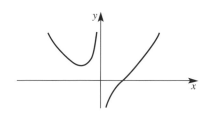

Kappa curve

$r = a \cot \theta$

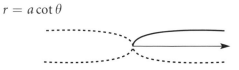

Maltese cross

$xy(x^2 - y^2) = x^2 + y^2$

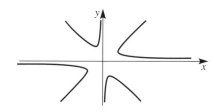

Piriform

$x = a(1 + \sin t), \quad y = \dfrac{a}{k} \cos t (1 + \sin t)$

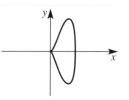

Deltoid

$x = 2a \cos t + a \cos 2t, \quad y = 2a \sin t + a \sin 2t$

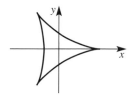

Answers

Chapter 1

Activity 1.1 (Page 3)

$$\cos^4 x = (\cos^2 x)^2$$
$$= \left(\tfrac{1}{2}(\cos 2x + 1)\right)^2$$
$$= \tfrac{1}{4}(\cos^2 2x + 2\cos 2x + 1)$$
$$= \tfrac{1}{4} \times \tfrac{1}{2}(\cos 4x + 1) + \tfrac{1}{2}\cos 2x + \tfrac{1}{4}$$
$$= \tfrac{1}{8}\cos 4x + \tfrac{1}{2}\cos 2x + \tfrac{3}{8}$$
$$\int \cos^4 x \, dx = \int \left(\tfrac{1}{8}\cos 4x + \tfrac{1}{2}\cos 2x + \tfrac{3}{8}\right) dx$$
$$= \tfrac{1}{32}\sin 4x + \tfrac{1}{4}\sin 2x + \tfrac{3}{8}x + c$$

Activity 1.2 (Page 4)

(i) $\displaystyle \sqrt{\frac{1}{2\pi}\int_0^{2\pi} a^2 \sin^2 t \, dt} = \frac{a}{\sqrt{2}}$

(ii) $a = 240\sqrt{2} \approx 339$

Activity 1.3 (Page 4)

(i) $\sin\theta \sin\phi = \tfrac{1}{2}(\cos(\theta - \phi) - \cos(\theta + \phi))$

(ii) (a) $\tfrac{1}{8}\sin 4x + \tfrac{1}{4}\sin 2x + c$

(b) $\tfrac{1}{6}\sin 3x - \tfrac{1}{14}\sin 7x + c$

Exercise 1A (Page 5)

1. (i) $\tfrac{1}{4}\sin 2x + \tfrac{1}{2}x + c$

   (ii) $\tfrac{1}{2}x - \tfrac{1}{12}\sin 6x + c$

   (iii) $\tan x + c$

   (iv) $-\cos x + \tfrac{1}{3}\cos^3 x + c$

   (v) $\tfrac{1}{32}\sin 4x - \tfrac{1}{4}\sin 2x + \tfrac{3}{8}x + c$

   (vi) $\sin x - \tfrac{2}{3}\sin^3 x + \tfrac{1}{5}\sin^5 x + c$

   (vii) $\tfrac{1}{2}\sec 2x + c$

   (viii) $\ln|\sin x| + c$

   (ix) $\ln|\tan x| + c$

2. (i) $-\tfrac{1}{3}\cos^3 x + c$

   (ii) $\tfrac{1}{12}\sin 6x + \tfrac{1}{2}x + c$

   (iii) $-\tfrac{1}{42}(3\cos 7x + 7\cos 3x) + c$

   (iv) $\tfrac{3}{2}x - 2\cos x - \tfrac{1}{4}\sin 2x + c$

   (v) $x - \tfrac{1}{2}\cos 2x + c$

   (vi) $\tfrac{1}{2}\tan^2 x + c$ or $\tfrac{1}{2}\sec^2 x + k$

3. (i) $\tfrac{1}{16}$ (ii) $\ln 2$ (iii) 1

   (iv) $1 - \dfrac{\pi}{4}$ (v) 0 (vi) $\dfrac{2\sqrt{2}}{7}$

4. (i)
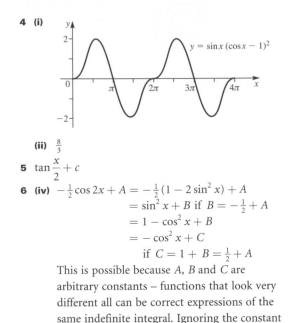

(ii) $\tfrac{8}{3}$

5. $\tan\dfrac{x}{2} + c$

6. (iv) $-\tfrac{1}{2}\cos 2x + A = -\tfrac{1}{2}(1 - 2\sin^2 x) + A$
   $$= \sin^2 x + B \text{ if } B = -\tfrac{1}{2} + A$$
   $$= 1 - \cos^2 x + B$$
   $$= -\cos^2 x + C$$
   $$\text{if } C = 1 + B = \tfrac{1}{2} + A$$

   This is possible because A, B and C are arbitrary constants – functions that look very different all can be correct expressions of the same indefinite integral. Ignoring the constant of integration can cause problems.

7. The constant of integration has been ignored.

Activity 1.4 (Page 8)

(i) The gradient is always negative.

(ii) $y = \arccos x \Rightarrow \cos y = x \Rightarrow -\sin y \dfrac{dy}{dx} = 1$

   $$\Rightarrow \frac{dy}{dx} = \frac{-1}{\sin y} = \frac{-1}{\pm\sqrt{1 - \cos^2 y}} = \frac{-1}{\pm\sqrt{1 - x^2}}$$

   Since $\dfrac{dy}{dx}$ is negative (from (i)), $\dfrac{dy}{dx} = -\dfrac{1}{\sqrt{1 - x^2}}$.

Activity 1.5 (Page 9)

The graphs in figure 1.8 are obtained by reflecting the graphs in figure 1.7 in $y = x$.

The gradient is always positive, tending to 0 as $x \to \pm\infty$. Maximum gradient $= 1$, when $x = 0$.

$y = \arctan x \Rightarrow \tan y = x \Rightarrow \sec^2 y \dfrac{dy}{dx} = 1$

$$\Rightarrow \frac{dy}{dx} = \frac{1}{\sec^2 y} = \frac{1}{1 + \tan^2 y} = \frac{1}{1 + x^2}.$$

Activity 1.6 (Page 9)

(i) $y = \text{arcsec } x \Leftrightarrow \sec y = x \Leftrightarrow \dfrac{1}{\cos y} = x$

   $$\Leftrightarrow \cos y = \frac{1}{x} \Leftrightarrow y = \arccos\left(\frac{1}{x}\right).$$

   For (ii) and (iii) the argument is similar.

Exercise 1B (Page 10)

1

	arcsine	arccosine	arctangent
Domain	$-1 \leqslant x \leqslant 1$	$-1 \leqslant x \leqslant 1$	all real numbers
Range	$-\dfrac{\pi}{2} \leqslant y \leqslant \dfrac{\pi}{2}$	$0 \leqslant y \leqslant \pi$	$-\dfrac{\pi}{2} < y < \dfrac{\pi}{2}$

3 $\arccos x + \arccos(-x) = \pi$

4 $-\dfrac{\pi}{2} \leqslant x \leqslant \dfrac{\pi}{2}$

6 (i) $\dfrac{1}{\sqrt{1 - x^2}}$

(ii) $\dfrac{5}{\sqrt{1 - 25x^2}}$

(iii) $\dfrac{6}{4 + 9x^2}$

(iv) $-\dfrac{3}{1 + (2 - 3x)^2}$

7 (i) $\dfrac{2}{\sqrt{1 - 4x^2}}$

(ii) $\dfrac{5}{1 + 25x^2}$

(iii) $\dfrac{6x}{\sqrt{1 - 9x^4}}$

(iv) $-\dfrac{2}{\sqrt{1 - 4x^2}}$

(v) $\dfrac{e^x}{1 + e^{2x}}$

(vi) $-\dfrac{2x}{1 + (1 - x^2)^2}$

(vii) $-\dfrac{10x}{\sqrt{1 - (5x^2 - 2)^2}}$

(viii) $-\dfrac{1}{2\sqrt{x(1 - x)}}$

8 $\arcsin \dfrac{x}{\sqrt{2}} - \dfrac{\pi}{4}$

9 $\dfrac{1}{\sqrt{1 - x^2}}, -\dfrac{1}{\sqrt{1 - x^2}}; c_2 = \dfrac{\pi}{2} + c_1$

10 (i) $n\pi$ or $2n\pi \pm \dfrac{\pi}{3}$

(ii) $2n\pi - \dfrac{\pi}{4}$

(iii) $2n\pi \pm \dfrac{\pi}{3} + \arcsin \dfrac{4}{5}$

(iv) $n\pi$ or $n\pi \pm \arctan \sqrt{\dfrac{1}{2}}$

(v) $4n\pi$ or $4n\pi \pm \dfrac{4\pi}{3}$

(vi) $(2n + 1)\pi$ or $2n\pi + 2\arcsin \dfrac{1}{\sqrt{5}}$

11

	arcsecant	arccosecant	arccotangent
Domain	$x \leqslant -1$ or $x \geqslant 1$	$x \leqslant -1$ or $x \geqslant 1$	all real numbers
Range	$0 \leqslant y \leqslant \pi$, $y \neq \dfrac{\pi}{2}$	$-\dfrac{\pi}{2} \leqslant y \leqslant \dfrac{\pi}{2}$, $y \neq 0$	$-\dfrac{\pi}{2} < y \leqslant \dfrac{\pi}{2}$, $y \neq 0$

12 (ii) (a) $-\dfrac{1}{|x|\sqrt{x^2 - 1}}$

(b) $-\dfrac{1}{1 + x^2}$

13 (i) $\dfrac{\pi}{2}$ provided $x \leqslant -1$ or $x \geqslant 1$

(ii) $-\dfrac{\pi}{2}$ if $x < 0$, $\dfrac{\pi}{2}$ if $x > 0$

Exercise 1C (Page 14)

1 (i) $\dfrac{1}{5}\arctan \dfrac{x}{5} + c$

(ii) $\arcsin \dfrac{x}{6} + c$

(iii) $\dfrac{5}{6}\arctan \dfrac{x}{6} + c$

(iv) $\dfrac{2}{5}\arctan \dfrac{2x}{5} + c$

(v) $\dfrac{1}{2}\arcsin \dfrac{2x}{3} + c$

(vi) $\dfrac{7}{\sqrt{3}}\arcsin \dfrac{\sqrt{3}x}{\sqrt{5}} + c$

2 (i) $\dfrac{\pi}{12}$ **(ii)** $\dfrac{\pi}{4}$ **(iii)** $\dfrac{7\pi}{36}$

(iv) $\dfrac{\pi}{12}$ **(v)** $\dfrac{\pi}{2\sqrt{6}}$ **(vi)** $\dfrac{\pi}{12\sqrt{10}}$

3 (i) $\dfrac{1}{12}\arctan \dfrac{4x}{3} + c$

❓ (Page 15)

No real roots $\Leftrightarrow B^2 - 4AC < 0$.

If $A < 0$, work with $\dfrac{-1}{-Ax^2 - Bx - C}$.

❓ (Page 16)

So that $Ax^2 + Bx + C$ can be rearranged as $p^2 - (qx + r)^2$.

Exercise 1D (Page 17)

1 (i) $\dfrac{1}{2}\arctan \dfrac{x + 2}{2} + c$

(ii) $7\arcsin \dfrac{x - 2}{3} + c$

(iii) $\dfrac{\sqrt{3}}{\sqrt{2}} \arctan \dfrac{\sqrt{2}x}{\sqrt{3}} + c$

(iv) $\dfrac{1}{2} \arctan \dfrac{3x+1}{2} + c$

(v) $\arcsin \dfrac{x-1}{2} + c$

(vi) $\dfrac{7}{2} \arcsin \dfrac{2x+1}{2} + c$

2 (i) $x \arcsin x + \sqrt{1-x^2} + c$

(ii) (a) $x \arccos x - \sqrt{1-x^2} + c$

(b) $x \arctan x - \frac{1}{2} \ln(1+x^2) + c$

(c) $x \text{arccot}\, x + \frac{1}{2} \ln(1+x^2) + c$

3 (i) $\dfrac{1}{2} a^2 \arcsin \dfrac{b}{a} + \dfrac{1}{2} b\sqrt{a^2 - b^2}$

(ii) Area of sector + area of triangle

4 (i) $\dfrac{1}{2} \arctan \dfrac{x-3}{2} + c$

(ii) $\dfrac{1}{2} \arcsin \dfrac{2x+3}{4} + c$

(iii) $\dfrac{1}{4} \arctan \dfrac{2x+5}{2} + c$

(iv) $-\dfrac{1}{x-3} + c$

(v) $\dfrac{1}{3} \arcsin \dfrac{3x+2}{3} + c$

5 (i) $\frac{1}{2} \ln(x^2+1) + \arctan x + c$

(ii) $\ln \dfrac{(x+1)^2}{x^2+1} + 2\arctan x + c$

(iii) $\sqrt{1-x^2} + \arcsin x + c$

(iv) $\ln \left| \dfrac{x+1}{\sqrt{x^2+1}} \right| + 2\arctan x + c$

6 (i) $\dfrac{\pi}{3}$

(ii) $\dfrac{1}{2} \left(\ln 58 + \arctan \dfrac{5}{3} \right) - \dfrac{\pi}{8} \approx 2.233$

7 $\dfrac{1}{x\sqrt{x^2-1}}; \dfrac{1}{a} \text{arcsec} \dfrac{x}{a} + c$

Chapter 2

Activity 2.1 (Page 21)

E.g. $\left(6, -\dfrac{\pi}{4} \right), \left(6, \dfrac{7\pi}{4} \right), \left(-6, -\dfrac{5\pi}{4} \right)$

Exercise 2A (Page 22)

1 Kite

2 (i) $\left(4, \dfrac{11\pi}{12} \right)$ and $\left(4, -\dfrac{5\pi}{12} \right)$

(ii) $\left(4, \dfrac{7\pi}{12} \right)$ or $\left(4, -\dfrac{\pi}{12} \right)$

(iii) $\left(\dfrac{4}{\sqrt{3}}, \dfrac{3\pi}{4} \right)$ and $\left(\dfrac{4}{\sqrt{3}}, -\dfrac{\pi}{4} \right),$

or $\left(4, -\dfrac{3\pi}{4} \right)$ and $\left(4\sqrt{3}, \dfrac{3\pi}{4} \right),$

or $\left(4, -\dfrac{3\pi}{4} \right)$ and $\left(4\sqrt{3}, -\dfrac{\pi}{4} \right)$

3 (ii) A(5.39, 0.38), B(8.71, 1.01), C(8.71, 1.64), D(5.39, 2.27)

(iii) B(4.64, 7.37), C(−0.58, 8.69), D(−3.45, 4.14)

4 (i) 4

(ii) $16 < r < 170,$ $\theta = -27$

(iii) (a) $99 < r < 107,$ $153 < \theta < 171$

(b) $16 < r < 99,$ $-81 < \theta < -63$

or $107 < r < 162,$ $-81 < \theta < -63$

(c) $16 < r < 99,$ $45 < \theta < 63$

or $107 < r < 162,$ $45 < \theta < 63$

or $162 < r < 170,$ $135 < \theta < 153$

or $99 < r < 107,$ $-9 < \theta < 9$

❓ (Page 25)

This uses $x = r\cos\theta$, $y = r\sin\theta$, with $r = \text{f}(\theta)$.

Exercise 2B (Page 26)

1 $x^2 + y^2 - 8y = 0$

2

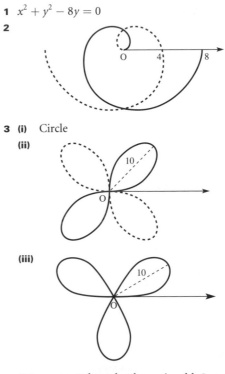

3 (i) Circle

(ii)

(iii)

(iv) n repeated petals when n is odd, $2n$ petals when n is even

4

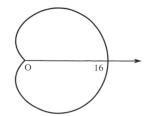

5 $x = a, y = b$

6 $x \cos \alpha + y \sin \alpha = p$

7 $\left(a, \pm \dfrac{\pi}{3} \right), \quad 2r = a \sec \theta$

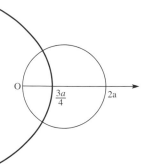

❓ (Page 28)

(a) $\delta\theta < 0, \delta r < 0, \delta A < 0,$
$\frac{1}{2}(r + \delta r)^2(-\delta\theta) < -\delta A < \frac{1}{2}r^2(-\delta\theta)$

(b) $\delta\theta > 0, \delta r < 0, \delta A > 0,$
$\frac{1}{2}(r + \delta r)^2 \delta\theta < \delta A < \frac{1}{2}r^2 \delta\theta$

(c) $\delta\theta < 0, \delta r > 0, \delta A < 0,$
$\frac{1}{2}r^2(-\delta\theta) < -\delta A < \frac{1}{2}(r + \delta r)^2(-\delta\theta)$

In all cases $\dfrac{\delta A}{\delta\theta}$ is between $\frac{1}{2}r^2$ and $\frac{1}{2}(r + \delta r)^2$, so the limiting argument holds as before.

Activity 2.3 (Page 29)

(i) $2\pi + \dfrac{3\sqrt{3}}{2}$

(ii) $\pi + 3\sqrt{3}$

Exercise 2C (Page 29)

1 It gives twice the area.

2 $\dfrac{64\pi}{3}$

3 $24\pi \pm 64$

4 $e^{4k\pi}$

5 $\dfrac{a^2}{2}$

6 (i)

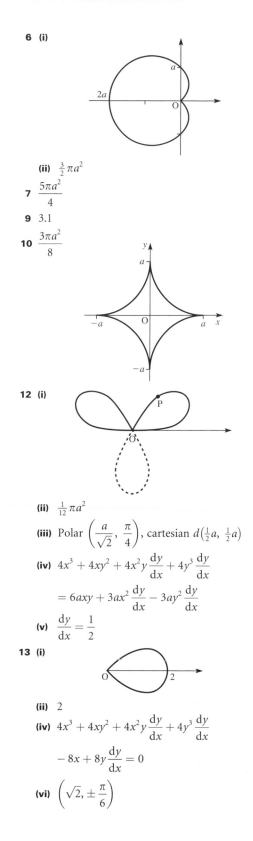

(ii) $\frac{3}{2}\pi a^2$

7 $\dfrac{5\pi a^2}{4}$

9 3.1

10 $\dfrac{3\pi a^2}{8}$

12 (i)

(ii) $\frac{1}{12}\pi a^2$

(iii) Polar $\left(\dfrac{a}{\sqrt{2}}, \dfrac{\pi}{4} \right)$, cartesian $d\left(\frac{1}{2}a, \frac{1}{2}a \right)$

(iv) $4x^3 + 4xy^2 + 4x^2 y \dfrac{dy}{dx} + 4y^3 \dfrac{dy}{dx}$
$= 6axy + 3ax^2 \dfrac{dy}{dx} - 3ay^2 \dfrac{dy}{dx}$

(v) $\dfrac{dy}{dx} = \dfrac{1}{2}$

13 (i)

(ii) 2

(iv) $4x^3 + 4xy^2 + 4x^2 y \dfrac{dy}{dx} + 4y^3 \dfrac{dy}{dx}$
$- 8x + 8y\dfrac{dy}{dx} = 0$

(vi) $\left(\sqrt{2}, \pm \dfrac{\pi}{6} \right)$

Chapter 3

Activity 3.1 (Page 33)

(i) $\dfrac{\pi}{2}$ (ii) $\dfrac{\pi}{6}$ (iii) $-\dfrac{3\pi}{4}$ (iv) $-\dfrac{2\pi}{3}$

Activity 3.2 (Page 34)

$\dfrac{\pi}{4}, \ -\dfrac{\pi}{4}, \ \dfrac{3\pi}{4}, \ -\dfrac{3\pi}{4}$

Exercise 3A (Page 35)

1 $1, 0$

2 $2, \pi$

3 $3, \dfrac{\pi}{2}$

4 $4, -\dfrac{\pi}{2}$

5 $\sqrt{2} \approx 1.414, \ \dfrac{\pi}{4}$

6 $\sqrt{50} \approx 7.071, \ -\dfrac{3\pi}{4}$

7 $2, \ -\dfrac{\pi}{3}$

8 $12, \dfrac{\pi}{6}$

9 $6, \dfrac{3\pi}{4}$

10 $8, \dfrac{\pi}{5}$

11 $0.25, 2.3$

12 $3, \pi - 3 \approx 0.142$

13 $5, -0.927$

14 $13, 2.747$

15 $8.062, 1.052$

16 $109.604, -2.128$

17   (i) $\alpha - \pi$ (ii) $-\alpha$ (iii) $\pi - \alpha$

     (iv) $\dfrac{\pi}{2} - \alpha$ (v) $\dfrac{\pi}{2} + \alpha$

18 $\cos(-\alpha) + j\sin(-\alpha)$

19 $3\left[\cos\left(\dfrac{\pi}{2} - \alpha\right) + j\sin\left(\dfrac{\pi}{2} - \alpha\right)\right]$

20 $\cos\left(\dfrac{\pi}{2} + \alpha\right) + j\sin\left(\dfrac{\pi}{2} + \alpha\right)$

21 $10[\cos(-\alpha) + j\sin(-\alpha)]$

22 $\sec\alpha(\cos\alpha + j\sin\alpha)$

23   (i)   Rhombus; $|z| = 2\cos\dfrac{\theta}{2}, \ \arg z = \dfrac{\theta}{2}$

     (iii) $2\sin\dfrac{\theta}{2}\left[\cos\left(\dfrac{\theta}{2} - \dfrac{\pi}{2}\right) + j\sin\left(\dfrac{\theta}{2} - \dfrac{\pi}{2}\right)\right]$

24   (i) $-3 - 4j, \ 11 - 2j$

     (ii) $-1 - 2j, \ -5$

     (iii) $\sqrt{5} \approx 2.236, \ \pm 2.034$ or $5, \pi$

     (iv) L is the circle centre $-\dfrac{5}{2}$, radius $\dfrac{5}{2}$

Exercise 3B (Page 37)

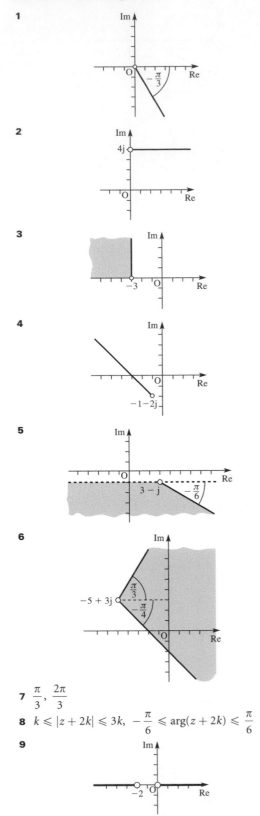

7 $\dfrac{\pi}{3}, \ \dfrac{2\pi}{3}$

8 $k \leqslant |z + 2k| \leqslant 3k, \ -\dfrac{\pi}{6} \leqslant \arg(z + 2k) \leqslant \dfrac{\pi}{6}$

10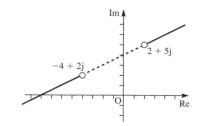

11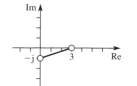

12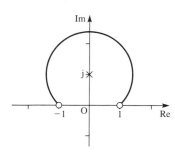

Activity 3.4 (Page 38)

(i) Rotation of vector z through $+\dfrac{\pi}{2}$

(ii) Half turn of vector z

$\left(= 2 \text{ successive } \dfrac{\pi}{2} \text{ rotations: } -1 = j \times j\right)$

Exercise 3C (Page 38)

1 $6\left(\cos\dfrac{7\pi}{12} + j\sin\dfrac{7\pi}{12}\right)$

2 $\dfrac{3}{2}\left(\cos\dfrac{\pi}{12} + j\sin\dfrac{\pi}{12}\right)$

3 $\dfrac{2}{3}\left[\cos\left(\dfrac{\pi}{12}\right) + j\sin\left(-\dfrac{\pi}{12}\right)\right]$

4 $\dfrac{1}{2}\left[\cos\left(-\dfrac{\pi}{4}\right) + j\sin\left(-\dfrac{\pi}{4}\right)\right]$

5 $9\left(\cos\dfrac{2\pi}{3} + j\sin\dfrac{2\pi}{3}\right)$

6 $32\left[\cos\left(-\dfrac{3\pi}{4}\right) + j\sin\left(-\dfrac{3\pi}{4}\right)\right]$

7 $432(\cos 0 + j\sin 0)$

8 $10\left(\cos\dfrac{3\pi}{4} + j\sin\dfrac{3\pi}{4}\right)$

9 $3\sqrt{2}\left(\cos\dfrac{7\pi}{12} + j\sin\dfrac{7\pi}{12}\right)$

10 Exceptions

   (i) if $z = 0$ then $\dfrac{1}{z}$ does not exist

   (iii) if z is real and negative then $\arg\left(\dfrac{1}{z}\right) = \arg z$

11 (i) Enlarge from O $\times 3$

   (ii) Enlarge from O $\times 2$ and rotate $+\dfrac{\pi}{2}$

   (iii) Complete the parallelogram $3z$, 0, $2jz$

   (iv) Reflect in the real axis

   (v) Find where the circle with centre O through z meets the positive real axis

   (vi) Complete the similar triangles 0, 1, z and 0, z, z^2

12 (a) All move in straight lines

   (i) from $-3j$ to $3j$

   (ii) from 2 to -2

   (iii) from $2 - 3j$ to $-2 + 3j$

   (iv) from j to $-j$

   (v) from 1 to 0 then back to 1

   (vi) from -1 to 0 then back to -1

  (b) All except **(v)** move round circles

   (i) once anticlockwise round $|z| = 3$, starting at 3

   (ii) once anticlockwise round $|z| = 2$, starting at $2j$

   (iii) once anticlockwise round $|z| = \sqrt{13}$, starting at $3 + 2j$

   (iv) once clockwise round $|z| = 1$, starting at 1

   (v) stationary at 1

   (vi) twice anticlockwise round $|z| = 1$, starting at 1

14 $\dfrac{\sqrt{3}-1}{4}$, $\dfrac{\sqrt{3}+1}{4}$; $\sqrt{2}\left(\cos\dfrac{3\pi}{4} + j\sin\dfrac{3\pi}{4}\right)$,

$\sqrt{10}\left(\cos\dfrac{\pi}{3} + j\sin\dfrac{\pi}{3}\right)$; $\dfrac{\sqrt{3}+1}{2\sqrt{2}}$

15 (ii) $\dfrac{\pi}{4}$, $\dfrac{5\pi}{6}$

   (iii) $8, -\dfrac{11\pi}{12}$

   (iv) perpendicular bisector of line from α to β

   (v) $\dfrac{13\pi}{24}$

16 (i) Points of knife have moduli < 1, which decrease on squaring; angle subtended by knife at the origin is doubled

   (ii) points of forearm have argument $\dfrac{\pi}{2}$ (vertical from O) which doubles to become π (horizontal from O) on squaring

   (iii) angles subtended by head and boots at O both double, but boots are further from O than head, so grow more

(iv) knife tip has argument $\frac{3\pi}{4}$, stomach has argument $-\frac{\pi}{4}$; both give argument $-\frac{\pi}{2}$ on doubling.

Exercise 3D (Page 41)

1 (i) $\dfrac{1-j}{\sqrt{2}}$

(ii) $-\dfrac{1+\sqrt{3}j}{2}$

(iii) $-\dfrac{\sqrt{3}+j}{2}$

(iv) $\dfrac{-1+j}{\sqrt{2}}$

2 (i) $-8+8\sqrt{3}j \approx -8+13.856j$

(ii) $-1024-1024j$

(iii) $-0.078+0.997j$

(iv) $-46\,656$

3 (i) $\cos 8\alpha - j\sin 8\alpha$

(ii) $\cos 2\beta - j\sin 2\beta$

(iii) $\cos^{10}\gamma(\cos 10\gamma + j\sin 10\gamma)$

(iv) $\dfrac{\cos 4\delta - j\sin 4\delta}{16\cos^4\delta}$

Activity 3.6 (Page 43)

(ii) $16\sin^5\theta - 20\sin^3\theta + 5\sin\theta$

Activity 3.7 (Page 43)

$\dfrac{\sin 5\theta - 5\sin 3\theta + 10\sin\theta}{16}$

Exercise 3E (Page 44)

1 $\dfrac{4t-4t^3}{1-6t^2+t^4}$, where $t = \tan\theta$

2 (i) $c^3 - 3cs^2 = 4c^3 - 3c$

(ii) $3c^2s - s^3 = 3s - 4s^3$

(iii) $\dfrac{3t-t^3}{1-3t^2}$

where $c=\cos\theta$, $s=\sin\theta$ and $t=\tan\theta$

3 $32c^6 - 48c^4 + 18c^2 - 1$, $32c^5 - 32c^3 + 6c$, where $c = \cos\theta$

4 $\dfrac{{}^nC_1 t - {}^nC_3 t^3 + \cdots}{1 - {}^nC_2 t^2 + {}^nC_4 t^4 - \cdots}$

5 (i) $\dfrac{\cos 4\theta + 4\cos 2\theta + 3}{8}$

(ii) $\dfrac{\sin 5\theta - 5\sin 3\theta + 10\sin\theta}{16}$

(iii) $\dfrac{-\cos 6\theta + 6\cos 4\theta - 15\cos 2\theta + 10}{32}$

(iv) $\dfrac{\cos 7\theta - \cos 5\theta - 3\cos 3\theta + 3\cos\theta}{64}$

(v) $\dfrac{-\sin 7\theta - \sin 5\theta + 3\sin 3\theta + 3\sin\theta}{64}$

7 (i) $-\frac{1}{192}\sin 6\theta + \frac{3}{64}\sin 4\theta - \frac{15}{64}\sin 2\theta + \frac{5}{16}\theta + k$

(ii) $\frac{2}{35}$

(iii) $\frac{4}{35}$

8 $\dfrac{\sin 2n\theta}{2\sin\theta}$

9 (i) $\cos n\theta + j\sin n\theta$, $\cos n\theta - j\sin n\theta$, $2\cos n\theta$, $2j\sin n\theta$

(iii) $p = \frac{1}{16}$, $q = \frac{1}{32}$, $r = -\frac{1}{16}$, $s = -\frac{1}{32}$

10 (i) Same as 9 **(i)**

(ii) $p = \frac{1}{16}$, $q = -\frac{1}{32}$, $r = -\frac{1}{16}$, $s = \frac{1}{32}$

11 0

Activity 3.8 (Page 46)

$e^{z+2\pi nj} = e^z \times e^{2\pi nj} = e^z(\cos 2\pi n + j\sin 2\pi n) = e^z \times 1.$

Exercise 3F (Page 48)

1 (i) -1

(ii) $\dfrac{1+j}{\sqrt{2}}$

(iii) $-1.209 + 0.698j$

(iv) $-13.129 + 15.201j$

2 $3 + 2k\pi j$

3 $-4 + \left(2k - \dfrac{1}{3}\right)\pi j$

4 All z

6 Rhombus

9 $\dot{z} = (\dot{r} + jr\dot{\theta})e^{j\theta}$, $\ddot{z} = (\ddot{r} - r\dot{\theta}^2 + j(2\dot{r}\dot{\theta} + r\ddot{\theta}))e^{j\theta}$, where the dot shows differentiation with respect to t. Components:

	radial	transverse
velocity	$\dot{r}$	$r\dot{\theta}$
acceleration	$\ddot{r} - r\dot{\theta}^2$	$2\dot{r}\dot{\theta} + r\ddot{\theta}$

10 $C = \dfrac{e^{3x}(3\cos 2x + 2\sin 2x)}{13} + c,$

$S = \dfrac{e^{3x}(-2\cos 2x + 3\sin 2x)}{13} + c'$

11 $\dfrac{e^{ax}(a\cos bx + b\sin bx)}{a^2 + b^2} + c,$ $\dfrac{e^{ax}(-b\cos bx + a\sin bx)}{a^2 + b^2} + c'$

Activity 3.9 (Page 49)

$S = 2^n \cos^n\dfrac{\theta}{2}\sin\dfrac{n\theta}{2}$

Exercise 3G (Page 50)

1 $\dfrac{\sin\theta + \sin(n-1)\theta - \sin n\theta}{2 - 2\cos\theta}$

2 (iii) $\displaystyle\sum_{r=0}^{n} {}^nC_r 2^{n-r}\sin\dfrac{2r\pi}{3} = 3^{n/2}\sin\dfrac{n\pi}{6}$

3 (i) $\cos k\theta + j\sin k\theta, \ \cos k\theta - j\sin k\theta$

(ii) $|w| = \sin\theta, \ \arg w = \theta - \dfrac{\pi}{2}$

Square roots have modulus $\sqrt{\sin\theta}$ and arguments $\dfrac{\theta}{2} - \dfrac{\pi}{4}, \ \dfrac{\theta}{2} + \dfrac{3\pi}{4}$.

(iii) $\dfrac{e^{j\theta}\cos\theta(1 - (e^{j\theta}\cos\theta)^n)}{1 - e^{j\theta}\cos\theta}$

(iv) $\dfrac{\cos\theta - \cos n\theta\cos^{n+1}\theta}{\sin\theta}$

4 (i) $\cos 2\theta + j\sin 2\theta, \ \cos 3\theta + j\sin 3\theta,$
$\cos n\theta + j\sin n\theta$

(ii) $1 + \dfrac{z}{3} + \dfrac{z^2}{9} + \dfrac{z^3}{27} + \cdots + \dfrac{z^n}{3^n} + \cdots$

(iii) $\dfrac{3}{3 - z}$

(iv) (a) $C = \dfrac{9 - 3\cos\theta}{10 - 6\cos\theta}$

(b) $S = \dfrac{3\sin\theta}{10 - 6\cos\theta}$

5 (i) $\cos\theta + j\sin\theta, \ \cos n\theta + j\sin n\theta, \ \cos n\theta - j\sin n\theta$

(iv) $C = \dfrac{2\cos\theta}{5 - 4\cos 2\theta}, \ S = \dfrac{6\sin\theta}{5 - 4\cos 2\theta}$

6 (i) $\cos n\theta + j\sin n\theta$

(ii) $\cos\theta, \ \dfrac{5}{4} + \cos\theta$

(iv) $C = \dfrac{2\cos\theta + 1}{5 + 4\cos\theta}, \ S = \dfrac{2\sin\theta}{5 + 4\cos\theta}$

7 $2^n \cos^n \dfrac{\beta}{2} \sin\left(\alpha + \dfrac{n\beta}{2}\right)$

Activity 3.10 (Page 51)

(i) ± 1

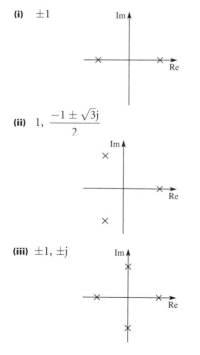

(ii) $1, \ \dfrac{-1 \pm \sqrt{3}j}{2}$

(iii) $\pm 1, \pm j$

Activity 3.11 (Page 52)

$\omega^r(\omega^r)^\star = |\omega^r|^2 = 1 = \omega^n$.

Therefore $(\omega^r)^\star = \dfrac{\omega^n}{\omega^r} = \omega^{n-r}$.

Activity 3.12 (Page 53)

The degree of the equation is now $n - 1$, since the $(jz)^n$ and $(-jz)^n$ terms now cancel. The working is the same, except that $\alpha + 1 = 0$ is now possible, when $k = \dfrac{n}{2}$. So the $n - 1$ roots are $z = \tan\dfrac{k\pi}{n}$, $k = 0, 1, 2, \ldots, n - 1$, $k \neq \dfrac{n}{2}$.

Exercise 3H (Page 53)

1 The fifth roots give alternate tenth roots, and their negatives (given by half turn about O) fill the gaps.

3 $-\alpha, \pm\alpha\omega, \pm\alpha\omega^2$

5 (iv) If and only if m and n have no common factor

6 $\dfrac{j}{2}, \ \dfrac{\pm\sqrt{3} + j}{2}$

7 $\cos\dfrac{k\pi}{3} + j\sin\dfrac{k\pi}{3}, \ k = 1, 2, 3, 4, 5$

9 $\dfrac{\cos\dfrac{2k\pi}{n}}{1 - \sin\dfrac{2k\pi}{n}}, \ k = 0, 1, 2, \ldots, n - 1$

(excluding $k = \dfrac{3n}{4}$ if n is a multiple of 4)

10 $\cot\dfrac{(2k + 1)\pi}{2n}, \ k = 0, 1, 2, \ldots, n - 1$

Activity 3.13 (Page 56)

$1.22 + 0.19j$

❓ (Page 56)

$\sqrt{-1}$ is ambiguous, meaning j at one stage and $-$j at another.

Exercise 3I (Page 57)

1 $\pm(0.90 + 2.79j)$

2 $\pm 1, \pm j$

3 $-119 - 120j, \ -3 + 2j, \ -2 - 3j, \ 3 - 2j$

4

5 $(z + 1 - 3j)^7 = 2187$

7 Regular n-gon with one vertex at O

9 (i) $2 + 2j, -2 + 2j, -2 - 2j, 2 - 2j$

(ii)

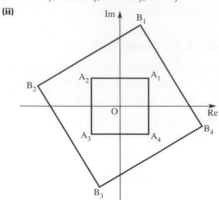

(iii) Rotate (centre O) through $+\dfrac{\pi}{6}$ and enlarge $\times 2$.
$B_1 B_2 = 8$.

(iv) $512 - 512\sqrt{3}j$

10 (i) $e^{j\theta} = \cos\theta + j\sin\theta$, $e^{-j\theta} = \cos\theta - j\sin\theta$

(ii) $2e^{j\alpha}$, where $\alpha = \pm\dfrac{\pi}{5}, \pm\dfrac{3\pi}{5}, \pi$

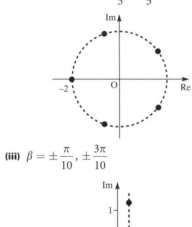

(iii) $\beta = \pm\dfrac{\pi}{10}, \pm\dfrac{3\pi}{10}$

11 (i) $\cos k\theta + j\sin k\theta, \cos k\theta - j\sin k\theta$

(ii) $\sqrt{2}e^{j\theta}$, where $\theta = \dfrac{\pi}{12}, \dfrac{5\pi}{12}, \dfrac{3\pi}{4}, -\dfrac{\pi}{4}, -\dfrac{7\pi}{12}, -\dfrac{11\pi}{12}$

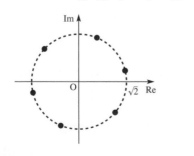

(iii) $-1 + j, 1 - j$

(iv) $p = \dfrac{1}{2\sqrt{2}}$,

$\alpha = \dfrac{\pi}{24}, \dfrac{5\pi}{24}, \dfrac{3\pi}{8}, -\dfrac{\pi}{8}, -\dfrac{7\pi}{24}, -\dfrac{11\pi}{24}$

13 (i) $8\left(\cos\dfrac{\pi}{10} + j\sin\dfrac{\pi}{10}\right)$

(ii) $\dfrac{1}{49}\left(\cos\left(-\dfrac{\pi}{4}\right) + j\sin\left(-\dfrac{\pi}{4}\right)\right)$

(iii) $\dfrac{1}{2187}\left(\cos\dfrac{7\pi}{12} + j\sin\dfrac{7\pi}{12}\right)$

14 (i) $\dfrac{-1 + j}{\sqrt{2}}, \dfrac{1 - j}{\sqrt{2}}, (j^{1/2})^3 = j^{3/2}$

(ii) Both $\dfrac{1 + \sqrt{3}j}{2}$

(iii) $-\pi < m \arg w < \pi$

15 (i) $\cos k\theta + j\sin k\theta, \cos k\theta - j\sin k\theta$

(ii) $\dfrac{e^{j\theta}(1 - e^{2nj\theta})}{1 - e^{2j\theta}}$, which simplifies to $\dfrac{\sin n\theta}{\sin\theta}e^{jn\theta}$
by using result **(i)**.

(iii) $\arg(C + jS) = n\theta$

(iv) $C = \dfrac{\sin n\theta \cos n\theta}{\sin\theta}, S = \dfrac{\sin^2 n\theta}{\sin\theta}$

(v) Let the side $A_{n-1}A_n$ be represented by the complex number w_n ($n = 1, 2, \ldots, 6$).
Then $|w_n| = 1$ (unit sides)
and
$$\arg(w_n) = \dfrac{\pi}{7} + (n - 1)\dfrac{2\pi}{7} = \dfrac{(2n - 1)\pi}{7}.$$

$\left(\text{Each external angle of the heptagon is } \dfrac{2\pi}{7}.\right)$

So $w_n = e^{(2n-1)j\pi/7}$ and
$z_n = w_1 + w_2 + \cdots + w_n$
(by vector addition round the heptagon from O).
$\arg(z_n) = \dfrac{1}{7}n\pi$ follows from **(iii)** with $\theta = \dfrac{\pi}{7}$.

16 He was essentially right, in the sense that by replacing $\sqrt{-1}$ by j and ∞ by n, and then letting $n \to \infty$ gives the limit π.

Activity 3.14 (Page 60)

$\arg\left(\dfrac{a - b}{c - b}\right) = \arg(a - b) - \arg(c - b)$
$= \angle XBA - \angle XBC = \angle ABC$

Activity 3.15 (Page 61)

$\arg\left(\dfrac{z + 3}{z - 2j}\right) = \dfrac{2\pi}{3}$

Activity 3.16 (Page 62)

The argument is as in Example 3.12, with the extra step of taking the conjugate which reflects triangle DEF to produce opposite similarity.

Exercise 3J (Page 64)

2

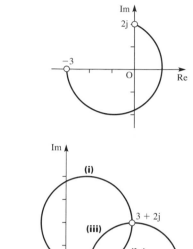

3

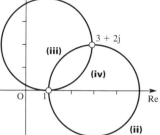

4 Converse is not true.

5 (i)

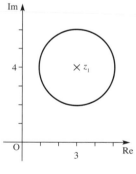

(ii)

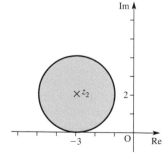

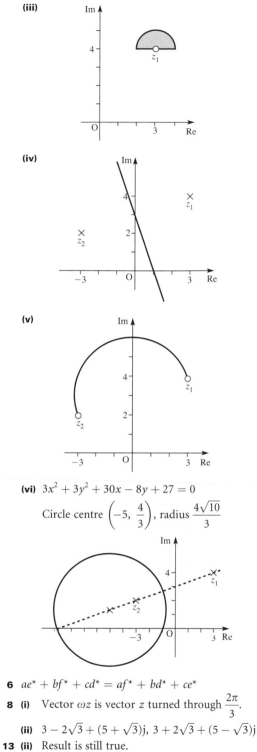

(iii)

(iv)

(v)

(vi) $3x^2 + 3y^2 + 30x - 8y + 27 = 0$

Circle centre $\left(-5, \dfrac{4}{3}\right)$, radius $\dfrac{4\sqrt{10}}{3}$

6 $ae^\star + bf^\star + cd^\star = af^\star + bd^\star + ce^\star$

8 (i) Vector ωz is vector z turned through $\dfrac{2\pi}{3}$.

(ii) $3 - 2\sqrt{3} + (5 + \sqrt{3})j$, $3 + 2\sqrt{3} + (5 - \sqrt{3})j$

13 (ii) Result is still true.

(iii) Let D coincide with A. Then S also coincides with A.

Chapter 4

Activity 4.1 (Page 71)

$1 - x + \dfrac{x^2}{2} - \dfrac{x^3}{6}$; $1 - \dfrac{x^4}{12} - \dfrac{x^6}{36}$; close to 1 when x is small.

Activity 4.2 (Page 71)

2.708

Exercise 4A (Page 72)

1 (i) $x - \dfrac{x^3}{6}$

(ii) $1 - \dfrac{x^2}{2} + \dfrac{x^4}{24}$

(iii) $1 + \dfrac{x^3}{3}$

2 Row 3 contains x times the reciprocals of factorials, and cell A5 contains the sum of these.

3 0.6065

5 $f'(0) = 0$, $f''(0) = -3$, $f^{(3)}(0) = 15$

6 $\dfrac{d}{dx}(e^x) = e^x$, $\int e^x dx = e^x + c$

7 (iii) 0.24%

9 (i) $1 - \tfrac{1}{2}x^2 + \tfrac{1}{8}x^4 - \tfrac{1}{48}x^6$

(ii) $1 - \tfrac{1}{2}x^2 + \tfrac{1}{8}x^4 - \tfrac{1}{48}x^6 + \tfrac{1}{384}x^8$; $0.8555 \pm 0.000\,15$

Activity 4.3 (Page 75)

If $f(x) = \cos x$ then $f'(x) = -\sin x$, $f''(x) = -\cos x$, $f^{(3)}(x) = \sin x$ and $f^{(4)}(x) = \cos x$. The pattern then repeats in a cycle of four. So $f^{(2r)}(0) = (-1)^r$ and $f^{(2r+1)}(0) = 0$.
The result follows.

Activity 4.4 (Page 75)

If $f(x) = (1 + x)^n$ then
$f^{(r)}(x) = n(n-1)(n-2)\ldots(n-r+1)(1+x)^{n-r}$
and $f^{(r)}(0) = n(n-1)(n-2)\ldots(n-r+1)$,
for $1 \leqslant r \leqslant n$. The result follows.

Exercise 4B (Page 76)

1 (i) $\ln x$ and its derivatives do not exist at $x = 0$.

(ii) If $f(x) = \ln(1 + x)$ then $f^{(r)}(x) = (-1)^{r+1}\dfrac{(r-1)!}{(1+x)^r}$
and $f^{(r)}(0) = (-1)^{r+1}(r-1)!$.
The result follows.

3 $\tfrac{1}{2} + \tfrac{1}{4}x - \tfrac{1}{48}x^3$

4 (i) 0.6456

(ii) 0.6911

(iii) $2x + \dfrac{2x^3}{3} + \dfrac{2x^5}{5}$; $x = \tfrac{1}{3}$ gives $\ln 2 \approx 0.6930$

5 (i) $\dfrac{1}{1 + (1+x)^2}$, $\dfrac{-2(1+x)}{(1+(1+x)^2)^2}$

(ii) $\tfrac{1}{4}\pi + \tfrac{1}{2}x - \tfrac{1}{4}x^2 + \cdots$

(iii) 0.324

6 (i) $a_0 = 2$

(ii) $2 + x - x^2 - \dfrac{x^3}{3} + \dfrac{x^4}{4} + \dfrac{x^5}{15} - \dfrac{x^6}{24}$

(iii)

Maclaurin approximation

7 (i) (a) $1 - \dfrac{\theta^2}{2!} + \dfrac{\theta^4}{4!} - \dfrac{\theta^6}{6!} + \cdots$

(b) $\theta - \dfrac{\theta^3}{3!} + \dfrac{\theta^5}{5!} - \dfrac{\theta^7}{7!} + \cdots$

(c) $1 + j\theta - \dfrac{\theta^2}{2!} - \dfrac{j\theta^3}{3!} + \dfrac{\theta^4}{4!} + \dfrac{j\theta^5}{5!} - \dfrac{\theta^6}{6!} - \dfrac{j\theta^7}{7!} + \cdots$

(ii) Same as (i) (c).

8 (ii) $a_1 = 1$, $a_2 = 0$

(iv) $x + \dfrac{x^3}{3!} + \dfrac{9x^5}{5!} + \cdots$
$+ \dfrac{(2r-1)^2(2r-3)^2 \ldots 5^2 \times 3^2}{(2r+1)!} x^{2r+1} + \cdots$

Activity 4.5 (Page 78)

(i) $\ln(1+x) = \displaystyle\int \dfrac{1}{1+x} dx$

$= \displaystyle\int (1 - x + x^2 - x^3 + \cdots) dx$

$= x - \dfrac{x^2}{2} + \dfrac{x^3}{3} - \dfrac{x^4}{4} + \cdots$

The constant of integration is zero because $\ln(1+x) = 0$ when $x = 0$.

(ii) The terms neglected in the series for e^x and $(1+x)^{-1}$ do not affect the product up to terms in x^3.

(iii) $\sec x = \dfrac{1}{\cos x} \approx \dfrac{1}{1 - \dfrac{x^2}{2!} + \dfrac{x^4}{4!}} = (1+y)^{-1}$.

Activity 4.6 (Page 79)

If $x = a$ is an approximation to the root of $f(x) = 0$ and the root is $x = a + h$ then $f(a + h) = 0$. But $f(a + h) \approx f(a) + hf'(a)$, so $f(a) + hf'(a) \approx 0$, so $h \approx -\dfrac{f(a)}{f'(a)}$.

This gives the Newton–Raphson approximation

$a - \dfrac{f(a)}{f'(a)}$ for the root.

Exercise 4C (Page 80)

1 (i) $3x - \frac{9}{2}x^3$
 (ii) $1 - 2x^2 + \frac{2}{3}x^4$
 (iii) $x^2 - \frac{1}{3}x^4$
 (iv) $x - \frac{1}{2}x^2 + \frac{1}{6}x^3 - \frac{1}{12}x^4$
 (v) $x - x^2 + \frac{1}{3}x^3$
 (vi) $1 + x + \frac{1}{2}x^2 - \frac{1}{8}x^4$
2 (i) $\frac{1}{2}\arcsin(2x) + c$
 (ii) $2x + \frac{4}{3}x^3 + \frac{12}{5}x^5 + \frac{40}{7}x^7 + \cdots$
3 (iv) $3.141\,59$
4 (i)

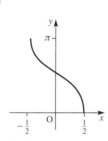

 (ii) $-2(1 - 4x^2)^{-\frac{1}{2}}$
 (iii) $x\arccos(2x) - \frac{1}{2}(1 - 4x^2)^{\frac{1}{2}} + c$
 (iv) $\dfrac{\pi}{2} - 2x - \dfrac{4}{3}x^3 - \dfrac{12}{5}x^5$
5 (i) $x + x^2 + \frac{1}{3}x^3 - \frac{1}{30}x^5 - \frac{1}{90}x^6$
 (ii) $x + x^2 + \frac{1}{3}x^3 - \frac{1}{12}x^5 - \frac{1}{36}x^6$; agrees with (i) as far as the term in x^4.
 (iii) $1 + x - \frac{1}{3}x^3$; the x^4 term of the product is not correct.
8 Given $0 < r < 1$, the area of the square

$$= \left(\frac{1}{1 - r}\right)^2 = 1 + 2r + 3r^2 + 4r^3 + 5r^4 + \cdots$$

Also the side of the square

$$= (1 - r)(1 + 2r + 3r^2 + 4r^3 + 5r^4 + \cdots)$$

$$= (1 - r)\left(\frac{1}{1 - r}\right)^2 = \frac{1}{(1 - r)}.$$

Chapter 5

Activity 5.1 (Page 86)

The six products in Sarrus' method are the six terms in the expansions of $\det M$ by the first column (for instance) with their correct signs; 13.

Exercise 5A (Page 87)

1 (i) 30
 (ii) -33
 (iii) -15
 (iv) -2
2 (i) (a) 5
   (b) 5
 (ii) (a) -5
   (b) -5
 Interchanging the rows and columns has not changed the determinant.
3 (i) 0
 (ii) 0
 With repeated columns, the value of each determinant is 0.
4 (i) (a) 2
   (b) -2
 (ii) (a) 13
   (b) -13
 In both cases, swapping two columns has multiplied the determinant by -1.
5 2, 3, 6; $\det(MN) = \det M \times \det N$
6 $\dfrac{-1 \pm \sqrt{41}}{2}$

Activity 5.2 (Page 90)

(i) (a) $\begin{pmatrix} x' \\ y' \\ z' \end{pmatrix} = E_1 \begin{pmatrix} x \\ y \\ z \end{pmatrix}$
 (b) A shear parallel to the z axis, each point moving q times its x co-ordinate.
 (c) $\begin{pmatrix} 1 & 0 & 0 \\ 0 & 1 & 0 \\ 0 & r & 1 \end{pmatrix}$
(ii) (c) P is mapped to P' by three successive shears; shears preserve volume.

Exercise 5B (Page 91)

1 (i) Columns 1 and 3 are identical.
 (ii) Columns 2 and 3 have been swapped.
 (iii) The columns have been cyclically interchanged.
 (iv) Substituting 3 for x makes columns 1 and 3 identical
   $\Rightarrow$ determinant $= 0$
   $\Rightarrow (x - 3)$ is a factor of the determinant (by the remainder theorem).
2 (ii) Stretching by scale factor k in one direction only multiplies volume by k.
 (iii) Multiplying any one column by constant k multiplies determinant by k.

3 **(i)** 430

(ii) −6020

(iii) $86x^3y$

4 **(ii)** A shear does not change volume.

5 **(i)** 43

(ii) 7

(iii) −1

6 $|\mathbf{a} \quad \mathbf{b} \quad \mathbf{a}+\mathbf{b}| = |\mathbf{a} \quad \mathbf{b} \quad \mathbf{a}| = 0$

7 **(iii)** $a_1B_1 + a_2B_2 + a_3B_3$; $\quad b_1C_1 + b_2C_2 + b_3C_3$;

$c_1A_1 + c_2A_2 + c_3A_3$; $\quad c_1B_1 + c_2B_2 + c_3B_3$

8 **(i)** $\begin{pmatrix} \Delta & 0 & 0 \\ 0 & \Delta & 0 \\ 0 & 0 & \Delta \end{pmatrix}$, $\dfrac{1}{\Delta}\begin{pmatrix} A_1 & A_2 & A_3 \\ B_1 & B_2 & B_3 \\ C_1 & C_2 & C_3 \end{pmatrix}$

(ii) No. (Yes if restricted to matrices whose determinant is not 0.)

9 Equation of the straight line joining (x_1, y_1), (x_2, y_2).

10 Expanding the determinant gives a cubic polynomial; 5, −8

12 **(i)** $(a - b)(b - c)(c - a)$

(ii) $(y - z)(z - x)(x - y)$

(iii) $(y - z)(z - x)(x - y)(x + y + z)$

(iv) $(y - z)(z - x)(x - y)(xy + yz + zx)$

13 $x(x + 1)(x - 1)^3$

Activity 5.3 (Page 93)

Of the nine elements, six are 0 as they are expansions by alien cofactors; the other three are Δ as they are expansions by each column in turn.

Activity 5.4 (Page 94)

(i) $\displaystyle\sum_{i=1}^{n} r_i c_i$

(ii) $\mathbf{MM}^{-1} = \mathbf{I} \Rightarrow (\mathbf{MM}^{-1})^{\mathrm{T}} = \mathbf{I}^{\mathrm{T}} = \mathbf{I}$
$\Rightarrow (\mathbf{M}^{-1})^{\mathrm{T}}\mathbf{M}^{\mathrm{T}} = \mathbf{I} \Rightarrow (\mathbf{M}^{-1})^{\mathrm{T}} = (\mathbf{M}^{\mathrm{T}})^{-1}$.

Activity 5.5 (Page 94)

If $\mathbf{M}$ has inverse $\mathbf{M}^{-1}$ then $\det(\mathbf{MM}^{-1}) = \det\mathbf{I} = 1$.
But $\det(\mathbf{MM}^{-1}) = \det\mathbf{M} \times \det(\mathbf{M}^{-1}) = 0$, since
$\det\mathbf{M} = 0$.
Therefore $\mathbf{M}$ has no inverse.

Exercise 5C (Page 96)

1 **(i)** $\dfrac{1}{3}\begin{pmatrix} 3 & 0 & -6 \\ -4 & 2 & 3 \\ 2 & -1 & 0 \end{pmatrix}$

(ii) none

(iii) $\begin{pmatrix} -0.06 & -0.1 & -0.1 \\ 0.92 & 0.2 & 0.7 \\ 0.66 & 0.1 & 0.6 \end{pmatrix}$

(iv) $\dfrac{1}{21}\begin{pmatrix} 34 & 11 & 32 \\ 9 & 6 & 6 \\ -38 & -16 & -37 \end{pmatrix}$

2 **(i)** $\begin{pmatrix} -1 & 0 & 2 \\ 9 & -7 & 3 \\ -5 & 7 & -4 \end{pmatrix}$

(ii) $7\mathbf{I}$

(iii) $7\mathbf{I}$

(iv) 7

(v) 49

(vi) $7\mathbf{M}$; $\operatorname{adj}(\operatorname{adj}\mathbf{M}) = (\det\mathbf{M})\mathbf{M}$

3 $\dfrac{1}{7}\begin{pmatrix} 2 & 18 & -11 \\ 2 & 39 & -25 \\ 3 & 41 & -27 \end{pmatrix}$; $x = 8$, $y = 4$, $z = -3$

4 $49\mathbf{I}$

(i) $\frac{1}{49}\mathbf{A}^{\mathrm{T}}$

(ii) 343

(iii) $49\mathbf{I}$

5 **(i)** $\begin{pmatrix} -5 & 4 & 6 \\ 14 & 16 & 13 \\ 4 & 9 & 8 \end{pmatrix}$, 77

(ii) $\begin{pmatrix} -9 & -4 & -9 \\ 10 & 7 & 14 \\ 8 & 14 & 21 \end{pmatrix}$, 77

(iii) 11

(iv) 7

6 **(i)** −1.5

(ii) −10

(iii) −2, 4

(iv) −1, 1, 2

9 **(i)** $\begin{pmatrix} ae - bd & 0 & 0 \\ 0 & cf & 0 \\ 0 & 0 & ae - bd \end{pmatrix}$

(ii) $f = \dfrac{ae - bd}{c}$ provided $c \neq 0$, $ae - bd \neq 0$

(iii) $\dfrac{1}{c(ae - bd)}\begin{pmatrix} ce & 0 & -bc \\ 0 & ae - bd & 0 \\ -cd & 0 & ac \end{pmatrix}$

(iv) $4\begin{pmatrix} 1 & -4 & 1 \\ 12 & 2k & -24 \\ 8 - k & 8 & 3k - 16 \end{pmatrix}$

(v) $x = -2k$, $y = k^2$, $z = 4k$

10 **(i)** See text, page 94.

(ii) Take determinants in part **(i)**.

(iii) $(\operatorname{adj}\mathbf{M})^{-1} = \dfrac{\operatorname{adj}(\operatorname{adj}\mathbf{M})}{\det(\operatorname{adj}\mathbf{M})} = \dfrac{\operatorname{adj}(\operatorname{adj}\mathbf{M})}{\Delta^2}$

But $(\operatorname{adj}\mathbf{M})^{-1} = \dfrac{\mathbf{M}}{\Delta}$ from part **(i)**.

The result follows.

These results are identities (or sets of identities) between the elements of $\mathbf{M}$, which are true for all values of these elements, even when $\mathbf{M}$ is singular.

Exercise 5D (Page 102)

1 A pair of lines intersecting at $\left(6\frac{1}{2}, \ -\frac{1}{2}\right)$

2 Inconsistent: distinct parallel lines in two dimensions

3 Coincident lines with infinitely many common points $(t, 4 - 2t)$

4 Inconsistent: distinct parallel lines in two dimensions

5 Inconsistent: planes forming a prism

6 A sheaf of planes with common line $(2\lambda + 1, 4\lambda + 1, -3\lambda + 5)$

7 Three planes with a unique common point $(3, -14, 8)$

8 Three planes with a unique common point $(-15, 24, -1)$

9 Three coincident planes $(\lambda, \mu, 2\lambda + \mu - 5)$

10 Inconsistent: planes forming a prism

11 $k = 4$, $(\frac{3}{2}, -2\lambda, \lambda)$; $k = -4$, no solution

12 The transformation either **(a)** collapses the whole plane to a line through O or **(b)** maps everything to O.

When $p = q = 0$ in **(a)** there is a line of points that map to O, and in **(b)** every point maps to O. When p and q are not both 0, there is either no solution (distinct parallel lines) or many solutions (coincident lines).

13 (i) Inconsistent: planes form a prism

(ii) $(\lambda - 2, \lambda, 2\lambda)$: planes form a sheaf

14 It makes no difference whether **A** is singular or non-singular.

15 14

16 (ii) (a) No solution: prism of planes

(b) $x = t$, $y = 3t - 4$, $z = 2t - 2$; sheaf

Activity 5.7 (Page 105)

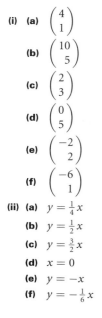

(i) (a) $\begin{pmatrix} 4 \\ 1 \end{pmatrix}$

(b) $\begin{pmatrix} 10 \\ 5 \end{pmatrix}$

(c) $\begin{pmatrix} 2 \\ 3 \end{pmatrix}$

(d) $\begin{pmatrix} 0 \\ 5 \end{pmatrix}$

(e) $\begin{pmatrix} -2 \\ 2 \end{pmatrix}$

(f) $\begin{pmatrix} -6 \\ 1 \end{pmatrix}$

(ii) (a) $y = \frac{1}{4}x$

(b) $y = \frac{1}{2}x$

(c) $y = \frac{3}{2}x$

(d) $x = 0$

(e) $y = -x$

(f) $y = -\frac{1}{6}x$

Activity 5.9 (Page 110)

(i) $\det(\mathbf{M} - \lambda\mathbf{I}) \equiv (\lambda_1 - \lambda)(\lambda_2 - \lambda)(\lambda_3 - \lambda)$ ⊛

Putting $\lambda = 0$ gives $\det\mathbf{M} = \lambda_1\lambda_2\lambda_3$

(ii) Coefficient of λ^2 on RHS of ⊛ $= \lambda_1 + \lambda_2 + \lambda_3$.

When expanding $\det(\mathbf{M} - \lambda\mathbf{I})$ the terms in λ^2 arise only from the product of the elements on the leading diagonal, $(a_1 - \lambda)(b_2 - \lambda)(c_3 - \lambda)$, since all other terms are linear in λ. The coefficient of λ^2 is $a_1 + b_2 + c_3$, and the result follows.

Exercise 5E (Page 110)

1 (i) 7, $k(3\mathbf{i} + 2\mathbf{j})$; 2, $k(\mathbf{i} - \mathbf{j})$ where $k \neq 0$

(ii) 4, $k(2\mathbf{i} - 3\mathbf{j})$; -1, $k(\mathbf{i} - 4\mathbf{j})$ where $k \neq 0$

(iii) $1 + \sqrt{2}$, $k(\sqrt{2}\mathbf{i} + \mathbf{j})$; $1 - \sqrt{2}$, $k(\sqrt{2}\mathbf{i} - \mathbf{j})$ where $k \neq 0$

(iv) 2 (repeated), $k(\mathbf{i} - \mathbf{j})$ where $k \neq 0$

(v) 1, $k(4\mathbf{i} + \mathbf{j})$; 0.3, $k(\mathbf{i} + 2\mathbf{j})$ where $k \neq 0$

(vi) p, $k\mathbf{i}$; q, $k\mathbf{j}$ where $k \neq 0$

2 (i) 3, $c\mathbf{i}$; 2, $c\mathbf{j}$; -1, $c(\mathbf{j} - 3\mathbf{k})$ where $c \neq 0$

(ii) 4, $c(\mathbf{i} - \mathbf{j} + 2\mathbf{k})$; 3, $c(\mathbf{i} - 2\mathbf{j} + 2\mathbf{k})$; -1, $c(9\mathbf{i} - 14\mathbf{j} - 2\mathbf{k})$ where $c \neq 0$

(iii) 4, $c(\mathbf{i} + \mathbf{j} + \mathbf{k})$; -3, $c(\mathbf{i} - 6\mathbf{j} + \mathbf{k})$; 0, $c(5\mathbf{i} + 9\mathbf{j} - 7\mathbf{k})$ where $c \neq 0$

(iv) 1, $c(\mathbf{i} + 5\mathbf{j} + \mathbf{k})$; 2 (repeated), $c(p\mathbf{i} + (2p + 4q)\mathbf{j} + q\mathbf{k})$ where $c \neq 0$ and p and q are not both 0

(v) 3, $c\mathbf{j}$; 2, $c(\mathbf{i} + \mathbf{k})$; -2, $c(\mathbf{i} - \mathbf{k})$ where $c \neq 0$

(vi) 9, $c(\mathbf{i} - \mathbf{k})$; 4, $c(\mathbf{i} + \mathbf{j} - 2\mathbf{k})$; 1, $c(\mathbf{i} + \mathbf{j} - \mathbf{k})$ where $c \neq 0$

3 (i) 1, $k(\mathbf{i} + \tan\theta\mathbf{j})$; -1, $k(\tan\theta\mathbf{i} - \mathbf{j})$

(ii) $\theta \neq n\pi \Rightarrow$ no real eigenvalues; $\theta = n\pi \Rightarrow$ eigenvalues are $(-1)^n$, and all non-zero vectors are eigenvectors.

4 (i) $\alpha + \beta$

(ii) $\alpha\beta$

6 (i) 9

(ii) $c(2\mathbf{i} + 5\mathbf{j} + 4\mathbf{k})$, 9; $c(\mathbf{i} - 2\mathbf{j} + 2\mathbf{k})$, -9 where $c \neq 0$

(iii) -729

8 (i) (a) 2, 3

(b) 4, 9

(c) 32, 243

(d) $\frac{1}{2}, \frac{1}{3}$

(ii) (a) 1, 2, 3

(b) 1, 4, 9

(c) 1, 32, 243

(d) 1, $\frac{1}{2}, \frac{1}{3}$

9 (i) $\mathbf{M}^n\mathbf{v}$ converges to $\mathbf{0}$

(ii) If $\lambda_1 = 1$, $\mathbf{M}^n\mathbf{v}$ converges to $\mathbf{s}_1$; if $\lambda_1 = -1$, $\mathbf{M}^n\mathbf{v}$ eventually alternates between $\pm\mathbf{s}_1$

(iii) The magnitude of $\mathbf{M}^n\mathbf{v}$ increases without limit; the direction of $\mathbf{M}^n\mathbf{v}$ becomes parallel to $\mathbf{s}_1$.

11 (i) $\mathbf{M} = \begin{pmatrix} 0.5 & 0.3 \\ 0.5 & 0.7 \end{pmatrix}$

(ii) $\mathbf{M}^2 \begin{pmatrix} 100 \\ 100 \end{pmatrix} = \begin{pmatrix} 76 \\ 24 \end{pmatrix}$

so 76 at Calgary, 124 at Vancouver

(iii) $\mathbf{x} = \begin{pmatrix} 75 \\ 125 \end{pmatrix}$; $\mathbf{Mx} = \lambda\mathbf{x}$ with $\lambda = 1$

(iv) 75 at Calgary, 125 at Vancouver

12 (iv) $4,\ c(3\mathbf{i} + \mathbf{j});\ 2,\ c(\mathbf{i} + \mathbf{j});$

$$\begin{pmatrix} r \\ w \end{pmatrix} = 475e^{4t}\begin{pmatrix} 3 \\ 1 \end{pmatrix} - 425e^{2t}\begin{pmatrix} 1 \\ 1 \end{pmatrix}$$

13 (i) Under $\mathbf{M}$ the image of a vector is attracted towards the eigenvector with the numerically largest eigenvalue; each multiplication by $\mathbf{M}$ maps the image closer to a multiple of that eigenvector. This does not happen if $\mathbf{v}_0 = \beta\mathbf{s}_2 + \gamma\mathbf{s}_3$, where $\mathbf{s}_2, \mathbf{s}_3$ are eigenvectors with other (numerically smaller) eigenvalues; rounding errors may also cause failures.

(ii) $\dfrac{x_n}{x_{n-1}}, \dfrac{y_n}{y_{n-1}}$ and $\dfrac{z_n}{z_{n-1}} \to$ a limit as $n \to \infty$. This limit is an eigenvalue, generally k, the largest eigenvalue (numerically).

Activity 5.10 (Page 116)

$\begin{vmatrix} 5-\lambda & 2 \\ 3 & 3-\lambda \end{vmatrix} = \lambda^2 - 8\lambda + 9.$

The characteristic equation is $\lambda^2 - 8\lambda + 9 = 0$.
By the Cayley–Hamilton theorem:
$\mathbf{M}^2 - 8\mathbf{M} + 9\mathbf{I} = 0 \Rightarrow \mathbf{M}^2 = 8\mathbf{M} - 9\mathbf{I}.$
Multiplying by $\mathbf{M}^n$ gives the result.

❓ (Page 116)

No. The suggested substitution is invalid since λ is a number and $\mathbf{M}$ is a matrix.

Exercise 5F (Page 117)

1 Note: the columns of $\mathbf{S}$ may be reversed provided the eigenvalues are also reversed. Each column of $\mathbf{S}$ may (independently) be multiplied by a non-zero constant.

(i) $\mathbf{S} = \begin{pmatrix} 4 & 1 \\ -3 & 1 \end{pmatrix},\quad \mathbf{\Lambda} = \begin{pmatrix} 2 & 0 \\ 0 & 9 \end{pmatrix}$

(ii) $\mathbf{S} = \begin{pmatrix} 4 & 5 \\ 2 & 3 \end{pmatrix},\quad \mathbf{\Lambda} = \begin{pmatrix} 2 & 0 \\ 0 & 1 \end{pmatrix}$

(iii) $\mathbf{S} = \begin{pmatrix} 1 & 5 \\ 1 & -3 \end{pmatrix},\quad \mathbf{\Lambda} = \begin{pmatrix} 1 & 0 \\ 0 & 0.2 \end{pmatrix}$

2 $\begin{pmatrix} 5 & 3 \\ 3 & 2 \end{pmatrix}\begin{pmatrix} 1 & 0 \\ 0 & 0.9 \end{pmatrix}\begin{pmatrix} 2 & -3 \\ -3 & 5 \end{pmatrix},$

$\begin{pmatrix} 4.0951 & -5.1585 \\ 2.0634 & -2.4390 \end{pmatrix}$; approximates to

$\begin{pmatrix} 10 & -15 \\ 6 & -9 \end{pmatrix}$

3 (i) $\begin{pmatrix} 876 & -1266 \\ 422 & -601 \end{pmatrix}$

(ii) $\begin{pmatrix} 524\,800 & -523\,776 \\ -523\,776 & 524\,800 \end{pmatrix}$

(iii) $\begin{pmatrix} 0.6667 & 0.3333 \\ 0.6666 & 0.3334 \end{pmatrix}$

4 e.g. (i) $\begin{pmatrix} 3 & 1 \\ 0 & 3 \end{pmatrix}$

(ii) $\begin{pmatrix} 1 & 0 \\ 0 & 1 \end{pmatrix}$

(iii) $\begin{pmatrix} 0 & 1 \\ 0 & 0 \end{pmatrix}$

(iv) $\begin{pmatrix} 1 & 3 \\ 0 & 0 \end{pmatrix} = \begin{pmatrix} 3 & 1 \\ -1 & 0 \end{pmatrix}\begin{pmatrix} 0 & 0 \\ 0 & 1 \end{pmatrix}\begin{pmatrix} 0 & -1 \\ 1 & 3 \end{pmatrix}$ or

$\begin{pmatrix} 6 & 4 \\ 3 & 2 \end{pmatrix} = \begin{pmatrix} 2 & 2 \\ -3 & 1 \end{pmatrix}\begin{pmatrix} 0 & 0 \\ 0 & 8 \end{pmatrix}\begin{pmatrix} \frac{1}{8} & -\frac{1}{4} \\ \frac{3}{8} & \frac{1}{4} \end{pmatrix}$

7 (i) $k, \begin{pmatrix} 1 \\ 0 \end{pmatrix}; 2, \begin{pmatrix} 3 \\ 2-k \end{pmatrix}$

(ii) $\begin{pmatrix} 1 & 3 \\ 0 & 2-k \end{pmatrix}$

(iii) $\begin{pmatrix} k^n & \frac{3(2^n - k^n)}{2-k} \\ 0 & 2^n \end{pmatrix}$

(iv) $p = 3,\ q = -2$

8 (i) 4

(ii) $k\begin{pmatrix} 1 \\ 0 \\ -1 \end{pmatrix}, k \neq 0$

(iii) (b) $p = \frac{1}{8}, q = -\frac{1}{8}, r = \frac{5}{4}$

(iv) $\frac{1}{2}\begin{pmatrix} -1 \\ -1 \\ 1 \end{pmatrix}$

9 $5;\ \begin{pmatrix} 1 & 1 & 1 \\ 1 & 1 & 0 \\ 0 & 1 & -1 \end{pmatrix}\begin{pmatrix} 5 & 0 & 0 \\ 0 & 4 & 0 \\ 0 & 0 & 2 \end{pmatrix}\begin{pmatrix} 1 & 1 & 1 \\ 1 & 1 & 0 \\ 0 & 1 & -1 \end{pmatrix}^{-1}$

10 (i) $2, 3$

(ii) $\begin{pmatrix} 1 \\ 2 \\ 2 \end{pmatrix}$

(iii) $p = 6, q = -11, r = 6$

11 (i) (a) $-2k - 8$

(b) $\dfrac{1}{2k+8}\begin{pmatrix} -2-2k & 1 & 2+k \\ 6 & 1 & -6-k \\ 12 & 2 & -4 \end{pmatrix}$

(ii) $k = -3$

(iii) $p = 2, q = 1, r = -2$

12 (i) 1

(ii) $\begin{pmatrix} 1 \\ -1 \end{pmatrix}, \begin{pmatrix} 5 \\ -3 \end{pmatrix}$

(iii) $\begin{pmatrix} 1 & 5 \\ -1 & -3 \end{pmatrix}$

14 (i) There are four such products, generally distinct, but **AB** has at most two distinct eigenvalues which may or may not be the product of an eigenvalue of **A** and an eigenvalue of **B**.

(ii) 'Proof' assumes that eigenvector of **A** is eigenvector of **B**.

Chapter 6

Activity 6.1 (Page 124)

$\cosh(-u) = \frac{1}{2}(e^{-u} + e^{u}) = \cosh u$; graph symmetrical about $u = 0$.
$\sinh(-u) = \frac{1}{2}(e^{-u} - e^{u}) = -\frac{1}{2}(e^{u} - e^{-u}) = -\sinh u$; graph has half-turn symmetry about the origin.

Activity 6.2 (Page 125)

$\cosh 2u = \cosh^2 u + \sinh^2 u$ (cf. $\cos 2\theta = \cos^2\theta - \sin^2\theta$)
$\cosh 2u = 2\cosh^2 u - 1$ (cf. $\cos 2\theta = 2\cos^2\theta - 1$)
$\cosh 2u = 1 + 2\sinh^2 u$ (cf. $\cos 2\theta = 1 - 2\sin^2\theta$)

Activity 6.3 (Page 125)

(i) $2\sinh u \cosh u$
$= \frac{1}{2}(e^u - e^{-u})(e^u + e^{-u}) = \frac{1}{2}(e^{2u} - e^{-2u}) = \sinh 2u$

(ii) $\sinh u \cosh v + \cosh u \sinh v$
$= \frac{1}{4}[(e^u - e^{-u})(e^v + e^{-v}) + (e^u + e^{-u})(e^v - e^{-v})]$
$= \frac{1}{4}[e^{u+v} + e^{u-v} - e^{-u+v} - e^{-u-v} + e^{u+v}$
$\quad -e^{u-v} + e^{-u+v} - e^{-u-v}]$
$= \frac{1}{4}[2e^{u+v} - 2e^{-u-v}] = \frac{1}{2}(e^{u+v} - e^{-(u+v)})$
$= \sinh(u+v)$

(iii) $\cosh u \cosh v + \sinh u \sinh v$
$= \frac{1}{4}[(e^u + e^{-u})(e^v + e^{-v}) + (e^u - e^{-u})(e^v - e^{-v})]$
$= \frac{1}{4}[e^{u+v} + e^{u-v} + e^{-u+v} + e^{-u-v} + e^{u+v} - e^{u-v}$
$\quad - e^{-u+v} + e^{-u-v}]$
$= \frac{1}{4}[2e^{u+v} + 2e^{-u-v}] = \frac{1}{2}(e^{u+v} + e^{-(u+v)})$
$= \cosh(u+v)$

Exercise 6A (Page 126)

1 $\cosh A - \cosh B = 2\sinh\dfrac{A+B}{2}\sinh\dfrac{A-B}{2}$,

$\sinh A + \sinh B = 2\sinh\dfrac{A+B}{2}\cosh\dfrac{A-B}{2}$,

$\sinh A - \sinh B = 2\cosh\dfrac{A+B}{2}\sinh\dfrac{A-B}{2}$

2 $\sinh 3u = 3\sinh u + 4\sinh^3 u$,
$\cosh 3u = 4\cosh^3 u - 3\cosh u$

3 (i) (a) $-\ln 3$
(b) $\ln\frac{3}{4}, \ln 2$
(c) No solution

(ii) $a+b, a-b, c$ all have the same sign and $b^2 + c^2 > a^2$

4 $x = \ln 3, y = \ln 2$

5 $1.62\,\text{m}, 22.3°$

7 (i) $4\cosh 4x$
(ii) $2x\sinh(x^2)$
(iii) $2\cosh x \sinh x$
(iv) $\cos x \cosh x - \sin x \sinh x$
(v) $\dfrac{1}{2}\left(1 + \dfrac{1}{x^2}\right)$
(vi) $5e^{10x}$
(vii) $3(1+x)^2\cosh^2 3x(\cosh 3x + 3(1+x)\sinh 3x)$
(viii) 1

8 $\frac{1}{2}(\cosh 2x + 1), \frac{1}{2}(\cosh 2x - 1)$;
$\frac{1}{4}\sinh 2x + \frac{1}{2}x + c, \frac{1}{4}\sinh 2x - \frac{1}{2}x + c$

9 (i) $\frac{1}{3}\cosh 3x + c$
(ii) $\frac{1}{2}\sinh(1+x^2) + c$
(iii) $x\cosh x - \sinh x + c$
(iv) $\sinh x + \frac{1}{3}\sinh^3 x + c$
(v) $\frac{1}{4}x\sinh 2x - \frac{1}{8}\cosh 2x - \frac{1}{4}x^2 + c$
(vi) $\frac{1}{18}e^{9x} - \frac{1}{2}e^{-x} + c$
(vii) $\frac{1}{5}\cosh^5 x - \frac{1}{3}\cosh^3 x + c$
(viii) $\frac{1}{28}\cosh 14x + \frac{1}{4}\cosh 2x + c$

11 $(\cosh x - \sinh x)^n = \cosh nx - \sinh nx$;
$\cosh 5x = 16\cosh^5 x - 20\cosh^3 x + 5\cosh x$,
$\sinh 5x = 16\sinh^5 x + 20\sinh^3 x + 5\sinh x$

12 (ii) 12
(iii) $\ln\frac{2}{9}$ or $\ln 2$
(iv) $\dfrac{6e^x}{4 + 9e^{2x}} = \dfrac{6}{4e^{-x} + 9e^x} = \dfrac{6}{f(x)}$.
$\displaystyle\int\dfrac{1}{f(x)}\,dx = \frac{1}{6}\arctan\!\left(\frac{3}{2}e^x\right) + c.$

Activity 6.4 (Page 128)

Function	Domain	Range	Even or odd
$\tanh x$	all x	$-1 < y < 1$	odd
$\coth x$	$x \neq 0$	$y > 1$ or $y < -1$	odd
$\operatorname{sech} x$	all x	$0 < y \leqslant 1$	even
$\operatorname{cosech} x$	$x \neq 0$	$y \neq 0$	odd

Exercise 6B (Page 128)

1 (i)

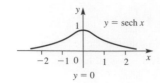

$y = \text{sech}\,x$

$y = 0$

(ii)

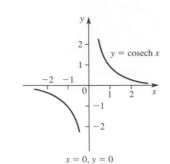

$y = \text{cosech}\,x$

$x = 0,\ y = 0$

(iii)

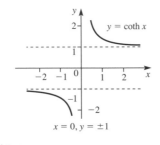

$y = \coth x$

$x = 0,\ y = \pm 1$

3 (i) $\pm\frac{1}{2}\ln 3$

(ii) $0,\ \ln 7$

(iii) $0,\ \frac{1}{2}\ln 2$

4 (i) $p = \frac{1}{2}\ln(2 + \sqrt{5}),\ q = \ln(1 + \sqrt{2})$

(ii) (a) $\tanh x < \sinh x < \text{sech}\,x < \cosh x$
$< \text{cosech}\,x < \coth x$

(b) $\tanh x < \text{sech}\,x < \sinh x < \text{cosech}\,x$
$< \cosh x < \coth x$

7 (i) $-\text{sech}\,x\tanh x$

(ii) $-\text{cosech}\,x\coth x$

(iii) $-\text{cosech}^2 x$

(iv) $\text{sech}\,x\,\text{cosech}\,x$

8 (i) $\ln(\cosh x) + c$

(ii) $\ln|\sinh x| + c$

(iii) $2\arctan(e^x) + c$

(iv) $\ln\left|\dfrac{e^x - 1}{e^x + 1}\right| + c$

9 $1 + \dfrac{x^2}{2!} + \dfrac{x^4}{4!} + \cdots + \dfrac{x^{2r}}{(2r)!} + \cdots$

10 (i) (b) $x^2 + \dfrac{x^6}{3!} + \dfrac{x^{10}}{5!} + \cdots + \dfrac{x^{4r+2}}{(2r+1)!} + \cdots$

(c) $f^{(5)}(0) = 0,\ f^{(6)}(0) = 120$

(ii) 0.0157

11 (ii) $1 + 2x^2 + \frac{5}{3}x^4$

12 (ii) $\frac{3}{16}$

Activity 6.5 (Page 131)

Function	Domain	Range
arcosh x	$x \geqslant 1$	$y \geqslant 0$
arsinh x	all x	all y
artanh x	$-1 < x < 1$	all y

Activity 6.6 (Page 132)

$y = \text{arsinh}\,x \Rightarrow x = \sinh y \Rightarrow 2x = e^y - e^{-y}$
$\Rightarrow (e^y)^2 - 2xe^y - 1 = 0$
$\Rightarrow e^y = x \pm \sqrt{x^2 + 1}$
$\Rightarrow y = \ln(x + \sqrt{x^2 + 1}).$

$\ln(x - \sqrt{x^2 + 1})$ does not exist since $x - \sqrt{x^2 + 1} < 0$.

Activity 6.7 (Page 133)

(i) $y = \text{arsinh}\,x \Rightarrow \sinh y = x \Rightarrow \cosh y \dfrac{dy}{dx} = 1$

$\Rightarrow \dfrac{dy}{dx} = \dfrac{1}{\cosh y} = \dfrac{1}{\pm\sqrt{\sinh^2 y + 1}} = \dfrac{1}{\pm\sqrt{x^2 + 1}}.$

Since the gradient of $y = \text{arsinh}\,x$ is always positive,

$\dfrac{dy}{dx} = \dfrac{1}{\sqrt{x^2 + 1}}.$

(ii) Let $x = au$. Then $dx = a\,du$ and

$\displaystyle \int \frac{1}{\sqrt{x^2 + a^2}}\,dx = \int \frac{1}{\sqrt{a^2 u^2 + a^2}}\,a\,du$

$\displaystyle = \int \frac{1}{a\sqrt{u^2 + 1}}\,a\,du$

$\displaystyle = \int \frac{1}{\sqrt{u^2 + 1}}\,du$

$\displaystyle = \text{arsinh}\,u + c = \text{arsinh}\left(\frac{x}{a}\right) + c.$

Exercise 6C (Page 134)

3

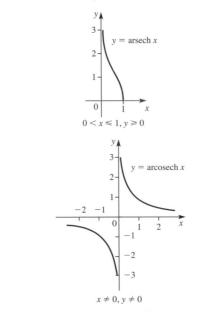

$y = \text{arsech}\,x$

$0 < x \leqslant 1,\ y \geqslant 0$

$y = \text{arcosech}\,x$

$x \neq 0,\ y \neq 0$

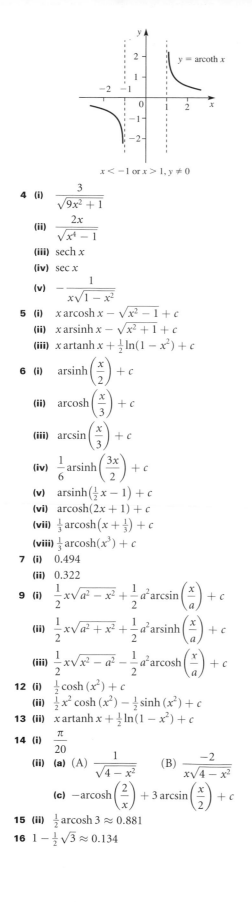

$x < -1$ or $x > 1$, $y \neq 0$

4 (i) $\dfrac{3}{\sqrt{9x^2 + 1}}$

(ii) $\dfrac{2x}{\sqrt{x^4 - 1}}$

(iii) $\operatorname{sech} x$

(iv) $\sec x$

(v) $-\dfrac{1}{x\sqrt{1 - x^2}}$

5 (i) $x \operatorname{arcosh} x - \sqrt{x^2 - 1} + c$

(ii) $x \operatorname{arsinh} x - \sqrt{x^2 + 1} + c$

(iii) $x \operatorname{artanh} x + \frac{1}{2} \ln(1 - x^2) + c$

6 (i) $\operatorname{arsinh}\left(\dfrac{x}{2}\right) + c$

(ii) $\operatorname{arcosh}\left(\dfrac{x}{3}\right) + c$

(iii) $\arcsin\left(\dfrac{x}{3}\right) + c$

(iv) $\dfrac{1}{6} \operatorname{arsinh}\left(\dfrac{3x}{2}\right) + c$

(v) $\operatorname{arsinh}\left(\frac{1}{2} x - 1\right) + c$

(vi) $\operatorname{arcosh}(2x + 1) + c$

(vii) $\frac{1}{3} \operatorname{arcosh}\left(x + \frac{1}{3}\right) + c$

(viii) $\frac{1}{3} \operatorname{arcosh}(x^3) + c$

7 (i) 0.494

(ii) 0.322

9 (i) $\dfrac{1}{2} x\sqrt{a^2 - x^2} + \dfrac{1}{2} a^2 \arcsin\left(\dfrac{x}{a}\right) + c$

(ii) $\dfrac{1}{2} x\sqrt{a^2 + x^2} + \dfrac{1}{2} a^2 \operatorname{arsinh}\left(\dfrac{x}{a}\right) + c$

(iii) $\dfrac{1}{2} x\sqrt{x^2 - a^2} - \dfrac{1}{2} a^2 \operatorname{arcosh}\left(\dfrac{x}{a}\right) + c$

12 (i) $\frac{1}{2} \cosh(x^2) + c$

(ii) $\frac{1}{2} x^2 \cosh(x^2) - \frac{1}{2} \sinh(x^2) + c$

13 (ii) $x \operatorname{artanh} x + \frac{1}{2} \ln(1 - x^2) + c$

14 (i) $\dfrac{\pi}{20}$

(ii) (a) (A) $\dfrac{1}{\sqrt{4 - x^2}}$ **(B)** $\dfrac{-2}{x\sqrt{4 - x^2}}$

(c) $-\operatorname{arcosh}\left(\dfrac{2}{x}\right) + 3 \arcsin\left(\dfrac{x}{2}\right) + c$

15 (ii) $\frac{1}{2} \operatorname{arcosh} 3 \approx 0.881$

16 $1 - \frac{1}{2} \sqrt{3} \approx 0.134$

Chapter 7

❓ (Page 138)

Periodic curve; contains loops.

Activity 7.1 (Page 140)

$|PA| = k|PB| \Rightarrow \sqrt{x^2 + y^2} = k\sqrt{(x - a)^2 + y^2}$

$\Rightarrow \left(x - \dfrac{k^2 a}{k^2 - 1}\right)^2 + y^2 = \left(\dfrac{ka}{k^2 - 1}\right)^2.$

❓ (Page 141)

$(-3, 0)$

❓ (Page 142)

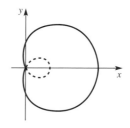

❓ (Page 143)

The parameter does not correspond to the angle the line OP makes with the x axis; using θ might suggest that it did.

Exercise 7A (Page 146)

1 (i) $y^2 = 4ax$

(ii) $\dfrac{x^2}{a^2} + \dfrac{y^2}{b^2} = 1$

(iii) $\dfrac{x^2}{a^2} - \dfrac{y^2}{b^2} = 1$

(iv) $xy = c^2$

2 $r = l - re \cos \theta \Rightarrow x^2 + y^2 = (l - ex)^2$

3 (i) $x = 6 \sin \theta \cos^2 \theta, \quad y = 6 \sin^2 \theta \cos \theta$

(ii) $r = 3 \sin 2\theta = 6 \sin \theta \cos \theta = 6\left(\dfrac{y}{r}\right)\left(\dfrac{x}{r}\right)$

$\Rightarrow r^3 = 6xy \Rightarrow (x^2 + y^2)^{\frac{3}{2}} = 6xy.$

4 $r = 2a \tan \theta \sin \theta \Rightarrow (r \cos \theta) r^2 = (2a \sin^2 \theta) r^2$

$\Rightarrow x(x^2 + y^2) = 2ay^2 \Rightarrow x^3 = y^2(2a - x).$

5 Substituting $y = tx$ in $x = \dfrac{2at^2}{1 + t^2}$

$\Rightarrow x = \dfrac{2ay^2}{x^2 + y^2} \Rightarrow (2a - x)y^2 = x^3.$

6 (i) $x = r\cos\theta = (2a\tan\theta\sin\theta)\cos\theta = 2a\sin^2\theta,$
$y = r\sin\theta = 2a\tan\theta\sin^2\theta$

(ii) $x = 2a\sin^2\theta = \dfrac{2at^2}{1+t^2},$
$y = 2a\tan\theta\sin^2\theta = \dfrac{2at^3}{1+t^2}$

7 They are all the same curve.

8 $y = \dfrac{a^3}{a^2 + a^2 t^2} = \dfrac{a^3}{a^2 + x^2}$

9 (i) $y = tx \Rightarrow x = \dfrac{y^2 - x^2}{y^2 + x^2} \Rightarrow y^2 = x^2\dfrac{(1+x)}{(1-x)}.$

(ii) $r\cos\theta = \dfrac{(r\sin\theta)^2 - (r\cos\theta)^2}{(r\sin\theta)^2 + (r\cos\theta)^2} = -\cos 2\theta$

$\Rightarrow \quad r = -\dfrac{\cos 2\theta}{\cos\theta}.$

10 $x^3 + y^3 = 3axy$

11 Link between the parametrics is explained by the substitution $t = \tan T$.

12 (i) A $y = 5$, B $x = 4$, C $x + y = 4$, D $2y = 3x - 2$

(ii) A $r = 5\operatorname{cosec}\theta$, B $r = 4\sec\theta$

C $r = \dfrac{4}{\cos\theta + \sin\theta}$, D $r = \dfrac{2}{3\cos\theta - 2\sin\theta}$

(iii) The cartesian equations of lines are far more elegant. Polar equations of straight lines are rarely used.

13 (ii)

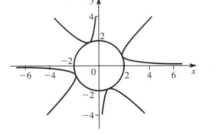

(iii) $r_{min} = \sqrt{\dfrac{4}{1}} = 2$, Therefore the curve touches the circle.

14 (i) (ii)

(v) $R^2 = 1 - p^4$, $\tan\alpha = p$

❓ (Page 148)

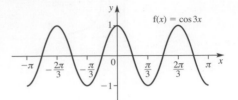

$f(x)$ is an even function; it is symmetrical about the y axis because $f(x) = f(-x)$. It is periodic with period $\dfrac{2\pi}{3}$.

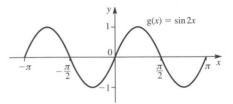

$g(x)$ is an odd function; it has rotation symmetry about the origin because $g(x) = -g(-x)$. It is periodic with period π.

Investigation (Page 149)

Parametric curves

(i) A$(6, 0)$, A$'(-6, 0)$, B$(0, 2)$, B$'(0, -2)$

(ii) Symmetrical about x axis since
$(x(2\pi - t), y(2\pi - t)) = (x(t), -y(t))$.
Symmetrical about y axis since
$(x(\pi - t), y(\pi - t)) = (-x(t), y(t))$.

(iii) $T = \dfrac{4\pi}{3}, \dfrac{5\pi}{3}$

(iv) The curve unfolds continuously in an anticlockwise sense from A. The full range from 0 to 2π is necessary.

(v) $x^2 + y^2 = 20 + 16\cos 2T$
$\Rightarrow (x^2 + y^2)_{max} = 6^2$, $(x^2 + y^2)_{min} = 2^2$.

Polar curves

(i) A$(-1, \pi)$, B$(3, 0)$

(ii) $\cos\theta = -\dfrac{1}{2} \Rightarrow \theta = \dfrac{2\pi}{3}, \dfrac{4\pi}{3}$

(iv) b affects the size of the curve (the maximum distance from the pole is $b + 1$) and determines whether there is a loop, a cusp or a dimple.

(v) The gradient of the tangent changes sign but the tangent does not exist when P is at the pole.

❓ (Page 151)

For the polar curves given, in any direction θ the two curves are separated by a distance a. However they are not, strictly speaking, parallel.

Investigation (Page 155)

$$x = (R + r)\cos T - |CM| \cos\left(\frac{r + R}{r}\right)T,$$

$$y = (R + r)\sin T - |CM| \sin\left(\frac{r + R}{r}\right)T$$

The statement is true.

Activity 7.2 (Page 157)

The same curve is drawn but they start from different points on the curve.

❓ (Page 159)

$$y = \frac{4x^2}{(2x - 1)} \Rightarrow \frac{dy}{dx} = \frac{8x^2 - 8x}{4x^2 - 4x + 1}$$

$$= \frac{8 - \dfrac{8}{x}}{4 - \dfrac{4}{x} + \dfrac{1}{x^2}} \rightarrow \frac{8 - 0}{4 - 0 + 0} = 2 \text{ as } x \rightarrow \infty.$$

This agrees with the gradient of the oblique asymptote found in Example 7.3.

❓ (Page 160)

All of the form $y = x^2 + c$.

❓ (Page 161)

There are $|n - 1|$ cusps or loops.

Activity 7.3 (Page 162)

n determines the order of rotational symmetry; k determines the number of cusps or dimples.

❓ (Page 162)

(i) D **(ii)** B **(iii)** A

Exercise 7B (Page 163)

1 (i) (a)

$r = 3(1 + \cos 2\theta)$
$r_{max} = 6$
Cusps at $\theta = \dfrac{\pi}{2}, \dfrac{3\pi}{2}$
Rotational symmetry of order 2
Symmetrical in initial line

(b)

$r = 1 + 2\cos\theta$
Touches circle $r = 3$
Loop for $\dfrac{2\pi}{3} < \theta < \dfrac{4\pi}{3}$
Loop touches circle $r = 1$
No rotational symmetry

2 (i) $\left(1 + \dfrac{1}{2^n}\right)$

(ii) The circle of radius 1, centre the origin, and the four points $(\pm 2, 0), (0, \pm 2)$

3 (i) $x + 3 + \dfrac{1}{2x - 1}$

(ii) $x = \dfrac{1}{2}, y = x + 3$

(iii) (a) $y = -1, x = 1.5$

(b) $x = 1, y = 2x + 1$

(c) $x = 3, x = -3, y = x + 2$

(d) $x = \frac{1}{3}, y = \frac{1}{3}$

(e) $x = -\frac{1}{6}, y = 2x - \frac{1}{3}$

4 (i) $(\sin^3 T)^{\frac{2}{3}} + (\cos^3 T)^{\frac{2}{3}} = \sin^2 T + \cos^2 T = 1$

(ii)

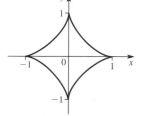

(iii) In general the curve $x = \cos^n T$, $y = \sin^n T$ contains points in the first quadrant for $n \notin \mathbb{N}$ unlike $x^{\frac{2}{n}} + y^{\frac{2}{n}} = 1$ which contains points in all four quadrants. The $\pm$ sign effectively gives the cartesian curve.

(iv) (a) $n = 1$

(b) $n = 0$

(c) $n = 2$

(v) (a) The curve tends to a cross consisting of line segments from $(-1, 0)$ to $(1, 0)$ and from $(0, -1)$ to $(0, 1)$.

(b) The curve tends to a square consisting of line segments parallel to the x and y axes, with vertices at $(1, 1), (-1, 1), (-1, -1)$ and $(1, -1)$.

5 (iii)

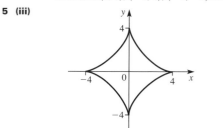

(iv) Same curve, but the path is traced out in the opposite direction and requires the smaller circle to travel around the larger circle three times.

6 (i) (a) Symmetry in both axes: $y \leftrightarrow -y$ leaves the equation unchanged, as does $x \leftrightarrow -x$. (Both substitutions together prove rotational symmetry of order 2.)

(b) Symmetry in the x axis: $y \leftrightarrow -y$ leaves the equation unchanged.

(c) Symmetry in line $y = x$: $y \leftrightarrow x$ leaves the equation unchanged.

(ii) Symmetry in line $y = x$.

7 (i) M is a clockwise rotation through $\dfrac{\pi}{2}$ radians about the origin.

(iii) The curve has rotational symmetry of order 4 about the origin.

8 (i) A circle centre $(0, 0)$, radius 1

(ii) Circles centre the origin

(iii) $r^2 = x^2 + y^2 = (k^2 + 1)$. A circle, centre $(0, 0)$, radius $\sqrt{k^2 + 1}$

(iv) The smallest possible radius occurs when $k = 0$, $r = 1$; this is the circle C.

9 (ii) Symmetrical about the x axis since $(x(\pi - t), y(\pi - t)) = (x(t), -y(t))$. Symmetrical about the y axis since $(x(t + \pi), y(t + \pi)) = (-x(t), y(t))$.

(iii) $(1, 0)$: $t = \dfrac{\pi}{2}$ $(-1, 0)$: $t = \dfrac{3\pi}{2}$

$(\sqrt{3}, 0)$: $t = \dfrac{\pi}{3}, \dfrac{2\pi}{3}$ $(-\sqrt{3}, 0)$: $t = \dfrac{4\pi}{3}, \dfrac{5\pi}{3}$

10 (ii) $d^2 = x^2 + y^2 = 5 + 4\sin(k + 1)T$ $\Rightarrow (d^2)_{\max} = 9$, $(d^2)_{\min} = 1$.

(iii)

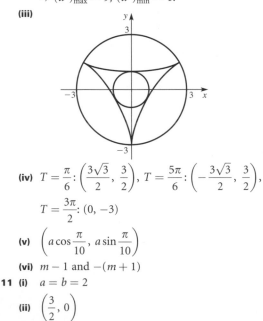

(iv) $T = \dfrac{\pi}{6}$: $\left(\dfrac{3\sqrt{3}}{2}, \dfrac{3}{2}\right)$, $T = \dfrac{5\pi}{6}$: $\left(-\dfrac{3\sqrt{3}}{2}, \dfrac{3}{2}\right)$, $T = \dfrac{3\pi}{2}$: $(0, -3)$

(v) $\left(a\cos\dfrac{\pi}{10}, a\sin\dfrac{\pi}{10}\right)$

(vi) $m - 1$ and $-(m + 1)$

11 (i) $a = b = 2$

(ii) $\left(\dfrac{3}{2}, 0\right)$

(iii) $\left(\dfrac{3}{2}, 0\right)\left(-\dfrac{3}{4}, \dfrac{3\sqrt{3}}{4}\right), \left(-\dfrac{3}{4}, -\dfrac{3\sqrt{3}}{4}\right)$

(iv) $d_{\max} = a + 1$, $d_{\min} = a - 1$ $x^2 + y^2 = (a + 1)^2$ and $x^2 + y^2 = (a - 1)^2$

(v) (a) Increasing a causes the curve to move further from the origin.

(b) Increasing b increases the order of rotational symmetry of the curve.

Investigation (Page 171)

As $n \to \infty$ the curve resembles a square.

❓ (Page 172)

(i) (a) Maximum or minimum distance of curve from pole

(b) Points where the tangent is perpendicular to the initial line

(c) Points where the tangent is parallel to the initial line

(ii) (a) Points where the tangent is parallel to the y axis

(b) Points where the tangent is parallel to the x axis

❓ (Page 173)

Maximum $3 + \sqrt{2}$, minimum $3 - \sqrt{2}$

❓ (Page 174)

In general, $\dfrac{dy}{dT}$ is easier to find than $\dfrac{dy}{dx}$.

Activity 7.4 (Page 174)

$$\frac{dx}{dT} = 2\sin T(12\sin^2 T - 11) = 0$$

$$\Rightarrow \quad T = 0, \pi, \sin^{-1}\frac{\pm\sqrt{33}}{6} \quad \Rightarrow \quad (6, 0), (-6, 0) \text{ and}$$

the four points $(\pm 0.385, \pm 2.553)$

Activity 7.5 (Page 177)

The containing rectangle has area $2\pi a \times 2a = 4\pi a^2$.

$$\int_0^{2\pi a} y\, dx = \int_0^{2\pi} a(1 - \cos T)\frac{dx}{dT}\, dT = \int_0^{2\pi} a^2(1 - \cos T)^2 dT$$

$$= a^2 \int_0^{2\pi} \left(1 - 2\cos T + \frac{1}{2}(\cos 2T + 1)\right) dT$$

$$= a^2 \left[\frac{3}{2}T - 2\sin T + \frac{1}{4}\sin 2T\right]_0^{2\pi} = 3\pi a^2 = \frac{3}{4}(4\pi a^2).$$

Activity 7.6 (Page 177)

$c = 1.14(292\ldots)$

Exercise 7C (Page 178)

1 (i) **(a)** $0 < k < 1$
   (b) $1 < k < 2$
   (c) $k \geqslant 2$
 (ii) $x = (k + \cos \theta) \cos \theta, \; y = (k + \cos \theta) \sin \theta$
 (iii) They correspond to the four vertical tangents.
 (iv) $\dfrac{dx}{d\theta} = -\sin \theta(k + 2 \cos \theta) = 0$ has four
   different roots for $0 < k < 2$, but only two
   roots (0 and π) for $k \geqslant 2$.

2 (i) $T = 0: \dfrac{dy}{dx} = \dfrac{3}{2} \quad T = \pi: \dfrac{dy}{dx} = -\dfrac{3}{2}$
 (ii) **(a)** $T = \dfrac{\pi}{4}: \left(1, \dfrac{\sqrt{2}}{2}\right)$
   (b) $T = \dfrac{\pi}{6}: \left(\dfrac{\sqrt{3}}{2}, 1\right)$

3 (ii) $\dfrac{dr}{d\theta} = n \sin \theta \cos \theta (\sin^{n-2} \theta - \cos^{n-2} \theta)$
 (iii) $\dfrac{dr}{d\theta} = 0 \Leftrightarrow \sin \theta = 0 \quad$ or $\quad \cos \theta = 0 \quad$ or
   (for $n \geqslant 3$) $\tan \theta = 1 \Leftrightarrow \theta = \dfrac{k\pi}{4} (k \in \mathbb{Z})$.
 (iv) $r = 2^{1 - \frac{n}{2}}$

4

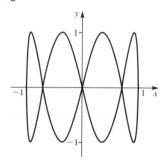

 (i) $y^2 = 16x^2(1 - x^2)(1 - 2x^2)^2$
 (ii) Substituting $-x$ for x and substituting $-y$ for y
   shows symmetry in both axes.
 (iii) $t = 0, \pi: (0, 0) \quad t = \dfrac{\pi}{4}, \dfrac{3\pi}{4}: \left(\dfrac{\sqrt{2}}{2}, 0\right)$
   $t = \dfrac{5\pi}{4}, \dfrac{7\pi}{4}: \left(-\dfrac{\sqrt{2}}{2}, 0\right)$
 (iv) $\dfrac{dy}{dt} = 0 \quad \Rightarrow \quad \cos 4t = 0$
   $\Rightarrow \quad y^2 = \sin^2 4t = (1 - \cos^2 4t) = 1$
   $\Rightarrow \quad y = \pm 1$.

6 (ii) $\dfrac{6}{5}$ and $-\dfrac{6}{5}$
 (iii) $(1.89, 1.76)$

7 (i)

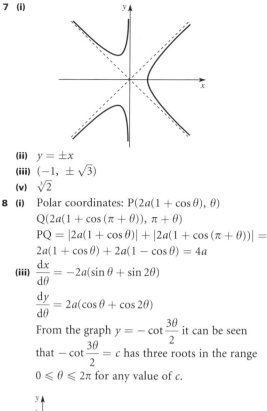

 (ii) $y = \pm x$
 (iii) $(-1, \pm\sqrt{3})$
 (v) $\sqrt[3]{2}$

8 (i) Polar coordinates: $P(2a(1 + \cos \theta), \theta)$
   $Q(2a(1 + \cos(\pi + \theta)), \pi + \theta)$
   $PQ = |2a(1 + \cos \theta)| + |2a(1 + \cos(\pi + \theta))| =$
   $2a(1 + \cos \theta) + 2a(1 - \cos \theta) = 4a$
 (iii) $\dfrac{dx}{d\theta} = -2a(\sin \theta + \sin 2\theta)$
   $\dfrac{dy}{d\theta} = 2a(\cos \theta + \cos 2\theta)$
   From the graph $y = -\cot \dfrac{3\theta}{2}$ it can be seen
   that $-\cot \dfrac{3\theta}{2} = c$ has three roots in the range
   $0 \leqslant \theta \leqslant 2\pi$ for any value of c.

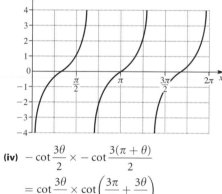

 (iv) $-\cot \dfrac{3\theta}{2} \times -\cot \dfrac{3(\pi + \theta)}{2}$
   $= \cot \dfrac{3\theta}{2} \times \cot \left(\dfrac{3\pi}{2} + \dfrac{3\theta}{2}\right)$
   $= \cot \dfrac{3\theta}{2} \times \dfrac{-1}{\cot \dfrac{3\theta}{2}} = -1$

9 (i) Both $t = -1$
 (ii) $-10 < t < -1$ moves away from origin in
   fourth quadrant; $-1 < t < 0$ moves towards
   origin in second quadrant; $t > 0$ loop in
   anticlockwise direction.
 (iii) $\dfrac{dy}{dx} = \dfrac{(2t - t^4)}{(1 - 2t^3)} \to -1$ as $t \to -1$.

(iv)

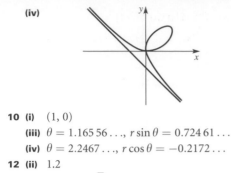

10 (i) $(1, 0)$

(iii) $\theta = 1.165\,56\ldots$, $r\sin\theta = 0.724\,61\ldots$

(iv) $\theta = 2.2467\ldots$, $r\cos\theta = -0.2172\ldots$

12 (ii) 1.2

(iii) $c = \dfrac{1 \pm \sqrt{2}}{2} \approx 1.2071$

Activity 7.7 (Page 184)

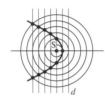

Activity 7.8 (Page 185)

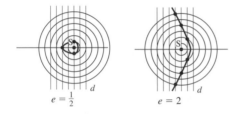

$e = \tfrac{1}{2}$ $e = 2$

Activity 7.9 (Page 186)

$e = 1$ gives a parabola, $0 < e < 1$ an ellipse, $e > 1$ a hyperbola. l affects the general dimensions of the conic but not the type of conic.

❓ (Page 188)

$b^2 = a^2(1 - e^2) \;\Rightarrow\; 9 = 16(1 - e^2) \;\Rightarrow\; e = \dfrac{\sqrt{7}}{4}$.

Focus $(ae, 0) = \left(\sqrt{7}, 0\right)$

Directrix $x = \dfrac{a}{e} = \dfrac{16}{\sqrt{7}}$

Activity 7.10 (Page 188)

As SS′ decreases, the ellipse becomes more circular.

❓ (Page 189)

See working for ellipse on pages 187–188.

❓ (Page 190)

Substituting $a = b$ in $a^2(1 - e^2) = -b^2$

$\Rightarrow \quad 1 - e^2 = -1 \quad \Rightarrow \quad e^2 = 2$.

❓ (Page 191)

Hyperbola: $0 \leqslant t < 2\pi$.

Rectangular hyperbola: $t \neq 0$

❓ (Page 191)

$x = a\cosh t$, $y = b\sinh t$ gives only the $x > 0$ branch of the hyperbola.

Exercise 7D (Page 195)

1 (i) $(\pm 5, 0)$, $(0, \pm\sqrt{7})$; A$(-3, 4)$, B$(3, 4)$, C$(3, -4)$, D$(-3, -4)$

(ii) $y^2 - x^2 = 7$

(iii) $|x| \geqslant 3$: $y^2 + ax^2 = 16 + 9a$ (ellipse)
$|x| < 3$: $y^2 - ax^2 = 16 - 9a$ (hyperbola)

(iv) $\left(\dfrac{dy}{dx}\right)_{\text{ell}} \left(\dfrac{dy}{dx}\right)_{\text{hyp}} = \left(-a\dfrac{x}{y}\right)\left(a\dfrac{x}{y}\right) = -a^2\dfrac{x^2}{y^2}$

$= -a^2 \dfrac{9}{16} = -1$ when $a = \tfrac{4}{3}$.

(v) $a = \dfrac{16}{9}$

2 (i) $x - py + ap^2 = 0$

3 (i) (a) $2x - (t_1 + t_2)y + 2at_1 t_2 = 0$

(c) $\left(\dfrac{a}{2}(t_1^2 + t_2^2),\, a(t_1 + t_2)\right)$

(ii) (a) $x - Ty + aT^2 = 0$

(c) $x - y + a = 0$, $x + y + a = 0$

6 (iv) $\dfrac{X^2}{a^2} + \dfrac{Y^2}{b^2} < 1$, (X, Y) inside the ellipse

(v) $X^2 + Y^2 = a^2 + b^2$

7 (i) $(b^2 - a^2m^2)x^2 - 2a^2mcx - a^2(b^2 + c^2) = 0$, $\dfrac{2a^2mc}{b^2 - a^2m^2}$

(ii) $(b^2 - a^2m^2)x^2 - 2a^2mcx - a^2c^2 = 0$, $\dfrac{2a^2mc}{b^2 - a^2m^2}$

10 $(3, 2)$, $(-3, -2)$

12 $t^3x - ty + c(1 - t^4) = 0$

13 $x = \tfrac{1}{2}h$, $y = \tfrac{1}{2}k$

14 (i) A circle centre $(0, 0)$, radius 1

(ii) Ellipses, with the major axis $y = x$ and the minor axis $y = -x$ for $k > 0$ but $\neq 1$. For $k < 0$ but $\neq -1$, the major axis is $y = -x$ and the minor axis $y = x$.

(iii) Rotation, centre the origin through $-45°$.

(iv) E has parametric equations

$$x = \frac{k+1}{\sqrt{2}}(\sin T + \cos T),$$

$$y = \frac{k-1}{\sqrt{2}}(\sin T - \cos T) \text{ and so the cartesian}$$

equation of E is $\dfrac{x^2}{(k+1)^2} + \dfrac{y^2}{(k-1)^2} = 1$.

This is the standard equation of an ellipse with the x axis for the major axis and the y axis for the minor axis for $k > 0$ but $\neq 1$, and vice versa for $k < 0$ but $\neq -1$. The lengths of the semi-axes are $(k+1)$ and $(k-1)$. This is a rotation of K through $-45°$ so K is an ellipse with axes $y = x$ and $y = -x$.

(v) Values of 1, -1 produce segments of the lines $y = x$ and $y = -x$ respectively. In these cases the parametric equations for x and y for the members of the family are

$k = 1$:

$x = \sin T + \cos T, y = \cos T + \sin T$

$\Rightarrow y = x$ for $-\sqrt{2} \leqslant x \leqslant \sqrt{2}$

$k = -1$:

$x = \sin T - \cos T, y = -\sin T + \cos T$

$\Rightarrow y = -x$ for $\sqrt{2} \leqslant x \leqslant \sqrt{2}$.

The value of $k = 0$ gives the circle C rather than an ellipse.

In this case the parametric equations for x and y for the member of the family are $x = \sin T$, $y = \cos T \Rightarrow x^2 + y^2 = 1$.

15 (i)

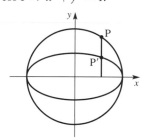

(ii) T is the angle between the x axis and the radius OQ, where $Q(a \cos T, a \sin T)$ is on the circle.

(iii) $\det \mathbf{M} = \dfrac{b}{a}$; area of ellipse $= \dfrac{b}{a} \times \pi a^2 = \pi ab$

16 (ii) $x^2 - y^2 = 1$

(iii) $xy = \dfrac{1}{2}$

Investigation (Page 200)

They do always touch. (See also Question 16 of Exercise 7D.)

Exercise 7E (Page 201)

1 (i) $x = \dfrac{p}{2}\cos T + \dfrac{q}{2}\sin T, \quad y = \dfrac{p}{2}\sin T + \dfrac{q}{2}\cos T$

(ii) $x = 4\cos T + 3\sin T, \quad y = 4\sin T + 3\cos T$

with range $0 \leqslant T \leqslant \dfrac{\pi}{2}$

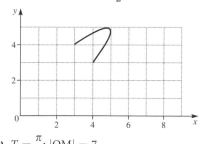

(iii) $T = \dfrac{\pi}{4}; |OM| = 7$

(iv) Now the range is $0 \leqslant T \leqslant 2\pi$.

(v) Appears to be an ellipse.

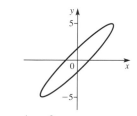

(vi) $\sin T = \dfrac{4y - 3x}{7}$,

$\cos T = \dfrac{4x - 3y}{7}$

$\Rightarrow 49 = (4y - 3x)^2 + (4x - 3y)^2$

$\Rightarrow 49 = 25y^2 + 25x^2 - 48xy$.

(vii) The substitution is equivalent to a rotation of the curve through $\dfrac{\pi}{4}$ about the origin in a clockwise direction. The line $y = x$ becomes the x axis and the line $y = -x$ becomes the y axis. The inclusion of $\sqrt{2}$ ensures that there is no enlargement. Hence the locus of M is an ellipse.

2 (i) $\angle AOD = t, \quad \angle COD = \theta$

At D: $y = \dfrac{2\theta}{\pi} = 1 - \dfrac{2t}{\pi}$

$\cot \theta = \tan t = \dfrac{x}{y}$

$$\Rightarrow \begin{cases} x = y\tan t = \left(1 - \dfrac{2t}{\pi}\right)\tan t \\ x = y\cot \theta = \dfrac{2\theta}{\pi}\cot \theta \end{cases}$$

(a) $D\left(\left(1 - \dfrac{2t}{\pi}\right)\tan t, 1 - \dfrac{2t}{\pi}\right)$

(b) $D\left(\dfrac{2\theta}{\pi}\cot \theta, \dfrac{2\theta}{\pi}\right)$

(ii) $\sin \theta = \dfrac{y}{OD} \quad \Rightarrow \quad r = OD = \dfrac{y}{\sin \theta} = \dfrac{2\theta}{\pi \sin \theta}$

(iii)

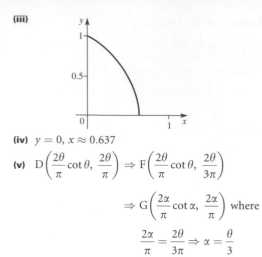

(iv) $y = 0$, $x \approx 0.637$

(v) $D\left(\dfrac{2\theta}{\pi}\cot\theta, \dfrac{2\theta}{\pi}\right) \Rightarrow F\left(\dfrac{2\theta}{\pi}\cot\theta, \dfrac{2\theta}{3\pi}\right)$

$$\Rightarrow G\left(\dfrac{2\alpha}{\pi}\cot\alpha, \dfrac{2\alpha}{\pi}\right) \text{ where}$$

$$\dfrac{2\alpha}{\pi} = \dfrac{2\theta}{3\pi} \Rightarrow \alpha = \dfrac{\theta}{3}$$

Therefore $\angle GOC = \frac{1}{3}\angle DOC$.

3 (ii) $y = \dfrac{2t^3}{1 + t^4}$

(iii)

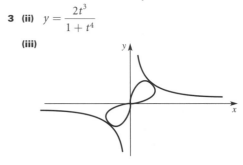

4 (i) $(\pm 2, 0)$

(ii) (a) $\lambda > -3$

(b) $-7 < \lambda < -3$

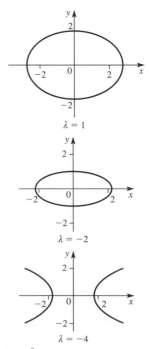

$\lambda = 1$

$\lambda = -2$

$\lambda = -4$

(iii) $\lambda = 3, -\frac{9}{2}$

5 (i) Circle $r = 2\cos\theta$; tangent $r = 2\sec\theta$

(iv) Cusp at O, symmetry about OCA, AR is an asymptote.

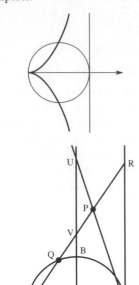

(v) (a)

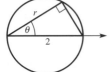

6 (i)

By the circle theorems it follows that C has the equation $r = 2\cos\theta$.

(iii) (a)

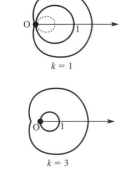

$k = 1$

(b)

$k = 3$

The former contains a loop, the latter a dimple.

(iv) (a) The loop of the limaçon is just inside the circle and the remainder just outside the circle.

(b) The limaçon approximates a circle, centre the point with polar co-ordinates $(2, 0)$.

(v) **(a)** By definition Q is the mid-point of PP′ and so is the centre of the circle C′ which has radius $k = 2$. If QQ′ is a diameter of C, then Q′ is the *only* point on C which is a distance 2 from Q.
Putting these together shows that C and C′ touch at Q′.

(b) Call the centre of C, M.
By circle theorems
$\angle OMQ' = 2 \times \angle OQQ' = 2\theta$.
$\Rightarrow$ Arc OQ on C $= 2\theta =$ Arc P′Q′ on C′.

7 (ii) A continuous closed curve; six cusps; maximum distance 6, minimum distance 4.

(iii) Curve has $(k + 1)$ cusps. Bounded by circles of radii $(k + 1)$, $(k − 1)$.

(v) Radius $(k + 1)$

8 (i)

x	$y = \sqrt{1 + \cos^2 2x}$
0	$\sqrt{2}$
$\dfrac{\pi}{6}$	$\dfrac{\sqrt{5}}{2}$
$\dfrac{\pi}{4}$	1
$\dfrac{\pi}{3}$	$\dfrac{\sqrt{5}}{2}$
$\dfrac{\pi}{2}$	$\sqrt{2}$
$\dfrac{3\pi}{4}$	1
π	$\sqrt{2}$
$\dfrac{5\pi}{4}$	1
$\dfrac{3\pi}{2}$	$\sqrt{2}$
$\dfrac{7\pi}{4}$	1
2π	$\sqrt{2}$

(ii)

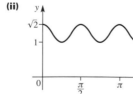

(iii) (iv)

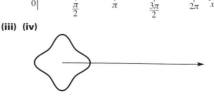

(v) concave for $0 < a < 1.6$; circle for $a = 2$; concave (with dimples) for $a > 2.5$.

9 (i) $a^2 = r^2 + (a\sqrt{2})^2 - 2ra\sqrt{2}\cos\theta \quad \Rightarrow$
$r = a(\sqrt{2}\cos\theta \pm \sqrt{\cos 2\theta})$.

(ii) $r = 2a\sqrt{\cos 2\theta}$

10 (i) Perpendicular bisector of ST

(iii) $DS = \dfrac{d}{3}$ and $DT = \dfrac{2d}{3}$, as required.

$r = \dfrac{d}{3}, -d$

P at D as above or at D′, where SD′ $= d$ and TD′ $= 2d$

(v) Symmetrical in the perpendicular bisector of ST

(vi) If $k > 1$, there are values of θ such that the expression $(1 - k^2 \sin^2\theta) < 0$, and so $\sqrt{1 - k^2 \sin^2\theta}$ is not real.

11 (i) Ellipse

(iii) $2r\dfrac{dr}{dT} = 12\sin T \cos T$

(iv) $(1, 1), (-1, -1); (-2, 2), (2, -2)$

(v) The axes are perpendicular. The major axis is $y = -x$ and the minor axis is $y = x$.

(vi) $45°$ anticlockwise

(vii) $(2\sqrt{2}\sin T, \sqrt{2}\cos T); \dfrac{x^2}{8} + \dfrac{y^2}{2} = 1$; this is the standard form of the equation of an ellipse; S is an ellipse; a curve and its image are congruent under rotation.

12 (i) $-\dfrac{\pi}{2} \leqslant \theta \leqslant \dfrac{\pi}{2}$ (or $0 \leqslant \theta \leqslant \dfrac{\pi}{2}$ and $\dfrac{3\pi}{2} \leqslant \theta < 2\pi$)

That P′ lies on curve follows from $2a\cos(\theta + \pi) + k = -(2a\cos\theta - k)$.

(ii)

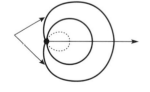

(iii) $k = 2a$

(iv) $\theta = \dfrac{\pi}{3}, \dfrac{5\pi}{3}$: points with horizontal tangents; $\theta = \pi$ is at the cusp.

13 (ii) $(x^2 + y^2)y^2 = a^2x^2$

(iii) Calculator plots $0 \leqslant \theta < 2\pi$, whereas the sketch is similar to $0 \leqslant \theta < \pi$. Using lines $y = \pm a$ by hand would give the full curve.

14 (i) $(2a \cos T \sin T, 2a \cos^2 T)$

(iii)

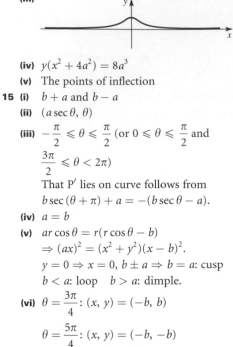

(iv) $y(x^2 + 4a^2) = 8a^3$

(v) The points of inflection

15 (i) $b + a$ and $b - a$

(ii) $(a \sec \theta, \theta)$

(iii) $-\dfrac{\pi}{2} \leqslant \theta \leqslant \dfrac{\pi}{2}$ (or $0 \leqslant \theta \leqslant \dfrac{\pi}{2}$ and

$\dfrac{3\pi}{2} \leqslant \theta < 2\pi$)

That P' lies on curve follows from
$b \sec(\theta + \pi) + a = -(b \sec \theta - a)$.

(iv) $a = b$

(v) $ar \cos \theta = r(r \cos \theta - b)$
$\Rightarrow (ax)^2 = (x^2 + y^2)(x - b)^2$.
$y = 0 \Rightarrow x = 0, b \pm a \Rightarrow b = a$: cusp
$b < a$: loop $b > a$: dimple.

(vi) $\theta = \dfrac{3\pi}{4}$: $(x, y) = (-b, b)$

$\theta = \dfrac{5\pi}{4}$: $(x, y) = (-b, -b)$

16 (iii)

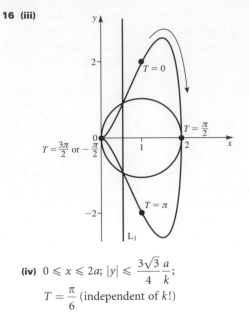

(iv) $0 \leqslant x \leqslant 2a$; $|y| \leqslant \dfrac{3\sqrt{3}}{4} \dfrac{a}{k}$;

$T = \dfrac{\pi}{6}$ (independent of k!)

Index